Vauxhall Carlton Owners Workshop Manual

A K Legg LAE MIMI

Models covered
All Vauxhall Carlton models with four-cylinder petrol engines
Saloon and Estate models, including special/limited editions
1796 cc & 1998 cc

Covers most features of Opel Omega
Does not cover air conditioning, or Diesel or six-cylinder engine models

(1469-3V2)

ABCDE
FG

Haynes Publishing Group
Sparkford Nr Yeovil
Somerset BA22 7JJ England

Haynes Publications, Inc
861 Lawrence Drive
Newbury Park
California 91320 USA

Acknowledgements

Thanks are due to Champion Spark Plug who supplied the illustrations showing spark plug conditions, to Holt Lloyd Limited who supplied the illustrations showing bodywork repair, and to Duckhams Oils who provided lubrication data. Certain other illustrations are the copyright of Vauxhall Motors Ltd, and are used with their permission. Thanks are also due to Vauxhall Motors for the supply of technical information and for the loan of project vehicles, to Sykes-Pickavant who provided some of the workshop tools, and to all those people at Sparkford who helped in the production of this manual.

A book in the **Haynes Owners Workshop Manual Series**

Printed by J. H. Haynes & Co. Ltd., Sparkford, Nr Yeovil, Somerset BA22 7JJ, England

ISBN 1 85010 908 7

British Library Cataloguing in Publication Data
A catalogue record for this book is available from the British Library

We take great pride in the accuracy of information given in this manual, but vehicle manufacturers make alterations and design changes during the production run of a particular vehicle of which they do not inform us. No liability can be accepted by the authors or publishers for loss, damage or injury caused by any errors in, or omissions from, the information given.

Restoring and Preserving our Motoring Heritage

Few people can have had the luck to realise their dreams to quite the same extent and in such a remarkable fashion as John Haynes, Founder and Chairman of the Haynes Publishing Group.

Since 1965 his unique approach to workshop manual publishing has proved so successful that millions of Haynes Manuals are now sold every year throughout the world, covering literally thousands of different makes and models of cars, vans and motorcycles.

A continuing passion for cars and motoring led to the founding in 1985 of a Charitable Trust dedicated to the restoration and preservation of our motoring heritage. To inaugurate the new Museum, John Haynes donated virtually his entire private collection of 52 cars.

Now with an unrivalled international collection of over 210 veteran, vintage and classic cars and motorcycles, the Haynes Motor Museum in Somerset is well on the way to becoming one of the most interesting Motor Museums in the world.

A 70 seat video cinema, a cafe and an extensive motoring bookshop, together with a specially constructed one kilometre motor circuit, make a visit to the Haynes Motor Museum a truly unforgettable experience.

Every vehicle in the museum is preserved in as near as possible mint condition and each car is run every six months on the motor circuit.

Enjoy the picnic area set amongst the rolling Somerset hills. Peer through the William Morris workshop windows at cars being restored, and browse through the extensive displays of fascinating motoring memorabilia.

From the 1903 Oldsmobile through such classics as an MG Midget to the mighty 'E' Type Jaguar, Lamborghini, Ferrari Berlinetta Boxer, and Graham Hill's Lola Cosworth, there is something for everyone, young and old alike, at this Somerset Museum.

Haynes Motor Museum

Situated mid-way between London and Penzance, the Haynes Motor Museum is located just off the A303 at Sparkford, Somerset (home of the Haynes Manual) and is open to the public 7 days a week all year round, except Christmas Day and Boxing Day.

Contents

Spark plug condition and bodywork repair colour pages between pages 32 and 33

Vauxhall Carlton CD Saloon

Vauxhall Carlton GL Estate

About this manual

Its aim

The aim of this manual is to help you get the best value from your vehicle. It can do so in several ways. It can help you decide what work must be done (even should you choose to get it done by a garage), provide information on routine maintenance and servicing, and give a logical course of action and diagnosis when random faults occur.

The manual has drawings and descriptions to show the function of the various components so that their layout can be understood. Then the tasks are described and photographed in a step-by-step sequence so that even a novice can do the work.

Its arrangement

The manual is divided into Chapters, each covering a logical sub-division of the vehicle. The Chapters are each divided into Sections, numbered with single figures, eg. 5; the Sections are divided into paragraphs, or into sub-sections and paragraphs.

It is freely illustrated, especially in those parts where there is a detailed sequence of operations to be carried out. There are two forms of illustration: figures and photographs. The figures are numbered in sequence with decimal numbers, according to their position in the Chapter – eg Fig. 6.4 is the fourth drawing/illustration in Chapter 6. Photographs carry the same number (either individually or in related groups) as the Section and paragraph to which they relate.

There is an alphabetical index at the back of the manual as well as a contents list at the front. Each Chapter is also preceded by its own individual contents list.

References to the 'left' or 'right' of the vehicle are in the sense of a person in the driver's seat facing forwards.

Unless otherwise stated, nuts and bolts are removed by turning anti-clockwise, and tightened by turning clockwise.

Vehicle manufacturers continually make changes to specifications and recommendations, and these, when notified, are incorporated into our manuals at the earliest opportunity.

We take great pride in the accuracy of information given in this manual, but vehicle manufacturers make alterations and design changes during the production run of a particular vehicle of which they do not inform us. No liability can be accepted by the authors or publishers for loss, damage or injury caused by any errors in, or omissions from, the information given.

Project vehicles

The vehicles used in the preparation of this manual, and which appear in many of the photographic sequences were: a 1.8i GL Saloon, a 2.0i GL Estate and a 2.0i CD Automatic Saloon.

Introduction to the Vauxhall Carlton

The Carlton covered by this manual was introduced to the UK market in November 1986. Although there is a similarity to its predecessor, the later version is much improved both mechanically and bodily. Independent rear suspension is fitted instead of the previous rigid axle, and both the engine and manual gearbox are new.

The 1.8 engine is available in both carburettor and fuel injection versions, but the 2.0 litre engine is only available in fuel injected form.

All models are equipped with both front and rear disc brakes. Anti-lock braking is fitted as standard on all high-specification models and later low-specification models, and was offered as an optional extra on all earlier low-specification models.

Being of conventional layout with reasonable access to most components, the Carlton should present no real problems to the home mechanic, except perhaps when overhauling the manual gearbox. A few special tools are necessary in order to carry out the latter work, but a little time spent making the tools suggested will mean that the work can be completed satisfactorily.

General dimensions, weights and capacities

Dimensions

	Saloon	Estate
Overall length	4687 mm (184.7 in)	4730 mm (186.4 in)
Overall width	1772 mm (69.8 in)	1772 mm (69.8 in)
Overall height (unladen)	1447 mm (57.0 in)	1481 mm (58.4 in)
Wheelbase	2730 mm (107.6 in)	2730 mm (107.6 in)
Front track	1447 mm (57.0 in)	1447 mm (57.0 in)
Rear track	1468 mm (57.8 in)	1465 mm (57.7 in)
Ground clearance (rear axle)	151 mm (5.9 in)	152 mm (6.0 in)

Weights

	Manual gearbox	Automatic transmission
Kerb weights (nominal):		
1.8 L Saloon	1150 kg (2535 lbs)	1175 kg (2590 lbs)
1.8i L Saloon	1175 kg (2590 lbs)	1200 kg (2646 lbs)
2.0i L Saloon	1200 kg (2646 lbs)	1220 kg (2690 lbs)
1.8 GL Saloon	1161 kg (2560 lbs)	1186 kg (2615 lbs)
1.8i GL Saloon	1184 kg (2610 lbs)	1209 kg (2665 lbs)
2.0i GL Saloon	1209 kg (2665 lbs)	1229 kg (2709 lbs)
1.8i CD Saloon	1194 kg (2632 lbs)	1219 kg (2687 lbs)
2.0i CD Saloon	1219 kg (2687 lbs)	1239 kg (2731 lbs)
1.8 L Estate	1220 kg (2690 lbs)	1245 kg (2745 lbs)
1.8i L Estate	1240 kg (2734 lbs)	1265 kg (2789 lbs)
2.0i L Estate	1255 kg (2767 lbs)	1275 kg (2811 lbs)
1.8 GL Estate	1231 kg (2714 lbs)	1256 kg (2769 lbs)
1.8i GL Estate	1249 kg (2754 lbs)	1274 kg (2809 lbs)
2.0i GL Estate	1264 kg (2787 lbs)	1284 kg (2831 lbs)
2.0i CD Estate	1274 kg (2809 lbs)	1294 kg (2853 lbs)
Gross vehicle weights:		
All 1.8 litre Saloons	1705 kg (3759 lbs)	1730 kg (3814 lbs)
All 2.0 litre Saloons	1730 kg (3814 lbs)	1745 kg (3847 lbs)
All 1.8 litre Estates	1840 kg (4057 lbs)	1865 kg (4112 lbs)
All 2.0 litre Estates	1865 kg (4112 lbs)	1880 kg (4145 lbs)
Maximum trailer weight limit:		
All Saloons	600 kg (1323 lbs)	600 kg (1323 lbs)
All Estates	565 kg (1245 lbs)	565 kg (1245 lbs)
Maximum roof load (including rack) — all models	100 kg (221 lbs)	100 kg (221 lbs)

Capacities

Engine oil (drain and refill, including filter)	4.5 litres (7.9 pints)
Cooling system	6.4 litres (11.3 pints)
Fuel tank:	
Saloon	75 litres (16.5 gallons)
Estate	70 litres (15.4 gallons)
Manual gearbox	1.2 litres (2.1 pints)
Automatic transmission (drain and refill)	2.5 litres (4.4 pints) approx
Final drive:	
Saloon	0.8 litre (1.4 pints)
Estate	1.0 litre (1.8 pints)
Washer fluid reservoir:	
Without headlamp washer	3.3 litres (5.8 pints)
With headlamp washer	5.7 litres (10.0 pints)
Brake hydraulic system	0.46 litres (0.8 pint)
Power-assisted steering	1.0 litre (1.8 pints)

Jacking, towing and wheel changing

Jacking

The jack supplied with the vehicle should only be used for wheel changing as described later.

When raising the vehicle for repair or maintenance, preferably use a trolley or hydraulic jack with a wooden block as an insulator to prevent damage to the underbody. Place the jack under a structural member at the points indicated, never raise the vehicle by jacking up under the engine sump, transmission casing or rear axle. If both front or both rear wheels are to be raised, jack up one side first and securely support it on an axle stand before raising the other side.

To avoid repetition, the procedures for raising the vehicle in order to carry out work under it is not included before each relevant operation described in this manual.

It is to be preferred and is certainly recommended that the vehicle is positioned over an inspection pit or raised on a lift. When such equipment is not available, use ramps or jack up the vehicle as previously described, but always supplement the lifting device with axle stands.

Towing

Towing eyes are provided at the front and rear of the vehicle. On Estate models the rear towing eye is concealed by a flap; it should only be used for emergency towing of another vehicle (photos).

Automatic transmission models should not be towed further than 30 miles (50 km) or faster than 30 mph (50 km/h). If these conditions cannot be met, or if transmission damage has already occurred, the rear of the vehicle should be suspended or alternatively the driveshafts disconnected.

When being towed, the gear lever should be in neutral on manual gearbox models or position 'N' on automatic transmission models. The ignition should be switched on to release the steering lock and allow operation of the stop lamps, horn and wipers. With the engine stopped more effort will be required to stop the vehicle and turn the steering wheel.

Wheel changing

To change a roadwheel, first park on a firm level surface if possible. Chock the wheel opposite the one being removed. Apply the handbrake and engage reverse gear (or 'P' on automatic transmission models). Pull off the wheel trim.

If the car is fairly new, the wheels and tyres will have been balanced

Front towing eye

Rear towing eye (Saloon)

Rear towing eye (Estate)

Spare wheel (Estate)

Jacking tools (Saloon)

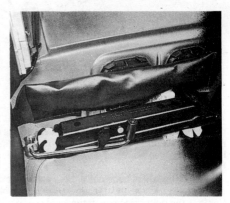
Jacking tools (Estate)

Loosening the wheel bolts

Vehicle jack in use

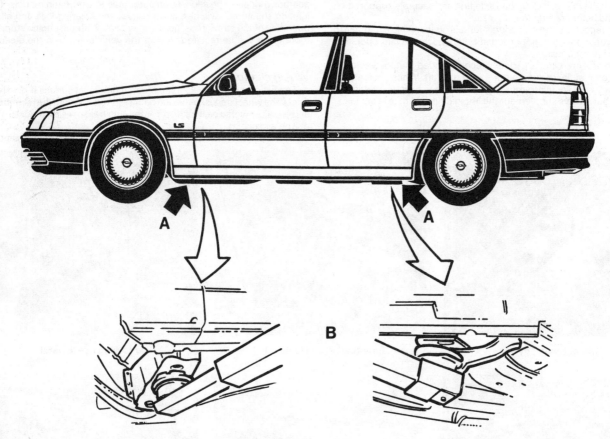

Jacking points

A　For vehicle jack　　　　　*B　For trolley jack or lift*

on the vehicle during production. To maintain this relationship, mark the position of the wheel relative to the hub. (This is not necessary if the tyre is to be removed for repair or renewal, since the balance will inevitably be altered.)

Loosen the wheel bolts half a turn each. Pull out the flap, fit the jack, and raise the vehicle until the wheel is just clear of the ground (photos). Remove the bolts and take off the wheel.

Fit the new wheel and secure it with the bolts. Tighten the bolts until they are snug, but do not try to tighten them fully yet. Lower the vehicle and remove the jack, then tighten the wheel bolts in criss-cross sequence. The use of a torque wrench is strongly recommended, especially when alloy wheels are fitted; see Chapter 10 Specifications for the recommended tightening torque. Refit the wheel trim and stow the tools. If a new wheel has been brought into service, have it balanced on the vehicle as soon as possible.

Buying spare parts and vehicle identification numbers

Buying spare parts

Spare parts are available from many sources, for example: Vauxhall dealers, other garages and accessory shops, and motor factors. Our advice regarding spare part sources is as follows:

Officially appointed Vauxhall dealers – This is the best source for parts which are peculiar to your vehicle and are otherwise not generally available (eg, complete cylinder heads, internal gearbox components, badges, interior trim etc). It is also the only place you should buy parts if your vehicle is still under warranty; non-Vauxhall components may invalidate the warranty. To be sure of obtaining the correct parts it will always be necessary to give the storeman your vehicle's engine and chassis number, and if possible, to take the 'old' part along for positive identification. Remember that some parts are available on a factory exchange scheme – any parts returned should always be clean. It obviously makes good sense to go straight to the specialists on your vehicle for this type of part, for they are best equipped to supply you.

Other garages and accessory shops – These are often very good places to buy materials and components needed for the maintenance of your vehicle (eg, spark plugs, bulbs, drivebelts, oils and greases, touch-up paint, filler paste etc.) They also sell general accessories, usually have convenient opening hours, charge lower prices and can often be found not far from home.

Motor factors – Good factors will stock all the more important components which wear out relatively quickly (eg, clutch components, pistons, valves, exhaust systems, brake cylenders/pipes/hoses/seals/shoes and pads etc). Motor factors will often provide new or reconditioned components on a part exchange basis – this can save a considerable amount of money.

Vehicle identification numbers

The *vehicle identification number* is located on the right-hand side of the engine compartment front panel on the identification plate. Additionally the number is stamped into the floor panel on the right-hand side of the driver's seat.

The *engine number* is stamped on the left-hand rear top face of the cylinder block (photo).

Engine number location

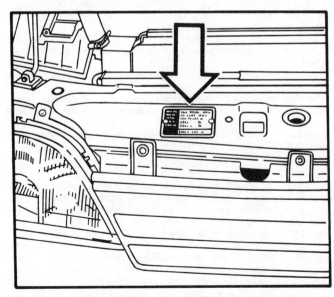

Vehicle identification number plate on the engine compartment front panel

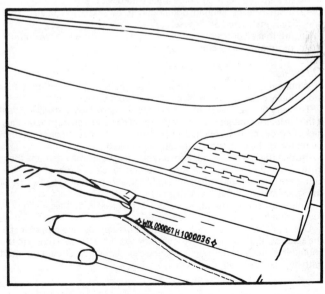

Vehicle identification number location on floor panel

General repair procedures

Whenever servicing, repair or overhaul work is carried out on the car or its components, it is necessary to observe the following procedures and instructions. This will assist in carrying out the operation efficiently and to a professional standard of workmanship.

Joint mating faces and gaskets

Where a gasket is used between the mating faces of two components, ensure that it is renewed on reassembly, and fit it dry unless otherwise stated in the repair procedure. Make sure that the mating faces are clean and dry with all traces of old gasket removed. When cleaning a joint face, use a tool which is not likely to score or damage the face, and remove any burrs or nicks with an oilstone or fine file.

Make sure that tapped holes are cleaned with a pipe cleaner, and keep them free of jointing compound if this is being used unless specifically instructed otherwise.

Ensure that all orifices, channels or pipes are clear and blow through them, preferably using compressed air.

Oil seals

Whenever an oil seal is removed from its working location, either individually or as part of an assembly, it should be renewed.

The very fine sealing lip of the seal is easily damaged and will not seal if the surface it contacts is not completely clean and free from scratches, nicks or grooves. If the original sealing surface of the component cannot be restored, the component should be renewed.

Protect the lips of the seal from any surface which may damage them in the course of fitting. Use tape or a conical sleeve where possible. Lubricate the seal lips with oil before fitting and, on dual lipped seals, fill the space between the lips with grease.

Unless otherwise stated, oil seals must be fitted with their sealing lips toward the lubricant to be sealed.

Use a tubular drift or block of wood of the appropriate size to install the seal and, if the seal housing is shouldered, drive the seal down to the shoulder. If the seal housing is unshouldered, the seal should be fitted with its face flush with the housing top face.

Screw threads and fastenings

Always ensure that a blind tapped hole is completely free from oil, grease, water or other fluid before installing the bolt or stud. Failure to do this could cause the housing to crack due to the hydraulic action of the bolt or stud as it is screwed in.

When tightening a castellated nut to accept a split pin, tighten the nut to the specified torque, where applicable, and then tighten further to the next split pin hole. Never slacken the nut to align a split pin hole unless stated in the repair procedure.

When checking or retightening a nut or bolt to a specified torque setting, slacken the nut or bolt by a quarter of a turn, and then retighten to the specified setting.

Locknuts, locktabs and washers

Any fastening which will rotate against a component or housing in the course of tightening should always have a washer between it and the relevant component or housing.

Spring or split washers should always be renewed when they are used to lock a critical component such as a big-end bearing retaining nut or bolt.

Locktabs which are folded over to retain a nut or bolt should always be renewed.

Self-locking nuts can be reused in non-critical areas, providing resistance can be felt when the locking portion passes over the bolt or stud thread.

Split pins must always be replaced with new ones of the correct size for the hole.

Special tools

Some repair procedures in this manual entail the use of special tools such as a press, two or three-legged pullers, spring compressors etc. Wherever possible, suitable readily available alternatives to the manufacturer's special tools are described, and are shown in use. In some instances, where no alternative is possible, it has been necessary to resort to the use of a manufacturer's tool and this has been done for reasons of safety as well as the efficient completion of the repair operation. Unless you are highly skilled and have a thorough understanding of the procedure described, never attempt to bypass the use of any special tool when the procedure described specifies its use. Not only is there a very great risk of personal injury, but expensive damage could be caused to the components involved.

Tools and working facilities

Introduction

A selection of good tools is a fundamental requirement for anyone contemplating the maintenance and repair of a motor vehicle. For the owner who does not possess any, their purchase will prove a considerable expense, offsetting some of the savings made by doing-it-yourself. However, provided that the tools purchased meet the relevant national safety standards and are of good quality, they will last for many years and prove an extremely worthwhile investment.

To help the average owner to decide which tools are needed to carry out the various tasks detailed in this manual, we have compiled three lists of tools under the following headings: *Maintenance and minor repair, Repair and overhaul,* and *Special.* The newcomer to practical mechanics should start off with the *Maintenance and minor repair* tool kit and confine himself to the simpler jobs around the vehicle. Then, as his confidence and experience grow, he can undertake more difficult tasks, buying extra tools as, and when, they are needed. In this way, a *Maintenance and minor repair* tool kit can be built-up into a *Repair and overhaul* tool kit over a considerable period of time without any major cash outlays. The experienced do-it-yourselfer will have a tool kit good enough for most repair and overhaul procedures and will add tools from the *Special* category when he feels the expense is justified by the amount of use to which these tools will be put.

It is obviously not possible to cover the subject of tools fully here. For those who wish to learn more about tools and their use there is a book entitled *How to Choose and Use Car Tools* available from the publishers of this manual.

Maintenance and minor repair tool kit

The tools given in this list should be considered as a minimum requirement if routine maintenance, servicing and minor repair operations are to be undertaken. We recommend the purchase of combination spanners (ring one end, open-ended the other); although more expensive than open-ended ones, they do give the advantages of both types of spanner.

Combination spanners - 10, 11, 12, 13, 14 & 17 mm
Adjustable spanner - 9 inch
Gearbox/rear axle drain plug key
Spark plug spanner (with rubber insert)
Spark plug gap adjustment tool
Set of feeler gauges
Brake bleed nipple spanner
Screwdriver - 4 in long x $^1/_4$ in dia (flat blade)
Screwdriver - 4 in long x $^1/_4$ in dia (cross blade)
Combination pliers - 6 inch
Hacksaw (junior)
Tyre pump
Tyre pressure gauge
Oil can
Fine emery cloth (1 sheet)
Wire brush (small)
Funnel (medium size)

Repair and overhaul tool kit

These tools are virtually essential for anyone undertaking any major repairs to a motor vehicle, and are additional to those given in the *Maintenance and minor repair* list. Included in this list is a comprehensive set of sockets. Although these are expensive they will be found invaluable as they are so versatile - particularly if various drives are included in the set. We recommend the ½ in square-drive type, as this can be used with most proprietary torque wrenches. If you cannot afford a socket set, even bought piecemeal, then inexpensive tubular box spanners are a useful alternative.

The tools in this list will occasionally need to be supplemented by tools from the *Special* list.

Sockets (or box spanners) to cover range in previous list
Reversible ratchet drive (for use with sockets)
Extension piece, 10 inch (for use with sockets)
Universal joint (for use with sockets)
Torque wrench (for use with sockets)
'Mole' wrench - 8 inch
Ball pein hammer
Soft-faced hammer, plastic or rubber
Screwdriver - 6 in long x $^5/_{16}$ in dia (flat blade)
Screwdriver - 2 in long x $^5/_{16}$ in square (flat blade)
Screwdriver - 1$^1/_2$ in long x $^1/_4$ in dia (cross blade)
Screwdriver - 3 in long x $^1/_8$ in dia (electricians)
Pliers - electricians side cutters
Pliers - needle nosed
Pliers - circlip (internal and external)
Cold chisel - $^1/_2$ inch
Scriber
Scraper
Centre punch
Pin punch
Hacksaw
Valve grinding tool
Steel rule/straight-edge
Allen keys (inc. splined/Torx type if necessary)
Selection of files
Wire brush (large)
Axle-stands
Jack (strong trolley or hydraulic type)

Special tools

The tools in this list are those which are not used regularly, are expensive to buy, or which need to be used in accordance with their manufacturers' instructions. Unless relatively difficult mechanical jobs are undertaken frequently, it will not be economic to buy many of these tools. Where this is the case, you could consider clubbing together with friends (or joining a motorists' club) to make a joint purchase, or borrowing the tools against a deposit from a local garage or tool hire specialist.

The following list contains only those tools and instruments freely available to the public, and not those special tools produced by the vehicle manufacturer specifically for its dealer network. You will find occasional references to these manufacturers' special tools in the text of this manual. Generally, an alternative method of doing the job without the vehicle manufacturers' special tool is given. However, sometimes, there is no alternative to using them. Where this is the case and the relevant tool cannot be bought or borrowed, you will have to entrust the work to a franchised garage.

> Valve spring compressor (where applicable)
> Piston ring compressor
> Balljoint separator
> Universal hub/bearing puller
> Impact screwdriver
> Micrometer and/or vernier gauge
> Dial gauge
> Stroboscopic timing light
> Dwell angle meter/tachometer
> Universal electrical multi-meter
> Cylinder compression gauge
> Lifting tackle
> Trolley jack
> Light with extension lead

Buying tools

For practically all tools, a tool factor is the best source since he will have a very comprehensive range compared with the average garage or accessory shop. Having said that, accessory shops often offer excellent quality tools at discount prices, so it pays to shop around.

There are plenty of good tools around at reasonable prices, but always aim to purchase items which meet the relevant national safety standards. If in doubt, ask the proprietor or manager of the shop for advice before making a purchase.

Care and maintenance of tools

Having purchased a reasonable tool kit, it is necessary to keep the tools in a clean serviceable condition. After use, always wipe off any dirt, grease and metal particles using a clean, dry cloth, before putting the tools away. Never leave them lying around after they have been used. A simple tool rack on the garage or workshop wall, for items such as screwdrivers and pliers is a good idea. Store all normal wrenches and sockets in a metal box. Any measuring instruments, gauges, meters, etc, must be carefully stored where they cannot be damaged or become rusty.

Take a little care when tools are used. Hammer heads inevitably become marked and screwdrivers lose the keen edge on their blades from time to time. A little timely attention with emery cloth or a file will soon restore items like this to a good serviceable finish.

Working facilities

Not to be forgotten when discussing tools, is the workshop itself. If anything more than routine maintenance is to be carried out, some form of suitable working area becomes essential.

It is appreciated that many an owner mechanic is forced by circumstances to remove an engine or similar item, without the benefit of a garage or workshop. Having done this, any repairs should always be done under the cover of a roof.

Wherever possible, any dismantling should be done on a clean, flat workbench or table at a suitable working height.

Any workbench needs a vice: one with a jaw opening of 4 in (100 mm) is suitable for most jobs. As mentioned previously, some clean dry storage space is also required for tools, as well as for lubricants, cleaning fluids, touch-up paints and so on, which become necessary.

Another item which may be required, and which has a much more general usage, is an electric drill with a chuck capacity of at least 5/16 in (8 mm). This, together with a good range of twist drills, is virtually essential for fitting accessories such as mirrors and reversing lights.

Last, but not least, always keep a supply of old newspapers and clean, lint-free rags available, and try to keep any working area as clean as possible.

Spanner jaw gap comparison table

Jaw gap (in)	Spanner size
0.250	1/4 in AF
0.276	7 mm
0.313	5/16 in AF
0.315	8 mm
0.344	11/32 in AF; 1/8 in Whitworth
0.354	9 mm
0.375	3/8 in AF
0.394	10 mm
0.433	11 mm
0.438	7/16 in AF
0.445	3/16 in Whitworth; 1/4 in BSF
0.472	12 mm
0.500	1/2 in AF
0.512	13 mm
0.525	1/4 in Whitworth; 5/16 in BSF
0.551	14 mm
0.563	9/16 in AF
0.591	15 mm
0.600	5/16 in Whitworth; 3/8 in BSF
0.625	5/8 in AF
0.630	16 mm
0.669	17 mm
0.686	11/16 in AF
0.709	18 mm
0.710	3/8 in Whitworth; 7/16 in BSF
0.748	19 mm
0.750	3/4 in AF
0.813	13/16 in AF
0.820	7/16 in Whitworth; 1/2 in BSF
0.866	22 mm
0.875	7/8 in AF
0.920	1/2 in Whitworth; 9/16 in BSF
0.938	15/16 in AF
0.945	24 mm
1.000	1 in AF
1.010	9/16 in Whitworth; 5/8 in BSF
1.024	26 mm
1.063	1 1/16 in AF; 27 mm
1.100	5/8 in Whitworth; 11/16 in BSF
1.125	1 1/8 in AF
1.181	30 mm
1.200	11/16 in Whitworth; 3/4 in BSF
1.250	1 1/4 in AF
1.260	32 mm
1.300	3/4 in Whitworth; 7/8 in BSF
1.313	1 5/16 in AF
1.390	13/16 in Whitworth; 15/16 in BSF
1.417	36 mm
1.438	1 7/16 in AF
1.480	7/8 in Whitworth; 1 in BSF
1.500	1 1/2 in AF
1.575	40 mm; 15/16 in Whitworth
1.614	41 mm
1.625	1 5/8 in AF
1.670	1 in Whitworth; 1 1/8 in BSF
1.688	1 11/16 in AF
1.811	46 mm
1.813	1 13/16 in AF
1.860	1 1/8 in Whitworth; 1 1/4 in BSF
1.875	1 7/8 in AF
1.969	50 mm
2.000	2 in AF
2.050	1 1/4 in Whitworth; 1 3/8 in BSF
2.165	55 mm
2.362	60 mm

Conversion factors

Length (distance)

Inches (in)	X 25.4	= Millimetres (mm)	X 0.0394	= Inches (in)
Feet (ft)	X 0.305	= Metres (m)	X 3.281	= Feet (ft)
Miles	X 1.609	= Kilometres (km)	X 0.621	= Miles

Volume (capacity)

Cubic inches (cu in; in³)	X 16.387	= Cubic centimetres (cc; cm³)	X 0.061	= Cubic inches (cu in; in³)
Imperial pints (Imp pt)	X 0.568	= Litres (l)	X 1.76	= Imperial pints (Imp pt)
Imperial quarts (Imp qt)	X 1.137	= Litres (l)	X 0.88	= Imperial quarts (Imp qt)
Imperial quarts (Imp qt)	X 1.201	= US quarts (US qt)	X 0.833	= Imperial quarts (Imp qt)
US quarts (US qt)	X 0.946	= Litres (l)	X 1.057	= US quarts (US qt)
Imperial gallons (Imp gal)	X 4.546	= Litres (l)	X 0.22	= Imperial gallons (Imp gal)
Imperial gallons (Imp gal)	X 1.201	= US gallons (US gal)	X 0.833	= Imperial gallons (Imp gal)
US gallons (US gal)	X 3.785	= Litres (l)	X 0.264	= US gallons (US gal)

Mass (weight)

Ounces (oz)	X 28.35	= Grams (g)	X 0.035	= Ounces (oz)
Pounds (lb)	X 0.454	= Kilograms (kg)	X 2.205	= Pounds (lb)

Force

Ounces-force (ozf; oz)	X 0.278	= Newtons (N)	X 3.6	= Ounces-force (ozf; oz)
Pounds-force (lbf; lb)	X 4.448	= Newtons (N)	X 0.225	= Pounds-force (lbf; lb)
Newtons (N)	X 0.1	= Kilograms-force (kgf; kg)	X 9.81	= Newtons (N)

Pressure

Pounds-force per square inch (psi; lbf/in²; lb/in²)	X 0.070	= Kilograms-force per square centimetre (kgf/cm²; kg/cm²)	X 14.223	= Pounds-force per square inch (psi; lbf/in²; lb/in²)
Pounds-force per square inch (psi; lbf/in²; lb/in²)	X 0.068	= Atmospheres (atm)	X 14.696	= Pounds-force per square inch (psi; lbf/in²; lb/in²)
Pounds-force per square inch (psi; lbf/in²; lb/in²)	X 0.069	= Bars	X 14.5	= Pounds-force per square inch (psi; lbf/in²; lb/in²)
Pounds-force per square inch (psi; lbf/in²; lb/in²)	X 6.895	= Kilopascals (kPa)	X 0.145	= Pounds-force per square inch (psi; lbf/in²; lb/in²)
Kilopascals (kPa)	X 0.01	= Kilograms-force per square centimetre (kgf/cm²; kg/cm²)	X 98.1	= Kilopascals (kPa)
Millibar (mbar)	X 100	= Pascals (Pa)	X 0.01	= Millibar (mbar)
Millibar (mbar)	X 0.0145	= Pounds-force per square inch (psi; lbf/in²; lb/in²)	X 68.947	= Millibar (mbar)
Millibar (mbar)	X 0.75	= Millimetres of mercury (mmHg)	X 1.333	= Millibar (mbar)
Millibar (mbar)	X 0.401	= Inches of water (inH₂O)	X 2.491	= Millibar (mbar)
Millimetres of mercury (mmHg)	X 0.535	= Inches of water (inH₂O)	X 1.868	= Millimetres of mercury (mmHg)
Inches of water (inH₂O)	X 0.036	= Pounds-force per square inch (psi; lbf/in²; lb/in²)	X 27.68	= Inches of water (inH₂O)

Torque (moment of force)

Pounds-force inches (lbf in; lb in)	X 1.152	= Kilograms-force centimetre (kgf cm; kg cm)	X 0.868	= Pounds-force inches (lbf in; lb in)
Pounds-force inches (lbf in; lb in)	X 0.113	= Newton metres (Nm)	X 8.85	= Pounds-force inches (lbf in; lb in)
Pounds-force inches (lbf in; lb in)	X 0.083	= Pounds-force feet (lbf ft; lb ft)	X 12	= Pounds-force inches (lbf in; lb in)
Pounds-force feet (lbf ft; lb ft)	X 0.138	= Kilograms-force metres (kgf m; kg m)	X 7.233	= Pounds-force feet (lbf ft; lb ft)
Pounds-force feet (lbf ft; lb ft)	X 1.356	= Newton metres (Nm)	X 0.738	= Pounds-force feet (lbf ft; lb ft)
Newton metres (Nm)	X 0.102	= Kilograms-force metres (kgf m; kg m)	X 9.804	= Newton metres (Nm)

Power

Horsepower (hp)	X 745.7	= Watts (W)	X 0.0013	= Horsepower (hp)

Velocity (speed)

Miles per hour (miles/hr; mph)	X 1.609	= Kilometres per hour (km/hr; kph)	X 0.621	= Miles per hour (miles/hr; mph)

Fuel consumption*

Miles per gallon, Imperial (mpg)	X 0.354	= Kilometres per litre (km/l)	X 2.825	= Miles per gallon, Imperial (mpg)
Miles per gallon, US (mpg)	X 0.425	= Kilometres per litre (km/l)	X 2.352	= Miles per gallon, US (mpg)

Temperature

Degrees Fahrenheit = (°C x 1.8) + 32

Degrees Celsius (Degrees Centigrade; °C) = (°F - 32) x 0.56

*It is common practice to convert from miles per gallon (mpg) to litres/100 kilometres (l/100km), where mpg (Imperial) x l/100 km = 282 and mpg (US) x l/100 km = 235

Safety first!

Professional motor mechanics are trained in safe working procedures. However enthusiastic you may be about getting on with the job in hand, do take the time to ensure that your safety is not put at risk. A moment's lack of attention can result in an accident, as can failure to observe certain elementary precautions.

There will always be new ways of having accidents, and the following points do not pretend to be a comprehensive list of all dangers; they are intended rather to make you aware of the risks and to encourage a safety-conscious approach to all work you carry out on your vehicle.

Essential DOs and DON'Ts

DON'T rely on a single jack when working underneath the vehicle. Always use reliable additional means of support, such as axle stands, securely placed under a part of the vehicle that you know will not give way.

DON'T attempt to loosen or tighten high-torque nuts (e.g. wheel hub nuts) while the vehicle is on a jack; it may be pulled off.

DON'T start the engine without first ascertaining that the transmission is in neutral (or 'Park' where applicable) and the parking brake applied.

DON'T suddenly remove the filler cap from a hot cooling system – cover it with a cloth and release the pressure gradually first, or you may get scalded by escaping coolant.

DON'T attempt to drain oil until you are sure it has cooled sufficiently to avoid scalding you.

DON'T grasp any part of the engine, exhaust or catalytic converter without first ascertaining that it is sufficiently cool to avoid burning you.

DON'T allow brake fluid or antifreeze to contact vehicle paintwork.

DON'T syphon toxic liquids such as fuel, brake fluid or antifreeze by mouth, or allow them to remain on your skin.

DON'T inhale dust – it may be injurious to health (see *Asbestos* below).

DON'T allow any spilt oil or grease to remain on the floor – wipe it up straight away, before someone slips on it.

DON'T use ill-fitting spanners or other tools which may slip and cause injury.

DON'T attempt to lift a heavy component which may be beyond your capability – get assistance.

DON'T rush to finish a job, or take unverified short cuts.

DON'T allow children or animals in or around an unattended vehicle.

DO wear eye protection when using power tools such as drill, sander, bench grinder etc, and when working under the vehicle.

DO use a barrier cream on your hands prior to undertaking dirty jobs – it will protect your skin from infection as well as making the dirt easier to remove afterwards; but make sure your hands aren't left slippery. Note that long-term contact with used engine oil can be a health hazard.

DO keep loose clothing (cuffs, tie etc) and long hair well out of the way of moving mechanical parts.

DO remove rings, wristwatch etc, before working on the vehicle – especially the electrical system.

DO ensure that any lifting tackle used has a safe working load rating adequate for the job.

DO keep your work area tidy – it is only too easy to fall over articles left lying around.

DO get someone to check periodically that all is well, when working alone on the vehicle.

DO carry out work in a logical sequence and check that everything is correctly assembled and tightened afterwards.

DO remember that your vehicle's safety affects that of yourself and others. If in doubt on any point, get specialist advice.

IF, in spite of following these precautions, you are unfortunate enough to injure yourself, seek medical attention as soon as possible.

Asbestos

Certain friction, insulating, sealing, and other products – such as brake linings, brake bands, clutch linings, torque converters, gaskets, etc – contain asbestos. *Extreme care must be taken to avoid inhalation of dust from such products since it is hazardous to health.* If in doubt, assume that they *do* contain asbestos.

Fire

Remember at all times that petrol (gasoline) is highly flammable. Never smoke, or have any kind of naked flame around, when working on the vehicle. But the risk does not end there – a spark caused by an electrical short-circuit, by two metal surfaces contacting each other, by careless use of tools, or even by static electricity built up in your body under certain conditions, can ignite petrol vapour, which in a confined space is highly explosive.

Always disconnect the battery earth (ground) terminal before working on any part of the fuel or electrical system, and never risk spilling fuel on to a hot engine or exhaust.

It is recommended that a fire extinguisher of a type suitable for fuel and electrical fires is kept handy in the garage or workplace at all times. Never try to extinguish a fuel or electrical fire with water.

Note: *Any reference to a 'torch' appearing in this manual should always be taken to mean a hand-held battery-operated electric lamp or flashlight. It does NOT mean a welding/gas torch or blowlamp.*

Fumes

Certain fumes are highly toxic and can quickly cause unconsciousness and even death if inhaled to any extent. Petrol (gasoline) vapour comes into this category, as do the vapours from certain solvents such as trichloroethylene. Any draining or pouring of such volatile fluids should be done in a well ventilated area.

When using cleaning fluids and solvents, read the instructions carefully. Never use materials from unmarked containers – they may give off poisonous vapours.

Never run the engine of a motor vehicle in an enclosed space such as a garage. Exhaust fumes contain carbon monoxide which is extremely poisonous; if you need to run the engine, always do so in the open air or at least have the rear of the vehicle outside the workplace.

If you are fortunate enough to have the use of an inspection pit, never drain or pour petrol, and never run the engine, while the vehicle is standing over it; the fumes, being heavier than air, will concentrate in the pit with possibly lethal results.

The battery

Never cause a spark, or allow a naked light, near the vehicle's battery. It will normally be giving off a certain amount of hydrogen gas, which is highly explosive.

Always disconnect the battery earth (ground) terminal before working on the fuel or electrical systems.

If possible, loosen the filler plugs or cover when charging the battery from an external source. Do not charge at an excessive rate or the battery may burst.

Take care when topping up and when carrying the battery. The acid electrolyte, even when diluted, is very corrosive and should not be allowed to contact the eyes or skin.

If you ever need to prepare electrolyte yourself, always add the acid slowly to the water, and never the other way round. Protect against splashes by wearing rubber gloves and goggles.

When jump starting a car using a booster battery, for negative earth (ground) vehicles, connect the jump leads in the following sequence: First connect one jump lead between the positive ($+$) terminals of the two batteries. Then connect the other jump lead first to the negative ($-$) terminal of the booster battery, and then to a good earthing (ground) point on the vehicle to be started, at least 18 in (45 cm) from the battery if possible. Ensure that hands and jump leads are clear of any moving parts, and that the two vehicles do not touch. Disconnect the leads in the reverse order.

Mains electricity and electrical equipment

When using an electric power tool, inspection light etc, always ensure that the appliance is correctly connected to its plug and that, where necessary, it is properly earthed (grounded). Do not use such appliances in damp conditions and, again, beware of creating a spark or applying excessive heat in the vicinity of fuel or fuel vapour. Also ensure that the appliances meet the relevant national safety standards.

Ignition HT voltage

A severe electric shock can result from touching certain parts of the ignition system, such as the HT leads, when the engine is running or being cranked, particularly if components are damp or the insulation is defective. Where an electronic ignition system is fitted, the HT voltage is much higher and could prove fatal.

Routine maintenance

Maintenance is essential for ensuring safety, and desirable for the purpose of getting the best in terms of performance and economy from your car. Over the years the need for periodic lubrication has been greatly reduced if not totally eliminated. This has unfortunately tended to lead some owners to think that, because no such action is required, the items either no longer exist, or will last forever. This is certainly not the case; it is essential to carry out regular visual examination as comprehensively as possible in order to spot any possible defects at an early stage before they develop into major expensive repairs.

The following service schedules are a list of the maintenance requirements and the intervals at which they should be carried out, as recommended by the manufacturers. Where applicable these procedures are covered in greater detail throughout this manual, near the beginning of each Chapter.

Where a vehicle covers a low annual mileage, follow the time intervals to determine when maintenance is due. Some fluids and components deteriorate with age as well as with use.

Vehicles which operate under adverse conditions (eg in extremes of temperature, or full-time trailer towing, or mainly on short journeys) may benefit from more frequent maintenance than specified. If in doubt consult a GM dealer.

Weekly or before a long journey

Check engine oil level (Chapter 1)
Check coolant level (Chapter 2)
Top up the washer reservoir (Chapter 12), adding a screen wash such as Turtle Wax High Tech Screen Wash
Check tyre pressures (cold), including the spare (Chapter 10)

Every 9000 miles (15 000 km) or 12 months   whichever comes first

---

Engine (Chapter 1)
Change engine oil and renew oil filter

Cooling system (Chapter 2)
Check cooling system for leaks
Check cooling fan/alternator drivebelt

Fuel and exhaust systems (Chapter 3)
Renew the air cleaner element
Check and adjust the idling speed and mixture
Examine the fuel lines
Lubricate the throttle controls
Clean the carburettor fuel inlet pipe strainer

Ignition system (Chapter 4)
Clean and check the distributor cap, rotor arm, HT leads and ignition coil

Automatic transmission (Chapter 6)
Check automatic transmission fluid level

Final drive and driveshafts (Chapter 8)
Check final drive unit oil level
Check driveshaft rubber bellows

Braking system (Chapter 9)
Check and if necessary top up the brake fluid level
Check brake pad linings for wear
Check the hydraulic brake lines and hoses for damage
Check vacuum servo unit operation

Suspension and steering (Chapter 10)
Check steering and suspension balljoints
Check power steering pump drivebelt
Check tyres for wear and damage

Bodywork and fittings (Chapter 11)
Lubricate hinges and locks (only at 9000, 27 000, 45 000 miles etc)
Check underbody protection

Electrical system (Chapter 12)
Check the washer system and wiper blades
Check the headlamp beam alignment
Check operation of all electrical equipment

Under-bonnet view of a 1.8 GL Saloon

1 Brake fluid reservoir
2 Brake vacuum servo unit
3 Steering gear
4 Throttle housing
5 Auxiliary air valve (step up valve) for power steering
6 Distributor
7 Engine oil filler cap

8 Engine oil level dipstick
9 Additional relay box
10 Front suspension top mounting
11 Power steering fluid reservoir
12 Washer fluid reservoir
13 Ignition coil

14 Battery
15 Top hose
16 Power steering pump
17 Thermostat housing
18 Radiator
19 Alternator/cooling fan drivebelt

20 Alternator
21 Air cleaner cover
22 Airflow sensor
23 Coolant expansion tank
24 Brake master cylinder
25 Ignition control unit

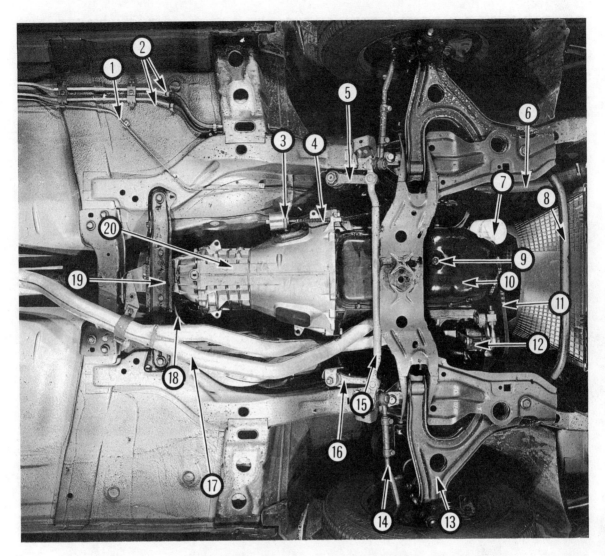

Front underside view of a 1.8 GL Saloon

1 Rear hydraulic brake line
2 Fuel feed and return pipes
3 Clutch release arm
4 Clutch cable
5 Steering drop arm
6 Bottom hose

7 Oil filter cartridge
8 Front anti-roll bar
9 Engine oil drain plug
10 Engine oil sump
11 Power steering pump
     drivebelt

12 Power steering pump
13 Front lower suspension arm
14 Steering tie-rod (side)
15 Steering tie-rod (centre)
16 Steering idler

17 Exhaust front downpipe
18 Speedometer cable
19 Manual gearbox rear
     mounting crossmember
20 Manual gearbox

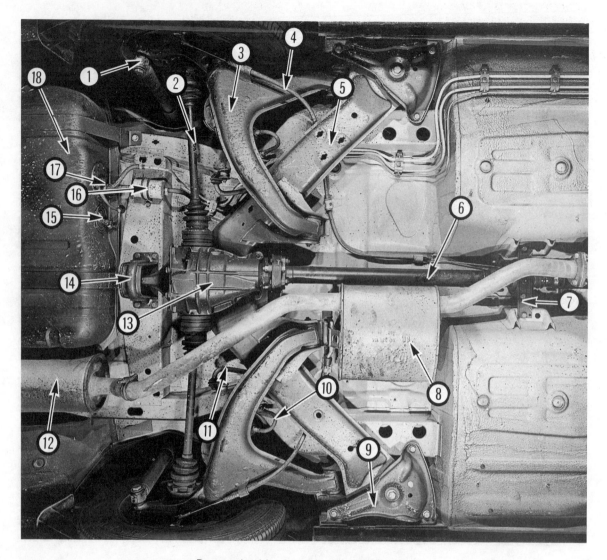

Rear underside view of a 1.8 GL Saloon

1 Rear shock absorber	6 Propeller shaft	10 Rear hydraulic brake hose	15 Fuel gauge sender unit
2 Driveshaft	7 Propeller shaft centre	11 Rear anti-roll bar	16 Fuel filter
3 Rear semi-trailing arm	bearing	12 Rear exhaust section	17 Tank-mounted fuel pump
4 Handbrake cable	8 Intermediate exhaust section	13 Final drive unit	18 Fuel tank
5 Rear suspension	9 Rear crossmember front	14 Final drive rear damping	
crossmember	mounting	bracket	

Every 18 000 miles (30 000 km) or two years – whichever comes first

Fuel and exhaust systems (Chapter 3)
Renew the fuel filter on fuel injection engines only

Ignition system (Chapter 4)
Renew the spark plugs

Clutch (Chapter 5)
Check clutch pedal adjustment

Manual gearbox (Chapter 6)
Check manual gearbox oil level

Braking system (Chapter 9)
Check handbrake shoe linings for wear

Suspension and steering (Chapter 10)
Check power steering fluid level

Bodywork and fittings (Chapter 11)
Check air conditioning system

Every 27 000 miles (45 000 km) or three years – whichever comes first

Automatic transmission (Chapter 6)
Change automatic transmission fluid

Every 36 000 miles (60 000 km) or four years – whichever comes first

Engine (Chapter 1)
Check timing belt

Every 63 000 miles (105 000 km) or seven years – whichever comes first

Engine (Chapter 1)
Renew timing belt

Annually, regardless of mileage

Braking system (Chapter 9)
Renew the hydraulic brake fluid

Every two years, regardless of mileage

Cooling system (Chapter 2)
Renew coolant

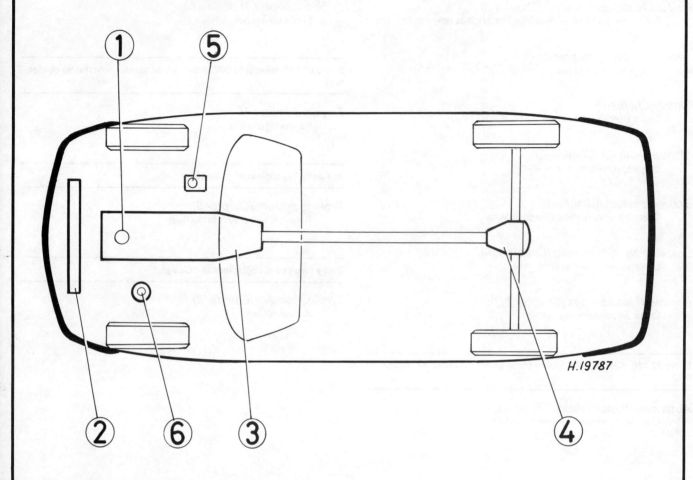

H.19787

Recommended lubricants and fluids

Component or system	Lubricant type/specifcation	Duckhams recomendation
Engine (1)	Multigrade engine oil, viscosity range SAE 10W/40 to 20W/50, to API SF/CC or better	Duckhams QXR, Hypergrade or 10W/40 Motor Oil
Cooling system (2)	Ethylene glycol based antifreeze, to GM spec GME L 6368, and soft water	Duckhams Universal Antifreeze and Summer Coolant
Manual gearbox (3)	Gear oil, GM type 19 40 761 (90 297 261)	Duckhams Hypoid 75W/90S
Automatic transmission (3)	Dexron II type ATF	Duckhams Uni-Matic or D-Matic

Final drive (4):
    Standard differential
    Limited slip differential
	Hypoid gear oil, viscosity SAE 90
	GM special lubricant 19 42 382 (9 293 688)
		Duckhams Hypoid 90S
		Duckhams Hypoid 90DL

Brake hydraulic system (5)	Hydraulic fluid to FMVSS 571 or 116, DOT 3 or 4, or SAE J1703	Duckhams Universal Brake and Clutch Fluid
Power steering (6)	Dexron II type ATF	Duckhams Uni-Matic or D-Matic

Fault diagnosis

Introduction

The vehicle owner who does his or her own maintenance according to the recommended schedules should not have to use this section of the manual very often. Modern component reliability is such that, provided those items subject to wear or deterioration are inspected or renewed at the specified intervals, sudden failure is comparatively rare. Faults do not usually just happen as a result of sudden failure, but develop over a period of time. Major mechanical failures in particular are usually preceded by characteristic symptoms over hundreds or even thousands of miles. Those components which do occasionally fail without warning are often small and easily carried in the vehicle.

With any fault finding, the first step is to decide where to begin investigations. Sometimes this is obvious, but on other occasions a little detective work will be necessary. The owner who makes half a dozen haphazard adjustments or replacements may be successful in curing a fault (or its symptoms), but he will be none the wiser if the fault recurs and he may well have spent more time and money than was necessary. A calm and logical approach will be found to be more satisfactory in the long run. Always take into account any warning signs or abnormalities that may have been noticed in the period preceding the fault – power loss, high or low gauge readings, unusual noises or smells, etc – and remember that failure of components such as fuses or spark plugs may only be pointers to some underlying fault.

The pages which follow here are intended to help in cases of failure to start or breakdown on the road. There is also a Fault Diagnosis Section at the end of each Chapter which should be consulted if the preliminary checks prove unfruitful. Whatever the fault, certain basic principles apply. These are as follows:

Verify the fault. This is simply a matter of being sure that you know what the symptoms are before starting work. This is particularly important if you are investigating a fault for someone else who may not have described it very accurately.

Don't overlook the obvious. For example, if the vehicle won't start, is there petrol in the tank? (Don't take anyone else's word on this particular point, and don't trust the fuel gauge either!) If an electrical fault is indicated, look for loose or broken wires before digging out the test gear.

Cure the disease, not the symptom. Substituting a flat battery with a fully charged one will get you off the hard shoulder, but if the underlying cause is not attended to, the new battery will go the same way. Similarly, changing oil-fouled spark plugs for a new set will get you moving again, but remember that the reason for the fouling (if it wasn't simply an incorrect grade of plug) will have to be established and corrected.

Don't take anything for granted. Particularly, don't forget that a 'new' component may itself be defective (especially if it's been rattling round in the boot for months), and don't leave components out of a fault diagnosis sequence just because they are new or recently fitted. When you do finally diagnose a difficult fault, you'll probably realise that all the evidence was there from the start.

Electrical faults

Electrical faults can be more puzzling than straightforward mechanical failures, but they are no less susceptible to logical analysis if the basic principles of operation are understood. Vehicle electrical wiring exists in extremely unfavourable conditions – heat, vibration and chemical attack – and the first things to look for are loose or corroded connections and broken or chafed wires, especially where the wires pass through holes in the bodywork or are subject to vibration.

All metal-bodied vehicles in current production have one pole of the battery 'earthed', ie connected to the vehicle bodywork, and in nearly all modern vehicles it is the negative (–) terminal. The various electrical components – motors, bulb holders etc – are also connected to earth, either by means of a lead or directly by their mountings. Electric current flows through the component and then back to the battery via the bodywork. If the component mounting is loose or corroded, or if a good path back to the battery is not available, the circuit will be incomplete and malfunction will result. The engine and/or gearbox are also earthed by means of flexible metal straps to the body or subframe; if these straps are loose or missing, starter motor, generator and ignition trouble may result.

Assuming the earth return to be satisfactory, electrical faults will be due either to component malfunction or to defects in the current supply. Individual components are dealt with in Chapter 12. If supply wires are broken or cracked internally this results in an open-circuit, and the easiest way to check for this is to bypass the suspect wire temporarily with a length of wire having a crocodile clip or suitable connector at each end. Alternatively, a 12V test lamp can be used to verify the presence of supply voltage at various points along the wire and the break can be thus isolated.

If a bare portion of a live wire touches the bodywork or other earthed metal part, the electricity will take the low-resistance path thus formed back to the battery: this is known as a short-circuit. Hopefully a short-circuit will blow a fuse, but otherwise it may cause burning of the insulation (and possibly further short-circuits) or even a fire. This is why it is inadvisable to bypass persistently blowing fuses with silver foil or wire.

Spares and tool kit

Most vehicles are supplied only with sufficient tools for wheel changing; the *Maintenance and minor repair* tool kit detailed in *Tools and working facilities,* with the addition of a hammer, is probably sufficient for those repairs that most motorists would consider attempting at the roadside. In addition a few items which can be fitted without too much trouble in the event of a breakdown should be carried. Experience and available space will modify the list below, but the following may save having to call on professional assistance:

Spark plugs, clean and correctly gapped
HT lead and plug cap – long enough to reach the plug furthest from the distributor
Distributor rotor
Drivebelt(s) – emergency type may suffice
Spare fuses
Set of principal light bulbs
Tin of radiator sealer and hose bandage
Exhaust bandage
Roll of insulating tape
Length of soft iron wire
Length of electrical flex
Torch or inspection lamp (can double as test lamp)

Carrying a few spares may save a long walk!

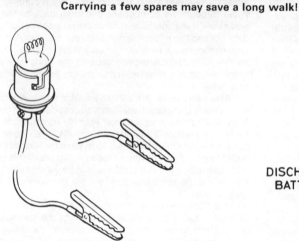

A simple test lamp is useful for tracing electrical faults

Battery jump leads
Tow-rope
Ignition water dispersant aerosol
Litre of engine oil
Sealed can of hydraulic fluid
Emergency windscreen
Worm drive clips

If spare fuel is carried, a can designed for the purpose should be used to minimise risks of leakage and collision damage. A first aid kit and a warning triangle, whilst not at present compulsory in the UK, are obviously sensible items to carry in addition to the above.

When touring abroad it may be advisable to carry additional spares which, even if you cannot fit them yourself, could save having to wait while parts are obtained. The items below may be worth considering:

Clutch and throttle cables
Cylinder head gasket
Alternator brushes
Starter motor brushes
Tyre valve core

One of the motoring organisations will be able to advise on availability of fuel etc in foreign countries.

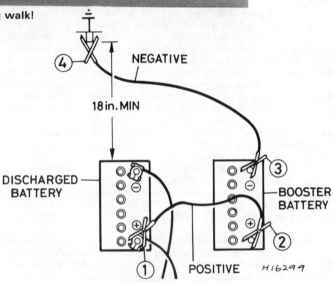

Jump start lead connections for negative earth vehicles — connect leads in order shown

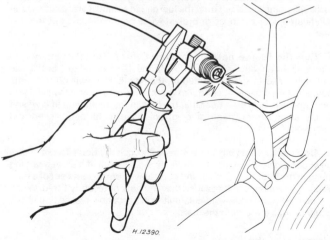

Crank engine and check for spark. Note use of insulated tool to hold plug lead

Engine will not start

Engine fails to turn when starter operated

Flat battery (recharge, use jump leads, or push start)
Battery terminals loose or corroded
Battery earth to body defective
Engine earth strap loose or broken
Starter motor (or solenoid) wiring loose or broken
Automatic transmission selector in wrong position, or inhibitor switch faulty
Ignition/starter switch faulty
Major mechanical failure (seizure)
Starter or solenoid internal fault (see Chapter 12)

Starter motor turns engine slowly

Partially discharged battery (recharge, use jump leads, or push start)
Battery terminals loose or corroded
Battery earth to body defective
Engine earth strap loose
Starter motor (or solenoid) wiring loose
Starter motor internal fault (see Chapter 12)

Starter motor spins without turning engine

Flywheel gear teeth damaged or worn
Starter motor mounting bolts loose

Engine turns normally but fails to start

Damp or dirty HT leads and distributor cap (crank engine and check for spark) – try moisture dispersant such as Holts Wet Start
No fuel in tank (check for delivery)
Excessive choke (hot engine) or insufficient choke (cold engine)
Fouled or incorrectly gapped spark plugs (remove and regap, or renew)
Other ignition system fault (see Chapter 4)
Other fuel system fault (see Chapter 3)
Poor compression (see Chapter 1)
Major mechanical failure (eg camshaft drive)

Engine fires but will not run

Insufficient choke (cold engine)
Air leaks at carburettor or inlet manifold
Fuel starvation (see Chapter 3)
Ignition fault (see Chapter 4)

Engine cuts out and will not restart

Engine cuts out suddenly — ignition fault

Loose or disconnected LT wires
Wet HT leads or distributor cap (after traversing water splash)
Coil failure (check for spark)
Other ignition fault (see Chapter 4)

Engine misfires before cutting out — fuel fault

Fuel tank empty
Fuel pump defective or filter blocked (check for delivery)
Fuel tank filler vent blocked (suction will be evident on releasing cap)
Carburettor needle valve sticking
Carburettor jets blocked (fuel contaminated)
Other fuel system fault (see Chapter 3)

Engine cuts out — other causes

Serious overheating
Major mechanical failure (eg camshaft drive)

Engine overheats

Ignition (no-charge) warning light illuminated

Slack or broken drivebelt — retension or renew (Chapter 2)

Ignition warning light not illuminated

Coolant loss due to internal or external leakage (see Chapter 2)
Thermostat defective
Low oil level
Brakes binding
Radiator clogged externally or internally
Thermo-viscous cooling fan not operating correctly
Engine waterways clogged
Ignition timing incorrect or automatic advance malfunctioning
Mixture too weak

Note: *Do not add cold water to an overheated engine or damage may result*

Low engine oil pressure

Gauge reads low or warning light illuminated with engine running

Oil level low or incorrect grade
Defective gauge or sender unit
Wire to sender unit earthed
Engine overheating
Oil filter clogged or bypass valve defective
Oil pressure relief valve defective
Oil pick-up strainer clogged
Oil pump worn or mountings loose
Worn main or big-end bearings

Note: *Low oil pressure in a high-mileage engine at tickover is not necessarily a cause for concern. Sudden pressure loss at speed is far more significant. In any event, check the gauge or warning light sender before condemning the engine.*

Engine noises

Pre-ignition (pinking) on acceleration

Incorrect grade of fuel
Ignition timing incorrect
Worn or maladjusted carburettor
Excessive carbon build-up in engine

Whistling or wheezing noises

Leaking vacuum hose
Leaking carburettor or manifold gasket
Blowing head gasket

Tapping or rattling

Faulty hydraulic valve lifter
Worn valve gear
Worn timing belt
Broken piston ring (ticking noise)

Knocking or thumping

Unintentional mechanical contact (eg fan blades)
Worn drivebelt
Peripheral component fault (generator, water pump etc)
Worn big-end bearings (regular heavy knocking, perhaps less under load)
Worn main bearings (rumbling and knocking, perhaps worsening under load)
Piston slap (most noticeable when cold)

Chapter 1 Engine

For information applicable to later models, see Supplement at end of manual

Contents

Specifications

Type	Four cylinder, in-line, single overhead camshaft

General

	1.8	**2.0**
Bore	84.8 mm (3.341 in)	86.0 mm (3.388 in)
Stroke	79.5 mm (3.132 in)	96.0 mm (3.388 in)
Displacement	1796 cc	1998 cc
Compression ratio	10.0 : 1	10.0 1

Maximum output:	
18SV	90 bhp (66 kW) @ 5200 rpm
18SEH	115 bhp (85 kW) @ 5600 rpm
20SE	122 bhp (90 kW) @ 5400 rpm

Maximum torque:	
18SV	109.2 lbf ft @ 3400 rpm
18SEH	118 lbf ft @ 4600 rpm
20SE	129 lbf ft @ 2600 rpm
Firing order	1-3-4-2 (No 1 at timing belt end of engine)

Valves

Valve timing:	**18SV**	**18SEH and 20SE**
Inlet opens BTDC	29°	23°
Inlet closes ABDC	65°	71°
Exhaust opens BBDC	66°	60°
Exhaust closes ATDC	29°	35°
Length	104 .2 mm (4.1055 in)	

Head diameter:	
Inlet	41.8 mm (1.6469 in)
Exhaust	36.5 mm (1.4381 in)
Seat angle	44°

Cylinder head

Valve play in guides:	
Inlet	0.015 to 0.042 mm (0.0006 to 0.0017 in)
Exhaust	0.03 to 0.06 mm (0.0012 to 0.0024 in)
Valve seat angle	45°
Overall height	95.75 to 96.25 mm (3.7725 to 3.7923 in)
Maximum distortion	0.025 mm (0.0010 in)

Pistons and bores

	Piston	Bore
0.5 mm Oversize combinations for 18SV and 18SEH engines	85.255 to 85.265 mm (3.3591 to 3.3594 in)	85.265 to 85.275 mm (3.3594 to 3.3598 in)
	85.265 to 85.275 mm (3.3594 to 3.3598 in)	85.275 to 85.285 mm (3.3598 to 3.3602 in)
	85.275 to 85.285 mm (3.3598 to 3.3602 in)	85.285 to 85.295 mm (3.3602 to 3.3606 in)
	85.285 to 85.295 mm (3.3602 to 3.3606 in)	85.295 to 85.305 mm (3.3606 to 3.3610 in)

	Piston	Bore
Oversize combinations for 20SE engine:		
0.5 mm	86.93 mm (3.4250 in)	86.97 mm (3.4266 in)
	86.94 mm (3.4254 in)	86.98 mm (3.4270 in)
	86.95 mm (3.4258 in)	86.99 mm (3.4274 in)
	86.96 mm (3.4262 in)	87.00 mm (3.4278 in)
1.0 mm	87.43 mm (3.4447 in)	87.47 mm (3.4463 in)
	87.44 mm (3.4451 in)	87.48 mm (3.4467 in)
	87.45 mm (3.4455 in)	87.49 mm (3.4471 in)
	87.46 mm (3.4459 in)	87.50 mm (3.4475 in)

Maximum bore ovality .... 0.013 mm (0.0005 in)
Maximum bore taper .... 0.013 mm (0.0005 in)
Piston projection above block .... 0.33 mm (0.0130 in)
Piston-to-bore clearance .... 0.02 to 0.04 mm (0.0008 to 0.0016 in)
Piston ring gap:
    Compression (1 and 2) .... 0.3 to 0.5 mm (0.0118 to 0.0197 in)
    Oil control ring .... 0.4 to 1.4 mm (0.0158 to 0.0591 in)

Crankshaft

Main bearing journal diameter (standard) .... 57.972 to 57.995 mm (2.2841 to 2.2850 in)
Crankpin journal diameter (standard) .... 48.971 to 48.987 mm (1.9295 to 1.9301 in)
Undersize .... −0.50 mm (−0.0197 in)
Maximum out-of-round .... 0.04 mm (0.0016 in)
Maximum run-out .... 0.03 mm (0.0012 in)
Endfloat .... 0.07 to 0.3 mm (0.003 to 0.012 in)
Maximum main bearing radial clearance .... 0.015 to 0.04 mm (0.0006 to 0.0016 in)
Maximum big-end bearing radial clearance .... 0.019 to 0.063 mm (0.0008 to 0.0025 in)

Camshaft

Endfloat .... 0.09 to 0.21 mm (0.004 to 0.008 in)
Maximum run-out .... 0.03 mm (0.0012 in)

Timing belt

Tension (using gauge KM-510-A):
    New belt, cold 4.5
    New belt, warm 7.5
    Used belt, cold 2.5
    Used belt, warm 7.0

Flywheel

Ring gear maximum run-out .... 0.5 mm (0.02 in)
Maximum machining of clutch face .... 0.3 mm (0.012 in)

Lubrication system

Oil type/specification .... Multigrade engine oil, viscosity range SAE 10W/40 to 20W/50, to API SF/CC or better (Duckhams QXR, Hypergrade, or 10W/40 Motor Oil)
Capacity (with filter) .... 4.5 litres (7.9 pints)
Difference between Min and Max on dipstick .... 1.0 litre (1.76 pints)
Oil pressure at idle (engine warm) .... 1.5 bar (21.75 lbf/in²)
Oil pump:
    Gear backlash .... 0.1 to 0.2 mm (0.004 to 0.008 in)
    Gear endfloat .... 0.03 to 0.10 mm (0.001 to 0.004 in)
Oil filter .... Champion G102 (all models)

Torque wrench settings

	Nm	lbf ft
Camshaft sprocket	45	33
Crankshaft pulley bolt:		
Stage 1	130	96
Stage 2	Plus 40 to 50°	Plus 40 to 50°
Pulley/vibration damper to sprocket	20	15
Flywheel/driveplate:		
Stage 1	60	44
Stage 2	Plus 30 to 45°	Plus 30 to 45°

Torque wrench settings (continued)

	Nm	lbf ft
Cylinder head bolts:		
Stage 1	25	19
Stage 2	Plus 60°	Plus 60°
Stage 3	Plus 60°	Plus 60°
Stage 4	Plus 60°	Plus 60°
Stage 5: Warm up engine, then	Plus 30°	Plus 30°
Main bearing cap:		
Stage 1	50	37
Stage 2	Plus 40 to 50°	Plus 40 to 50°
Big-end cap:		
Stage 1	35	26
Stage 2	Plus 45 to 60°	Plus 45 to 60°
Sump	5	4
Oil drain plug	45	33

1   General description

The engine is of four-cylinder, in-line type with a single overhead camshaft, mounted conventionally at the front of the car. The cylinder head is of alloy and the cylinder block of cast iron.

The crankshaft is supported in five bearings, and the centre bearing incorporates flanges to control the endfloat.

The connecting rods are attached to the crankshaft by horizontally split shell bearings, and to the pistons by gudgeon pins which are an interference fit in the connecting rod small-end. The aluminium alloy pistons are fitted with three piston rings: two compression rings and a three segment oil control ring.

The camshaft is driven by a toothed rubber belt from the crankshaft, and operates the valves via rocker arms. The rocker arms are supported at their pivot end by hydraulic self-adjusting valve lifters (tappets), which automatically take up any clearance between the rocker arm and the valve stems. The inlet and exhaust valves are each closed by a single spring and operate in guides pressed into the cylinder head.

Engine lubrication is by a bi-rotor pump located in a housing attached to the front of the cylinder block. The oil pump is driven by the crankshaft, while the distributor rotor arm and, on carburettor models, the fuel pump, are driven by the camshaft. Blow-by gases in the crankcase are fed to the camshaft housing by an external tube and thereafter drawn into the inlet manifold via a hose.

2   Routine maintenance

1   Carry out the following procedures at the intervals given in *Routine Maintenance* at the front of this manual.

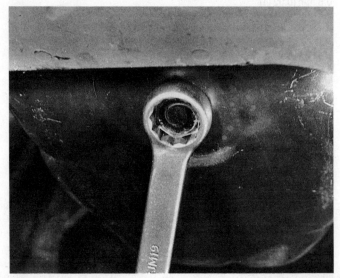

2.6 Engine oil drain plug

Check/renew timing belt

2   Unclip and remove the timing belt covers, and examine the full length of the timing belt for signs of damage and fraying.
3   Check the tension of the timing belt, and if necessary adjust as described in Section 13.
4   Refit the covers.

Change engine oil and renew oil filter

5   Position the vehicle over an inspection pit, or apply the handbrake, jack up the front and support it on axle stands.
6   Place a suitable container beneath the sump, then unscrew the drain plug (photo)
7   While the oil is draining, unscrew the oil filter cartridge using a strap wrench (photo).
8   Clean the drain plug and sump, then refit the plug and tighten it to the specified torque.
9   Clean the filter contact area on the oil pump.
10   Smear a film of oil on the new oil filter rubber gasket. Screw on the oil filter and tighten by hand only.
11   Remove the filler cap on the front of the camshaft cover and fill the engine with the specified quantity and grade of oil. Refit the cap.
12   Lower the car to the ground.
13   With the car on level ground, remove the oil level dipstick and wipe it clean, then re-insert it and remove it again. The oil level should be up to the maximum mark.
14   If necessary top up the level, noting that the distance between the minimum and maximum level marks represents approximately 1.0 litre (1.76 pints) (photos).

3   Major operations possible with engine in car

The following major operations can be carried out without removing the engine from the car:
(a)   Removal and refitting of cylinder head
(b)   Removal and refitting of sump
(c)   Removal and refitting of oil pump
(d)   Removal and refitting of timing belt
(e)   Removal and refitting of pistons and connecting rods
(f)   Removal and refitting of flywheel
(g)   Removal and refitting of engine mountings
(h)   Removal and refitting of camshaft
(i)   Renewal of the crankshaft front and rear oil seals

4   Major operation requiring engine removal

The following major operation is only possible after removal of the engine.
(a)   Removal and refitting of crankshaft and main bearings

5   Method of engine removal

Although it is possible to remove the engine together with the

Fig.1.1 Cutaway view of the 2.0 litre injection engine (Sec 1)

manual gearbox or automatic transmission, it is recommended that the engine be removed separately. A strong hoist will still be necessary as the engine alone is of considerable weight. The engine is removed upwards from the engine compartment.

6   Engine – removal

1   Remove the bonnet as described in Chapter 11.

2   Disconnect the battery negative lead.

3   Remove the air cleaner on carburettor models, or disconnect and remove the air duct from the throttle housing and airflow sensor on fuel injection models.

4   Remove the radiator as described in Chapter 2.

5   Disconnect the accelerator cable, choke cable, automatic transmission kickdown cable, and cruise control cable as applicable.

6   Unbolt the power-assisted steering pump and bracket assembly and place it on one side (photos). There is no need to disconnect the hoses.

2.7   Removing the oil filter cartridge

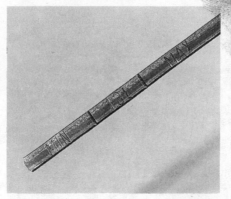

2.14A   Engine oil level dipstick markings

2.14B   Topping up the engine oil

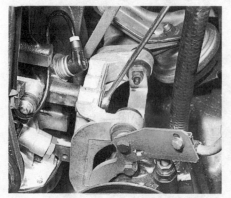

6.6A   Unscrew the bolts ...

6.6B   ... and remove the power steering pump and bracket assembly

6.8   Heater hose connections at the bulkhead

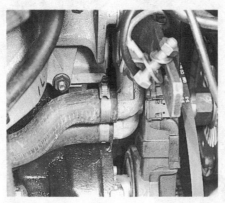

6.11A   Hose connections to the front coolant housing

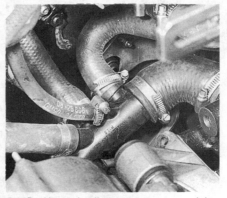

6.11B   Hoses leading to water pump inlet

7   If fitted, remove the air conditioning compressor (Chapter 11) and place it on one side without disconnecting the refrigerant hoses.

8   Disconnect the heater hoses at the bulkhead (photo)

9   Disconnect and plug the fuel feed and return hoses. Unbolt the mounting bracket from the inlet manifold.

10   Disconnect the HT cable from the ignition coil.

11   Note the location of the coolant hoses on the right-hand side of the engine then disconnect them (photos). Also disconnect the brake vacuum servo hose.

12   Unbolt the engine earth strap(s) (photo).

13   Disconnect the top hose from the thermostat housing.

14   Note the location and routing of the engine wiring harness, and make a simple drawing of it if necessary. Disconnect and remove the harness. To ensure quick and accurate refitting, identify each wire with tape as it is removed. On fuel injection models the harness must be disconnected on the top of the engine (photo) and at the airflow sensor.

15   Apply the handbrake, then jack up the front of the car and support it on axle stands.

16   Unbolt the exhaust downpipe from the exhaust manifold and remove the gasket. Where applicable unbolt the exhaust bracket at the rear of the gearbox.

17   Unbolt and remove the gearbox front cover.

18   On manual gearbox models disconnect the clutch cable from the release arm and gearbox.

19   On automatic transmission models unscrew the bolts securing the torque converter to the driveplate with reference to Chapter 6.

20   Unscrew the lower bolts securing the gearbox to the engine.

21   Lower the car to the ground.

22   Attach a hoist to the engine and just take its weight. Lifting eyes are provided at the front and rear of the engine.

23   Support the gearbox with a trolley jack.

24   Unscrew the nuts from the top of both engine mountings, and unbolt the right-hand mounting bracket from the block (photos).

25   Unscrew the upper bolts securing the gearbox to the engine.

26   Pull the engine forwards to disengage it from the gearbox/automatic transmission. On automatic transmission models make sure that the torque converter is held firmly in contact with the transmission oil pump, otherwise it could fall out and fluid would be spilled.

6.12 Engine earth strap

6.14 Wiring harness connector on the top of the fuel injection engine

6.24A Front left-hand engine mounting

6.24B Removing the engine mounting nuts

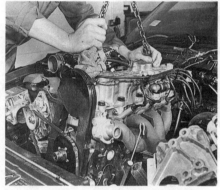

6.27 Lifting the engine from the engine compartment

27   When clear of the gearbox, lift the engine from the engine compartment while guiding it past the surrounding components (photo).
28   If the engine is to be dismantled, drain the oil and refit the drain plug before lowering the engine onto the workbench.

7 Engine dismantling – general

The engine should be dismantled in a clean area away from dust and dirt. Avoid working with the engine directly on a concrete floor, as grit presents a real source of trouble.

It is advisable to have suitable containers to hold small items, as this will help when reassembling the engine.

Thoroughly clean all components with a suitable solvent and wipe dry ready for inspection. Internal channels are best blown through with an air line.

Always obtain complete sets of gaskets when dismantling the engine, and fit them all.

When possible refit nuts, bolts and washers in their locations as this helps to protect the threads from damage and will also be helpful when the engine is being reassembled.

Retain unserviceable items until the new parts are obtained, so that the new part can be checked against the old part, to ensure that the correct item has been supplied.

8 Engine ancillaries – removal

Although the items listed may be removed separately with the engine installed, it is more appropriate to take these off after the engine has been removed from the car when extensive dismantling is being

carried out. The items are:

Carburettor or fuel injection components (Chapter 3)
Fuel pump on carburettor models (Chapter 3)
Inlet and exhaust manifolds (Chapter 3)
Clutch (Chapter 5)
Spark plugs, distributor cap and plate, and ignition inductive impulse sensor (Chapter 4)
Alternator and bracket (Chapter 12)
Thermo-viscous cooling fan, thermostat, and temperature gauge sender unit (Chapter 2)

9 Engine – complete dismantling

1   Using a screwdriver, prise the oil seal for the distributor plate from the rear of the camshaft housing (photo).
2   Unscrew and remove the oil pressure switch (photo).
3   Remove the oil dipstick.
4   Disconnect the crankcase ventilation hose from the camshaft cover (photo).
5   On fuel injection models use an Allen key to unscrew the auxiliary air valve bracket from the camshaft housing (photo). Recover the gasket.
6   Unbolt the camshaft cover and remove the cork gasket. Note the location of the HT lead bracket (photos).
7   Remove the cooling fan pulley by holding the hub stationary with a spanner while removing the pulley screws (photos).
8   Unclip and remove the two timing belt covers (photos).
9   Turn the engine with a spanner on the crankshaft pulley bolt until the mark on the camshaft sprocket is aligned with the pointer on the top of the rear timing belt cover. Also align the notch in the crankshaft pulley with the pointer on the lower part of the rear timing belt cover (photos).
10   Using an Allen key, loosen the three bolts securing the water pump to the block.

9.1 Prising the oil seal from the rear of the camshaft housing

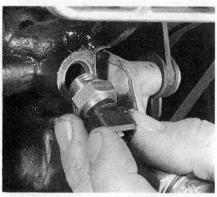

9.2 Removing the oil pressure switch

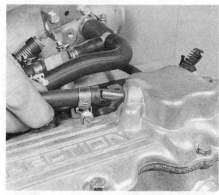

9.4 Disconnecting the crankcase ventilation hose

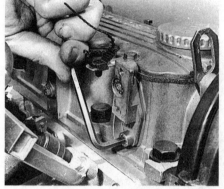

9.5 Removing the auxiliary air valve bracket on the fuel injection engine

9.6A Removing the camshaft cover ...

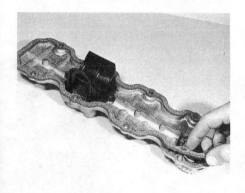

9.6B ... and gasket

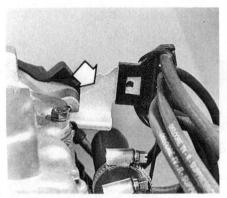

9.6C HT lead bracket (arrowed)

9.7A Remove the screws ...

9.7B ... and withdraw the cooling fan pulley

9.8A Release the clips ...

9.8B ... and remove the timing belt upper cover ...

9.8C ... and lower cover

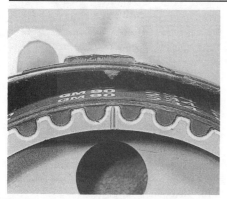

9.9A   Camshaft sprocket and cover timing marks

9.9B   Crankshaft pulley notch and timing pointer

9.12   Tool for holding the flywheel stationary

9.13   Removing the crankshaft pulley/vibration damper

9.14   Removing the timing belt

9.15A   Slide off the crankshaft sprocket ...

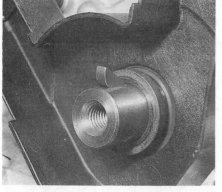

9.15B   ... remove the Woodruff key ...

9.15C   ... and spacer

9.16A   Unscrew the securing bolt ...

11   Unscrew and remove the bolt securing the water pump section of the timing belt cover to the oil pump housing.
12   Unscrew the crankshaft pulley bolt while holding the flywheel/driveplate stationary using a wide blade screwdriver in the starter ring gear teeth. Alternatively make up the tool shown (photo) to hold the flywheel.
13   Unbolt the crankshaft pulley/vibration damper from the sprocket (photo).
14   Rotate the water pump body anti-clockwise. Remove the timing belt from the water pump, camshaft and crankshaft sprockets (photo).
15   Slide the crankshaft sprocket from the front of the crankshaft, then remove the Woodruff key and spacer (photos).
16   Hold the camshaft sprocket stationary using a tool as shown (photo), then unscrew the securing bolt. Remove the sprocket from the front of the camshaft (photo).
17   Unscrew and remove the three securing bolts and washers, and withdraw the water pump from the block.
18   Unbolt and remove the rear timing belt cover (photo).
19   Unscrew the oil filter from the oil pump housing (photo).
20   Unbolt the cooling fan hub bracket from the block (photo).

21   Unbolt the front coolant and thermostat housing from the cylinder head, and remove the O-ring seal (photos).
22   Remove the crankcase ventilation tube from the camshaft housing and block by disconnecting the hose and unscrewing the flange bolts (photos). Recover the gasket.
23   Working in a spiral pattern from outside to inside, slacken each cylinder head bolt by a quarter turn. Following the same sequence slacken the bolts a further half turn, then remove them completely. Note that the cylinder head bolts must be renewed as a complete set whenever they are disturbed; obtain a new set of bolts for reassembly.
24   Lift off the camshaft housing and camshaft.
25   Lift the cylinder head from the block. Careful use of a wooden or hide mallet may be necessary to release the head, but do not attempt to wedge any tool between the joint faces.
26   Remove the gasket from the block (photo).
27   Unscrew the camshaft thrustplate bolts, remove the thrustplate and withdraw the camshaft from the camshaft housing (photos).
28   Remove the rocker arms and thrustpads from the cylinder head. Withdraw the hydraulic valve lifters and immerse them in a container of clean engine oil to prevent the oil from draining. Keep all components

9.16B ... and remove the camshaft sprocket

9.18 Removing the rear timing belt cover

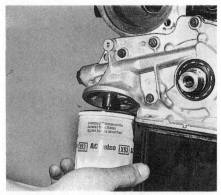

9.19 Removing the oil filter

9.20 Cooling fan hub bracket removal

9.21A Unscrew the bolts ...

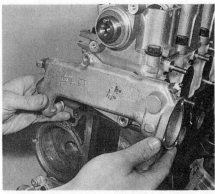

9.21B ... and remove the front coolant and thermostat housing ...

9.21C ... and O-ring seal

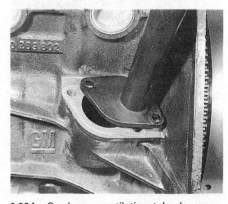

9.22A Crankcase ventilation tube lower flange ...

9.22B ... and upper connecting hose

9.26 Head gasket on the block

9.27A Unscrew the bolts (arrowed) ...

9.27B ... remove the thrustplate ...

Are your plugs trying to tell you something?

Normal.
Grey-brown deposits, lightly coated core nose. Plugs ideally suited to engine, and engine in good condition.

Heavy Deposits.
A build up of crusty deposits, light-grey sandy colour in appearance.
Fault: Often caused by worn valve guides, excessive use of upper cylinder lubricant, or idling for long periods.

Lead Glazing.
Plug insulator firing tip appears yellow or green/yellow and shiny in appearance.
Fault: Often caused by incorrect carburation, excessive idling followed by sharp acceleration. Also check ignition timing.

Carbon fouling.
Dry, black, sooty deposits.
Fault: over-rich fuel mixture.
Check: carburettor mixture settings, float level, choke operation, air filter.

Oil fouling.
Wet, oily deposits. Fault: worn bores/piston rings or valve guides; sometimes occurs (temporarily) during running-in period.

Overheating.
Electrodes have glazed appearance, core nose very white – few deposits. Fault: plug overheating. Check: plug value, ignition timing, fuel octane rating (too low) and fuel mixture (too weak).

Electrode damage.
Electrodes burned away; core nose has burned, glazed appearance. Fault: pre-ignition. Check: for correct heat range and as for 'overheating'.

Split core nose.
(May appear initially as a crack). Fault: detonation or wrong gap-setting technique.
Check: ignition timing, cooling system, fuel mixture (too weak).

WHY DOUBLE COPPER IS BETTER FOR YOUR ENGINE.

Unique Trapezoidal Copper Cored Earth Electrode — 50% Larger Spark Area

Copper Cored Centre Electrode

Champion Double Copper plugs are the first in the world to have copper core in both centre <u>and</u> earth electrode. This innovative design means that they run cooler by up to 100°C – giving greater efficiency and longer life. These double copper cores transfer heat away from the tip of the plug faster and more efficiently. Therefore, Double Copper runs at cooler temperatures than conventional plugs giving improved acceleration response and high speed performance with no fear of pre-ignition.

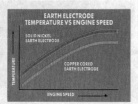

Champion Double Copper plugs also feature a unique trapezoidal earth electrode giving a 50% increase in spark area. This, together with the double copper cores, offers greatly reduced electrode wear, so the spark stays stronger for longer.

 FASTER COLD STARTING

 FOR UNLEADED OR LEADED FUEL

 ELECTRODES UP TO 100°C COOLER

 BETTER ACCELERATION RESPONSE

 LOWER EMISSIONS

 50% BIGGER SPARK AREA

 THE LONGER LIFE PLUG

Plug Tips/Hot and Cold.
Spark plugs must operate within well-defined temperature limits to avoid cold fouling at one extreme and overheating at the other.
Champion and the car manufacturers work out the best plugs for an engine to give optimum performance under all conditions, from freezing cold starts to sustained high speed motorway cruising.
Plugs are often referred to as hot or cold. With Champion, the higher the number on its body, the hotter the plug, and the lower the number the cooler the plug.

Plug Cleaning
Modern plug design and materials mean that Champion no longer recommends periodic plug cleaning. Certainly don't clean your plugs with a wire brush as this can cause metal conductive paths across the nose of the insulator so impairing its performance and resulting in loss of acceleration and reduced m.p.g.
However, if plugs are removed, always carefully clean the area where the plug seats in the cylinder head as grit and dirt can sometimes cause gas leakage.
Also wipe any traces of oil or grease from plug leads as this may lead to arcing.

CHAMPION

DOUBLE COPPER

1

This photographic sequence shows the steps taken to repair the dent and paintwork damage shown above. In general, the procedure for repairing a hole will be similar; where there are substantial differences, the procedure is clearly described and shown in a separate photograph.

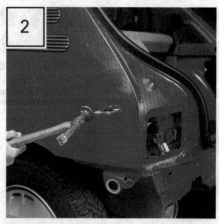

2

First remove any trim around the dent, then hammer out the dent where access is possible. This will minimise filling. Here, after the large dent has been hammered out, the damaged area is being made slightly concave.

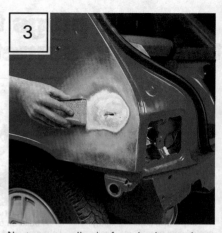

3

Next, remove all paint from the damaged area by rubbing with coarse abrasive paper or using a power drill fitted with a wire brush or abrasive pad. 'Feather' the edge of the boundary with good paintwork using a finer grade of abrasive paper.

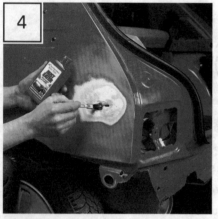

4

Where there are holes or other damage, the sheet metal should be cut away before proceeding further. The damaged area and any signs of rust should be treated with Turtle Wax Hi-Tech Rust Eater, which will also inhibit further rust formation.

5

For a large dent or hole mix Holts Body Plus Resin and Hardener according to the manufacturer's instructions and apply around the edge of the repair. Press Glass Fibre Matting over the repair area and leave for 20-30 minutes to harden. Then ...

5A

... brush more Holts Body Plus Resin and Hardener onto the matting and leave to harden. Repeat the sequence with two or three layers of matting, checking that the final layer is lower than the surrounding area. Apply Holts Body Plus Filler Paste as shown in Step 5B.

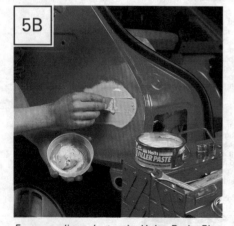

5B

For a medium dent, mix Holts Body Plus Filler Paste and Hardener according to the manufacturer's instructions and apply it with a flexible applicator. Apply thin layers of filler at 20-minute intervals, until the filler surface is slightly proud of the surrounding bodywork.

5C

For small dents and scratches use Holts No Mix Filler Paste straight from the tube. Apply it according to the instructions in thin layers, using the spatula provided. It will harden in minutes if applied outdoors and may then be used as its own knifing putty.

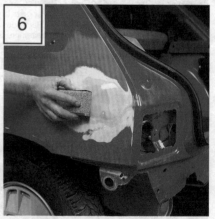

6

Use a plane or file for initial shaping. Then, using progressively finer grades of wet-and-dry paper, wrapped round a sanding block, and copious amounts of clean water, rub down the filler until glass smooth. 'Feather' the edges of adjoining paintwork.

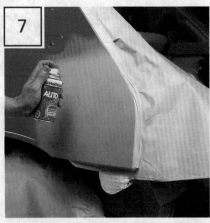

Protect adjoining areas before spraying the whole repair area and at least one inch of the surrounding sound paintwork with Holts Dupli-Color primer.

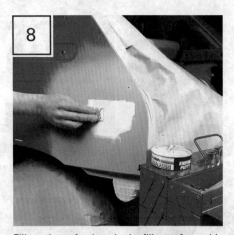

Fill any imperfections in the filler surface with a small amount of Holts Body Plus Knifing Putty. Using plenty of clean water, rub down the surface with a fine grade wet-and-dry paper – 400 grade is recommended – until it is really smooth.

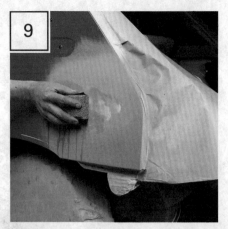

Carefully fill any remaining imperfections with knifing putty before applying the last coat of primer. Then rub down the surface with Holts Body Plus Rubbing Compound to ensure a really smooth surface.

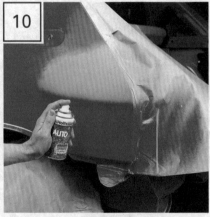

Protect surrounding areas from overspray before applying the topcoat in several thin layers. Agitate Holts Dupli-Color aerosol thoroughly. Start at the repair centre, spraying outwards with a side-to-side motion.

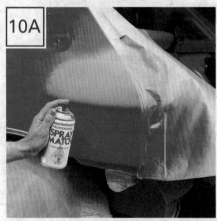

If the exact colour is not available off the shelf, local Holts Professional Spraymatch Centres will custom fill an aerosol to match perfectly.

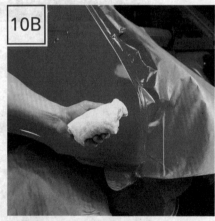

To identify whether a lacquer finish is required, rub a painted unrepaired part of the body with wax and a clean cloth.

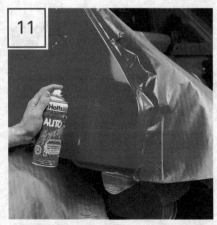

If *no* traces of paint appear on the cloth, spray Holts Dupli-Color clear lacquer over the repaired area to achieve the correct gloss level.

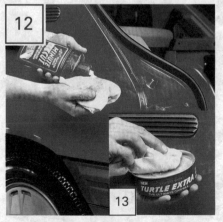

The paint will take about two weeks to harden fully. After this time it can be 'cut' with a mild cutting compound such as Turtle Wax Minute Cut prior to polishing with a final coating of Turtle Wax Extra.

When carrying out bodywork repairs, remember that the quality of the finished job is proportional to the time and effort expended.

HAYNES No1 for DIY

Haynes publish a wide variety of books besides the world famous range of *Haynes Owners Workshop Manuals*. They cover all sorts of DIY jobs. Specialist books such as the *Improve and Modify* series and the *Purchase and DIY Restoration Guides* give you all the information you require to carry out everything from minor modifications to complete restoration on a number of popular cars. In addition there are the publications dealing with specific tasks, such as the *Car Bodywork Repair Manual* and the *In-Car Entertainment Manual*. The *Household DIY* series gives clear step-by-step instructions on how to repair everyday household objects ranging from toasters to washing machines.

Whether it is under the bonnet or around the home there is a Haynes Manual that can help you save money. Available from motor accessory stores and bookshops or direct from the publisher.

9.27C ... and withdraw the camshaft

9.28A Removing the rocker arms ...

9.28B ... thrust pads ...

9.28C ... and hydraulic valve lifters

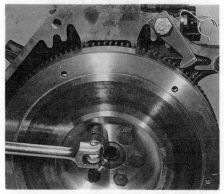

9.29A Unscrew the bolts ...

9.29B ... and lift the flywheel from the crankshaft

9.31A Unscrew the bolts ...

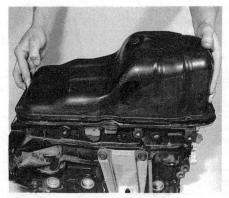

9.31B ... and remove the sump

9.32A Remove the baffle plate ...

identified for position to ensure correct reassembly (photo).

29 Hold the flywheel/driveplate stationary using the method described in paragraph 12, then unscrew the bolts and lift the unit from the crankshaft (photos). Discard the flywheel/driveplate bolts; new retaining bolts must be obtained for refitting.

30 Turn the engine upside-down on the workbench. Place cloth rags around it to absorb the water and oil which escapes.

31 Unscrew the sump bolts and remove the sump (photos).

32 Remove the baffle plate and pull the rubber gasket from its edge (photos).

33 Unbolt the oil pick-up tube from the block, and oil pump (photo).

34 Unbolt the oil pump from the block and remove the gasket

(photos).

35 Mark the big-end caps and connecting rods in relation to each other using a centre punch, and numbering them from the front of the engine.

36 Lay the block on its side then unscrew the No. 1 cylinder big-end bolts and tap off the cap (photo). Using the handle of a hammer tap the connecting rod and piston through the top of the block. Temporarily refit the cap to the connecting rod keeping the bearing shells in their original positions.

37 Repeat the procedure on the remaining pistons and connecting rods. Note that all the big-end cap bolts must be renewed whenever they are disturbed; obtain a new set of bolts for reassembly.

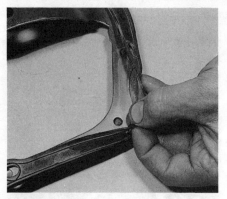

9.32B　... and pull off the rubber gasket

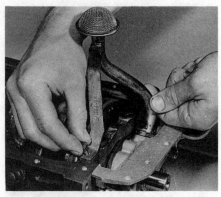

9.33　Oil pick-up tube removal

9.34A　Oil pump showing mounting bolts

9.34B　Removing the oil pump

9.36　Big-end cap removal

9.38　No.1 main bearing cap

38　The main bearing caps should already be marked with numbers starting at the front of the engine. However if there are none, mark them with a centre punch (photo).

39　Position the block upside-down again, then unscrew the main bearing bolts and remove the caps (photo). Take care to keep the bearing shells with their respective caps. Note that the main bearing cap bolts must be renewed whenever they are disturbed; obtain a new set of bolts for reassembly.

40　Lift the crankshaft out of the crankcase and remove the oil seal (photo).

41　Remove the upper halves of the main bearing shells from the crankcase and place them with their respective main bearing caps (photo).

10　Sump – removal and refitting with engine in car

1　Apply the handbrake. Jack up the front of the car and support it on axle stands.

2　Unscrew the drain plug and drain the engine oil into a suitable container. When completed, wipe the plug clean, refit it and tighten.

3　Unscrew the nuts from the top of both engine mountings.

4　Using a hoist or an engine support bar across the engine compartment, raise the engine approximately 25 mm (1 inch).

5　On automatic transmission models unbolt both engine mounting brackets.

6　Unscrew the sump bolts, and withdraw the sump forwards over the crossmember.

7　Withdraw the baffle plate forwards while turning it to clear the oil pick-up tube.

8　Pull the rubber gasket from the edge of the baffle plate.

9　If necessary unbolt the oil level sensor from the sump and remove the gasket (photos).

10　Thoroughly clean the sump and baffle plate, and clean the joint face on the crankcase.

11　Fit a new rubber gasket to the baffle plate.

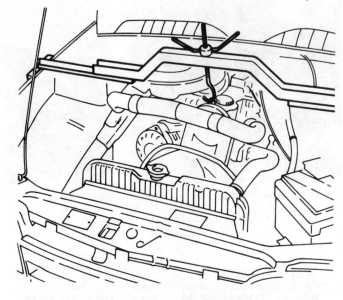

Fig. 1.2 Using an engine support bar when removing the sump (Sec 10)

12　Apply sealant to GM spec 15 03 294 (90 001 871) to both sides of the gasket at the corners only.

13　Position the baffle plate on the crankcase, then fit the sump beneath it. Hold the sump temporarily with two or three bolts.

14　Apply locking fluid to the threads of the bolts then insert and tighten them progressively in diagonal sequence to the specified torque.

9.39 Removing the centre main bearing cap

9.40 Lifting the crankshaft out of the crankcase

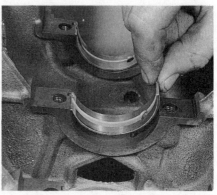

9.41 Removing No.4 main bearing shell

10.9A Oil level sensor and retaining bolts

10.9B Inner view of the oil level sensor

11.5 Locating peg on the engine mounting (arrowed)

15   On automatic transmission models refit the engine mounting brackets and tighten the bolts.
16   Lower the engine and tighten the engine mounting nuts. Disconnect the hoist.
17   Lower the car to the ground.
18   Fill the engine with the specified quantity and grade of oil.

11   Engine mountings – renewal

1   Apply the handbrake. Jack up the front of the car and support it on axle stands.
2   Unscrew the nuts from the top of both engine mountings.
3   Using a hoist or an engine support bar across the engine compartment, raise the engine approximately 25 mm (1 inch).
4   Unscrew the lower nuts and remove the engine mountings. On automatic transmission models it will be necessary to unbolt the engine mounting brackets.
5   Fit the new mountings using a reversal of the removal procedure, but make sure that the pegs on the mountings engage with the cut-outs on the brackets (photo).

12   Cylinder head – removal and refitting with engine in car

1   Disconnect the battery negative lead.
2   Remove the inlet and exhaust manifolds as described in Chapter 3.
3   Remove the spark plugs, distributor cap, and rotor arm as described in Chapter 4.
4   Unclip and remove the upper timing belt cover.
5   Remove the thermo-viscous cooling fan and drivebelt as described in Chapter 2.
6   Unbolt the camshaft cover and remove the cork gasket. Note the location of the HT lead bracket.

7   Turn the engine with a spanner on the crankshaft pulley bolt until the mark on the camshaft sprocket is aligned with the pointer on the top of the rear timing belt cover. Also align the notch in the crankshaft pulley with the pointer on the lower part of the rear timing belt cover.
8   Using an Allen key, loosen the three bolts securing the water pump to the block. Rotate the water pump body anti-clockwise and remove the timing belt from the camshaft sprocket.
9   Hold the camshaft stationary with a spanner on the rear flats, then unscrew the securing bolt and remove the sprocket.
10   Unbolt the rear timing belt cover from the cylinder head.
11   Loosen the clips and disconnect the crankcase ventilation hose from the camshaft housing.
12   Working in a spiral pattern from outside to inside, slacken each cylinder head bolt by a quarter turn. Following the same sequence slacken the bolts a further half turn, then remove them completely. Note that the cylinder head bolts must be renewed as a complete set whenever they are disturbed; obtain a new set of bolts for reassembly.
13   Lift off the camshaft housing and camshaft.
14   Lift the cylinder head from the block. Careful use of a wooden or hide mallet may be necessary to release the head, but do not attempt to wedge any tool between the joint faces.
15   Remove the gasket from the block and clean the mating faces thoroughly.
16   Check that Nos 1 and 4 pistons are still at top dead centre with the crankshaft pulley notch and pointer aligned.
17   Check that both location dowels are inserted in the block. Locate the new head gasket on the block with the 'TOP' marking uppermost and at the front.
18   Locate the cylinder head on the block so that the dowels engage in their holes. Check that the hydraulic valve lifters, thrustpads and rocker arms are correctly located.
19   Apply a uniform bead of jointing compound to the mating face on top of the cylinder head using a soft brush to ensure even coverage.
20   Check that the dowel on the front of the camshaft is uppermost, then lower the camshaft housing onto the head.

21   Insert new cylinder head bolts and tighten them in the sequence shown in Fig.1.3 to the specified torque. Note that the bolts must be tightened to an initial torque then angle-tightened in stages.
22   Refit the crankcase ventilation hose and tighten the clips.
23   Insert and tighten the rear timing belt cover bolts.
24   Refit the camshaft sprocket and tighten the bolt.
25   Check that the crankshaft pulley and camshaft sprocket timing marks are correctly aligned. Reconnect the timing belt without disturbing the sprockets and apply some tension by moving the water pump clockwise.
26   Ideally the tension gauge specified by GM (KM-510-A) should be used to adjust the timing belt tension. If this is available, proceed as follows.
27   Turn the water pump clockwise to apply moderate tension to the belt then tighten the bolts. Rotate the crankshaft half a turn clockwise to tension the belt between the camshaft and crankshaft sprockets. Fit the tension gauge between the camshaft and water pump sprockets and

check that the reading is as given in the Specifications.
28   If adjustment is necessary move the water pump clockwise to increase or anti-clockwise to decrease the tension. Rotate the crankshaft through one full turn and repeat the test.
29   If the tension gauge is not available an appropriate setting may be made by checking if it is possible to twist the belt through 90° with the thumb and finger.
30   With the adjustment correct, tighten the water pump bolts to the specified torque (Chapter 2) and recheck the timing mark alignment.
31   Refit the camshaft cover along with a new gasket, then refit the retaining bolts and washers, and tighten them securely. Note that, to cure the problem of oil loss from beneath the cover retaining bolt heads, modified washers have been introduced; these can be purchased from your Vauxhall dealer.
32   Refit the thermo-viscous cooling fan and drivebelt with reference to Chapter 2.
33   Refit the upper timing belt cover.

14.1A   Removing the oil pump rear cover

14.1B   View of the oil pump gears

14.2A   Checking the endfloat of the oil pump outer gear ...

14.2B   ... and inner gear

14.2C   Checking the oil pump gear backlash

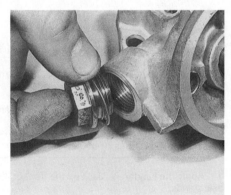

14.4A   Unscrew the plug ...

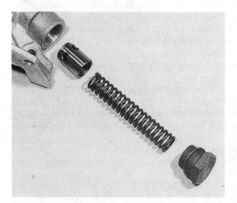

14.4B   ... and remove the relief valve spring and piston

14.5   Removing the oil temperature sensor

14.6   By-pass valve in oil pump (arrowed)

14.7 Tightening the oil pump rear cover screws

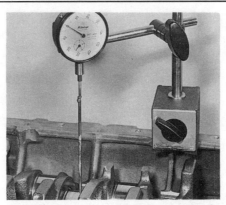

14.9 Checking the crankshaft run-out

14.13A Identification numbers on the main bearing shells (except centre)

14.13B Identification numbers on the centre main bearing shells

14.13C Identification numbers on the big-end bearing shells

14.13D Piston, connecting rod and big-end components

34   Refit the spark plugs, distributor cap and rotor arm with reference to Chapter 4.
35   Refit the inlet and exhaust manifolds with reference to Chapter 3.
36   Reconnect the battery negative lead.
37   Start the engine and run it to normal operating temperature.
38   Stop the engine and angle-tighten the cylinder head bolts by the specified amount in the sequence shown in Fig 1.3. It is not necessary to re-tighten the bolts.

13   Timing belt – renewal with engine in car

1   Disconnect the battery negative lead.
2   Remove the spark plugs (Chapter 4)
3   Remove the thermo-viscous cooling fan, drivebelt, and fan cowling as described in Chapter 2. If applicable, remove the power steering pump and air conditioning compressor drivebelts.
4   Drain the cooling system (Chapter 2).
5   Unclip and remove the timing belt covers.
6   Turn the engine with a spanner on the crankshaft pulley bolt until the mark on the camshaft sprocket is aligned with the pointer on the top of the rear timing belt cover. Also align the notch in the crankshaft pulley with the pointer on the lower part of the rear timing belt cover.
7   Using an Allen key, loosen the three bolts securing the water pump to the block.
8   Apply the handbrake and engage 4th gear. Alternatively, and essential on automatic transmission models, remove the starter and hold the flywheel/driveplate stationary using a wide-bladed screwdriver in the starter ring gear teeth.
9   Unscrew the crankshaft pulley bolt then unbolt the pulley from the sprocket.
10   Rotate the water pump body anti-clockwise and remove the timing belt from the sprockets.

11   Locate the new timing belt temporarily on the sprockets.
12   Locate the crankshaft pulley on the crankshaft sprocket and insert the bolts. Insert the centre bolt.
13   Hold the flywheel/driveplate stationary then tighten first the outer bolts, then the centre bolt to the specified torque.
14   Disconnect the timing belt and align the timing marks on the camshaft sprocket and crankshaft pulley with the pointers on the rear cover. Reconnect the belt without disturbing the sprockets, and apply some tension by moving the water pump clockwise.
15   Tension the timing belt with reference to Section 12, paragraphs 26 to 30.
16   Refit the timing belt covers.
17   Refit and tension the drivebelt(s).
18   Refit the cooling fan and fan cowling.
19   Refit the spark plugs (Chapter 4).
20   Refill the cooling system (Chapter 2)
21   Reconnect the battery negative lead.

14   Engine components – examination and renovation

Oil pump

1   Using an impact driver, extract the cross-head screws and remove the rear cover (photos).
2   With a straight edge and feeler blades, check the endfloat of the two gears then check the backlash between the two gears (photos).
3   If any of the clearances are outside the specified tolerances, it is recommended that the oil pump is renewed, although individual parts are available.
4   Unscrew the plug and remove the relief valve spring and piston (photos). Examine them for wear and damage.

14.26   Checking a piston ring gap

14.45   Spigot bearing in the rear of the crankshaft

14.47   Core plugs in the cylinder block

15.2A   Compress the valve spring and remove the collets

15.2B   Removing the valve spring retainer ...

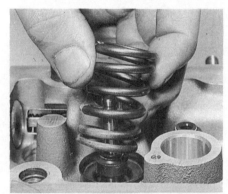

15.2C   ... spring ...

5   If necessary unscrew the oil temperature sensor (photo).
6   Check that the bypass valve ball is seating correctly (photo). If necessary, pull out the old valve and press in a new one.
7   Thoroughly clean all components then reassemble them in reverse order, using a new plug sealing washer (photo).

Crankshaft
8   Examine the crankpin and main journal surfaces for signs of scoring or scratches, and check the ovality and taper of the crankpins and main journals. If the bearing surface dimensions do not fall within the tolerance ranges given in the Specifications at the beginning of the Chapter, the crankpins and/or main journals will have to be reground.
9   Check the crankshaft for run-out by mounting it in the crankcase using the front and rear bearing shells only. With a dial test gauge probe on the centre main journal, rotate the crankshaft (photo).
10   Big-end and crankpin wear is accompanied by distinct metallic knocking, particularly noticed when the engine is pulling from low revs, and also some loss of oil pressure. Main bearing and main journal wear is accompanied by severe engine vibration rumble, getting progressively worse as engine revs increase, and again by loss of oil pressure.
11   If the crankshaft requires regrinding, take it to an engine reconditioning specialist, who will machine it for you and supply the correct undersize bearing shells.
12   On some engines, the crankshaft journal diameters are machined undersize in production to allow for greater manufacturing tolerances.

Big-end and main bearing shells
13   Inspect the big-end and main bearing shells for signs of general wear, scoring, pitting and scratches. The bearings should be matt grey in colour. With lead-indium bearings, should a trace of copper colour be noticed, the bearings are badly worn as the lead bearing material has worn away to expose the indium underlay. Renew the bearings if they are in this condition or if there are any signs of scoring or pitting. **You are strongly advised to renew the bearings – regardless of their condition – at time of major overhaul. Refitting used bearings is a false economy (photos).**
14   The undersizes available are designed to correspond with

crankshaft regrind sizes. The bearings are in fact, slightly more than the stated undersize as running clearances have been allowed for during their manufacture.

Cylinder bores
15   The cylinder bores must be examined for taper, ovality, scoring and scratches. Start by carefully examining the top of the cylinder bores. If they are at all worn a very slight ridge will be found on the thrust side. This marks the top of the piston travel. The owner will have a good indication of the bore wear prior to dismantling the engine, or removing the cylinder head. Excessive oil consumption accompanied by blue smoke from the exhaust can be caused by worn cylinder bores and piston rings.
16   Measure the bore diameter across the block and just below any ridge. This can be done with an internal micrometer or a dial gauge. Compare this with the diameter of the bottom of the bore, which is not subject to wear. If no measuring instruments are available, use a piston from which the rings have been removed and measure the gap between it and the cylinder wall with a feeler gauge.
17   Refer to the Specifications. If the cylinder wear exceeds the permitted tolerances then the cylinders will need reboring.
18   If the cylinders have already been bored out to their maximum it may be possible to have liners fitted. This situation will not often be encountered.

Connecting rods
19   Examine the mating faces of the big-end caps to see if they have ever been filed in a mistaken attempt to take up wear. If so, the offending rods must be renewed.
20   Check the alignment of the rods visually, and if all is not well, take the rods to your local agent for checking on a special jig.

Pistons and piston rings
21   If the pistons and/or rings are to be re-used, remove the rings from the pistons. Three strips of tin or 0.38 mm (0.015 in) feeler gauges should be prepared and the top ring then sprung open just sufficiently to allow them to be slipped behind the ring. The ring can then be slid off the

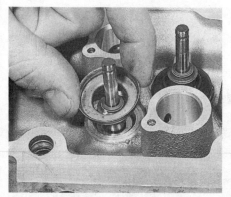

15.2D ... inlet valve spring seat ...

15.3 ... and valve

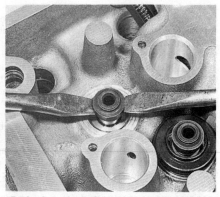

15.4A Levering off the inlet valve stem oil seal

15.4B Removing the exhaust valve stem oil seal ...

15.4C ... and valve rotator

15.5 Piston crown

piston upwards without scoring or scratching the piston lands.

22 Repeat the process for the second and third rings.

23 Mark the rings or keep them in order so they may be refitted in their original locations.

24 Inspect the pistons to ensure that they are suitable for re-use. Check for cracks, damage to the piston ring grooves and lands, and scores or signs of picking-up the piston walls.

25 Clean the ring grooves using a piece of old piston ring ground to a suitable width and scrape the deposits out of the grooves, taking care not to remove any metal or score the piston lands. Protect your fingers – piston rings are sharp.

26 Check the rings in their respective bores. Press the ring down to the unworn lower section of the bore (use a piston to do this, and keep the ring square in the bore). Measure the ring end gap and check that it is within the tolerance allowed (see Specifications) (photo). Also check the ring's side clearance in its groove. If these measurements exceed the specified tolerances the rings will have to be renewed, and if the ring grooves in the pistons are worn new pistons may be needed.

27 Proprietary piston rings are available which are reputed to reduce oil consumption due to bore wear without the expense of a rebore. Depending on the degree of wear, the improvement produced by fitting such rings may be short-lived.

28 If new rings (or pistons and rings) are to be fitted to an existing bore the top ring must be stepped to clear the wear ridge at the top of the bore, or the bore must be de-ridged.

29 Check the clearance and end gap of any new rings, as described in paragraph 26. If a ring is slightly tight in its groove it may be rubbed down using an oilstone or a sheet of carborundum paper laid on a sheet of glass. If the end gap is inadequate the ring can be carefully ground until the specified clearance is achieved.

30 If new pistons are to be installed they will be selected from the grades available (see Specifications), after measuring the bores as described in paragraph 16. Normally the appropriate oversize pistons are supplied by the repairer when the block is rebored.

31 Removing and refitting pistons on the connecting rod is a job for your dealer or specialist repairer. Press equipment and a means of accurately heating the connecting rod will be required for removal and insertion of the gudgeon pin.

Camshaft

32 With the camshaft removed, examine the bearing surfaces for signs of wear. If evident, a new camshaft housing will probably be required.

33 The camshaft itself should show no marks or scoring on the journal or cam lobe surfaces. If evident, renew the camshaft.

34 The thrustplate should appear unworn and without grooves. In any event, check the camshaft endfloat, and fit a new plate where necessary.

Timing belt

35 Closely inspect the belt for cracking, fraying or tooth deformation. Where evident, renew the belt. The belt should be renewed in any case at the intervals shown in *Routine maintenance* at the front of this manual.

36 Whenever re-using the timing belt always note its running direction in order to prevent subsequent noisy operation.

Hydraulic valve lifters, rockers and thrustpads

37 Any sign of wear in a hydraulic valve lifter can only be rectified by renewal as the unit cannot be dismantled.

38 Inspect the rockers and thrustpads for wear or grooving, and renew if necessary.

Flywheel/driveplate

39 If the teeth on the starter ring gear are badly worn, it is possible to renew the ring gear separately only on the flywheel.

40 Either split the ring with a cold chisel after making a cut with a hacksaw blade between two teeth, or use a soft-headed hammer (not steel) to knock the ring off, striking it evenly and alternately at equally spaced points. Take great care not to damage the flywheel during this process, and protect your eyes from flying fragments.

41 Clean and polish with emery cloth four evenly spaced areas on the

outside face of the new starter ring.

42   Heat the ring evenly with a flame until the polished portions turn
dark blue. Alternatively heat the ring in a bath of oil to a temperature of
200°C. (If a naked flame is used take adequate fire precautions.) Hold
the ring at this temperature for five minutes and then quickly fit it to the
flywheel, so the chamfered portion of the teeth faces the gearbox side
of the flywheel. Wipe all oil off the ring before fitting it.

43   The ring should be tapped gently down onto its register and left to
cool naturally when the contraction of the metal on cooling will ensure
that it is a secure and permanent fit. Great care must be taken not to
overheat the ring, indicated by its turning light metallic blue. If this
happens the temper of the ring will be lost.

44   If the clutch contact surface of the flywheel is scored or on close
inspection shows evidence of small hair cracks, caused by overheating,
it may be possible to have the flywheel surface ground provided the
overall thickness of the flywheel is not reduced too much. Consult a
specialist engine repairer and if it is not possible, renew the flywheel
complete.

45   If the needle bearing in the centre of the crankshaft flange is worn,
fill it with grease and tap in a close-fitting rod. Hydraulic pressure will
remove it. Tap the new bearing into position and apply a little grease
(photo).

Cylinder block

46   Check that all internal oil and waterways are clear of sediment or
obstructions.

47   If a core plug (photo) is leaking, it may be renewed by driving a
screwdriver into it and prising it out of the block. Clean the seating then
use a large drift or two hammer heads to drive in the new plug. The use
of sealant is not usually necessary.

48   The crankshaft main bearing bolts and the cylinder head bolts
should be renewed as a matter of course.

---

15 Cylinder head – overhaul

1   Clean the external surfaces of the cylinder head.

2   Remove the valves by compressing the valve spring with a suitable
valve spring compressor and lifting out the collets. Release the compressor and remove the valve spring retainer and spring. Remove the
inlet valve spring seat (photos).

3   Remove the valves, keeping them identified for location to ensure
correct refitting (photo).

4   Lever the valve stem oil seals from the valve guides, then remove
the exhaust valve rotators (photos)

5   With the valves removed, clean the carbon from them and from the
combustion chambers and ports. The piston crowns can also be
cleaned at this stage but take care not to allow carbon to drop between
the pistons and bores (photo). To prevent this, clean two pistons at a
time with them at the top of their bores and press a little grease between
the pistons and bores. Seal off the remaining cylinders, and oil and water
channels with paper. After cleaning, move the pistons down the bore
and wipe out the grease which will contain the particles of carbon.

6   Examine the heads of the valves and the valve seats for pitting and

15.8 Grinding in the valves

burning. If the pitting on valve and seat is slight it can be removed by
grinding the valves and seats together with coarse, and then fine, valve
grinding paste. If the pitting is deep, the valves will have to be reground
on a valve grinding machine and the seats will have to be recut with a
valve seat cutter. Both these operations are a job for your local GM
dealer or motor engineering specialist.

7   Check the valve guides for wear by inserting the valve in the guide
and attempting to move the valve from side to side. If the specified play
is exceeded the valve guides should be renewed by a GM dealer.

8   When grinding slightly-pitted valves and valve seats with carborundum paste, proceed as follows. Apply a little coarse grinding paste to
the valve head, and using a suction-type valve grinding tool, grind the
valve into its seat with a rotary movement, lifting the valve and turning it
from time to time (photo). A light spring under the valve head will assist
in this operation. When a dull matt, even surface finish appears on both
the valve and the valve seat, clean off the coarse paste. Repeat the
grinding operation with a fine grinding paste until a continuous ring of
light grey matt finish appears on both valve and valve seat. Carefully
clean off all traces of grinding paste.

9   Check the valve springs for damage and if possible compare their
length with that of a new spring. Renew them if necessary.

10   Using a straight edge and feeler blade check the joint face of the
cylinder head for distortion (photo). If greater than the maximum
amount given in the Specifications it may be possible to have the head
machined flat. Consult a GM dealer if necessary.

11   An oil pressure regulating valve in the cylinder head stabilises the
oil pressure applied to the valve lifters (photo). To renew the valve,
access is gained by removing the plug in the head. The old valve must

15.10 Checking the cylinder head for
distortion

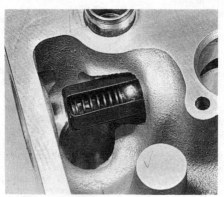

15.11 Oil pressure regulating valve in the
cylinder head

15.13 Pressing the valve stem oil seals
onto the guides

16.3 Lubricating the upper main bearing shells

16.4 Gently tap the crankshaft to make sure it is seated correctly

16.5A Checking the crankshaft endfloat with a feeler blade ...

16.5B ... and dial test indicator

16.6 Lubricating the lower main bearing shells

16.7A Coating the rear main bearing cap joint face with sealant

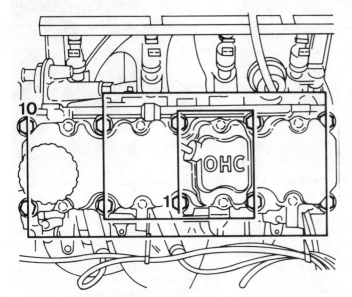

Fig. 1.3 Cylinder head bolt tightening sequence (Sec 16)

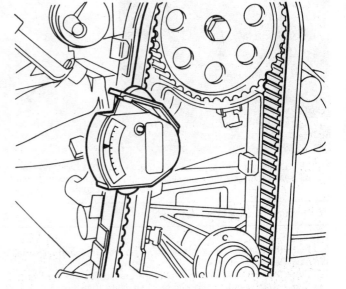

Fig. 1.4 Checking the timing belt tension with a tension gauge (Sec 16)

be crushed and its remains extracted, then a thread (M10) is cut in the valve seat to allow removal using a suitable bolt. A new valve and plug can then be driven into position. Care must be taken to keep foreign matter and swarf out of the oilways, and it is probably best to have the valve renewed by a GM dealer if necessary.

12 Commence reassembly by locating the exhaust valve rotators over their respective valve guides.

13 Press the valve stem oil seals onto the guides (photo).

14 To fit the valves, lubricate the valve stem with engine oil and insert it in the valve guide. On the inlet valve, refit the spring seat.

15 Refit the spring and spring retainer, then use the valve spring compressor to compress the spring until the collets can be fitted in position in the slots in the valve stem. Release the compressor slowly, and check that the collets are seated correctly.

16 After fitting all the valves, tap the tops of the springs lightly to ensure correct seating of the collets.

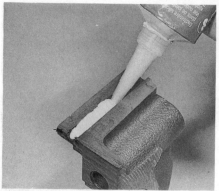

16.7B   Filling the rear main bearing cap grooves with RTV jointing compound

16.8   Fitting the rear main bearing cap

16.9   Making sure the grooves are full of sealant

16.10A   Torque-tightening the main bearing cap bolts

16.10B   Angle-tightening the main bearing cap bolts

16.12A   Using a piece of celluloid as a guide sleeve when fitting the crankshaft rear oil seal

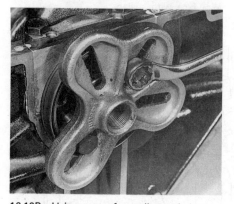

16.12B   Using part of a puller and the old oil seal to fit the new oil seal

16.17A   The arrow on the piston crown must point towards the front of the engine

16.17B   Inserting the piston (with piston ring compressor) into the cylinder

16   Engine – complete reassembly

1   Place the cylinder block upside-down on the bench and wipe clean the main bearing shell seats.
2   Press the main bearing shells onto the crankcase, making sure that the tags engage with the special grooves. Note that the centre shell incorporates thrust flanges.
3   Lubricate the shells with clean engine oil (photo).
4   Carefully lower the crankshaft into the crankcase. Rotate it several times and check that it is correctly seated by gently tapping the webs with a mallet (photo).
5   Check that the crankshaft endfloat is as given in the Specifications by either using a feeler gauge between the flanged centre main bearing shell and the crankshaft thrust face, or by using a dial test indicator on the crankshaft rear flange (photo).
6   Clean the backs of the lower main bearing shells and the caps, then press them into position. Lubricate the shells with clean oil (photo).

7   Coat the joint face of the rear main bearing cap with sealant to GM spec 15 04 200 (8 983 368). This sealant is available is 200 ml tubes. Fill the side grooves of the cap with RTV jointing compound or sealant to GM spec 15 04 294 (90 001 851) (photos).
8   Fit the rear main bearing cap, then insert the new bearing cap bolts and tighten them to the specified torque setting (photo). If required, the crankshaft rear oil seal may be fitted at the same time.
9   Insert more sealant into the side grooves until it is certain that they are full (photo).
10   Refit the remaining main bearing caps, then fit the new bearing cap bolts and tighten them to the specified torque setting. Make sure that the front cap is exactly flush with the end face of the crankcase. Note that the bolts must be tightened to an initial torque then angle-tighten (photos).
11   Rotate the crankshaft and check that it turns freely with no signs of binding or tight spots.
12   Lubricate the lips of the new crankshaft rear oil seal with grease. Cut a length of celluloid to act as a guide sleeve for the oil seal and locate it on the crankshaft rear flange. Locate the oil seal on the sleeve and

16.19A Torque-tightening the big-end bolts

16.19B Angle-tightening the big-end bolts

16.23 Oil pump gasket on the front of the block

16.26A Using a piece of celluloid as a guide sleeve when fitting the crankshaft front oil seal

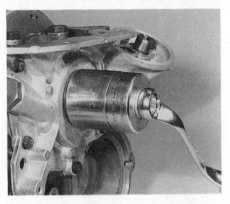

16.26B Using a socket to press in the crankshaft front oil seal

16.27 O-ring seal on the oil pick-up tube

16.29 Applying sealant to the corners of the sump gasket

16.30 Applying locking fluid to the sump bolts

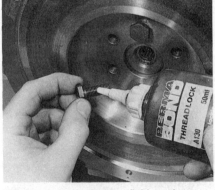

16.32A Applying locking fluid to the flywheel bolts

press it into the rear main bearing cap until flush. Part of a pulley may be used effectively to press in the oil seal using two flywheel bolts and using the old oil seal to apply even pressure (photos). Remove the puller and celluloid.

13 Lay the block on its side and lubricate the cylinder bores and crankshaft journals liberally with oil.

14 Space the piston rings around the pistons so that their end gaps are 180° apart. In the case of the oil scraper ring, offset the gaps in the upper and lower rails by 25 to 50 mm (1 to 2 in) to right and left of the end gap of the centre section.

15 Clean the backs of the big-end bearing shells and the caps and connecting rods, then press the shells into position.

16 Turn the crankshaft so that the journal for No 1 cylinder is at bottom dead centre.

17 Fit a piston ring compressor to No 1 piston then insert it into No 1 cylinder with the arrow on the piston crown pointing towards the front of the engine (photos). The land extensions on the piston underside, the connecting rod and the big-end bearing cap should be towards the rear

of the engine.

18 Using the handle of a hammer, tap the piston through the ring compressor while guiding the connecting rod onto the journal.

19 Fit the big-end bearing cap, ensuring it is fitted the correct way around, then insert the new big-end bearing bolts. Tighten the bolts first to the Stage 1 torque setting, and then angle-tighten them through the specified amount (see Specifications at the start of this Chapter) (photos).

20 Check that the crankshaft turns freely taking into consideration the resistance of the piston rings.

21 Repeat the procedure given in paragraphs 16 to 20 for the remaining pistons.

22 Turn the block upside down on the bench.

23 Position a new oil pump gasket on the front of the block and retain it with a little grease (photo).

24 If necessary prise the old oil seal from the oil pump.

25 Refit the oil pump then insert and tighten the bolts.

26 Cut a length of celluloid and wrap it around the crankshaft nose.

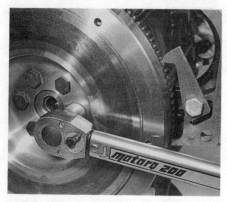

16.32B Torque-tightening the flywheel bolts

16.32C Alternative position for the flywheel locking tool (arrowed)

16.32D Angle-tightening the flywheel bolts

16.34 Location dowel on the block

16.35 'TOP' marking on the cylinder head gasket

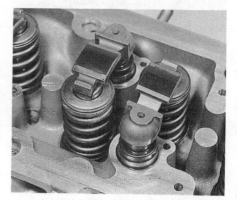

16.36 Rockers fitted to the valves

16.37 Cylinder head located on the block

16.38 Prising out the camshaft housing front oil seal

16.39 Lubricating the bearing surfaces in the camshaft housing

Smear a little grease on the lips of the new oil seal and locate it on the celluloid. Press the oil seal to start it, then use a suitable socket and the crankshaft pulley bolt to press the oil seal in until flush (photos). Remove the celluloid and socket.

27   Fit a new O-ring seal to the oil pick-up tube then refit the tube and tighten the bolts (photo).

28   Fit a new sump gasket to the baffle plate.

29   Apply sealant to GM spec 15 03 294 (90 001 871) to both sides of the gasket at the corners only, and locate the baffle plate on the crankcase (photo).

30   Refit the sump. Apply locking fluid to the threads of the bolts, then insert and tighten them progressively in diagonal sequence to the specified torque (photo).

31   Position the engine upright on the workbench using blocks of wood.

32   Locate the flywheel/driveplate on the rear of the crankshaft. Apply locking fluid to the threads of the new bolts, then insert and tighten

them progressively, while holding the flywheel stationary using the method described in Section 9, paragraph 12. Note that the bolts must be tightened to an initial torque then angle-tightened (photos).

33   Turn the engine so that Nos 1 and 4 pistons are at top dead centre.

34   Check that both location dowels are inserted in the block and that the joint faces on the block and cylinder head are clean (photo).

35   Locate the new head gasket on the block with the 'TOP' marking uppermost and at the front (photo).

36   Refit the hydraulic valve lifters, thrustpads and rocker arms to the cylinder head in their original positions (photo). If new hydraulic valve lifters are being used, initially immerse each one in a container of clean engine oil and compress by hand several times to charge them.

37   Locate the cylinder head on the block so that the dowels engage in their holes (photo).

38   Prise the old oil seal from the front of the camshaft housing (photo). Clean the seating and drive in the new oil seal using a block of wood. Smear the oil seal lips with grease.

16.40 Checking the camshaft endfloat

16.41A Apply jointing compound on the cylinder head ...

16.41B ... and brush it to an even coverage

16.42A Camshaft dowel positioned uppermost

16.42B Camshaft housing on the cylinder head

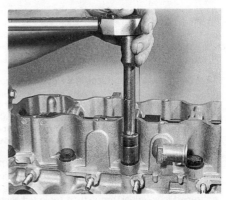

16.43A Torque-tightening the cylinder head bolts

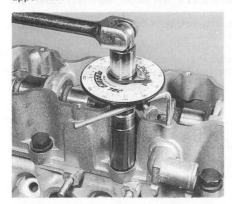

16.43B Angle-tightening the cylinder head bolts

16.44 Crankcase ventilation tube refitted

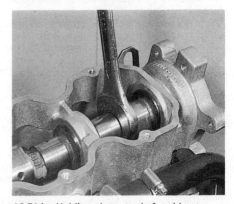

16.51A Holding the camshaft with an open-ended spanner

16.51B Tightening the camshaft sprocket bolt

16.54A Tightening the crankshaft pulley outer bolts ...

16.54B ... and centre bolt

16.55 Tensioning the timing belt

16.59 Checking that the timing belt turns through 90°

39 Oil the bearing surfaces in the camshaft housing (photo).
40 Carefully insert the camshaft into the housing. Refit the camshaft thrustplate and tighten the bolts. Using a feeler blade as shown (photo) check that the camshaft endfloat is as given in the Specifications.
41 Apply a uniform bead of jointing compound to the mating face on the cylinder head using a soft brush to ensure even coverage (photos).
42 Turn the camshaft so that the dowel at the front is uppermost (photo), then lower the camshaft housing onto the head.
43 Insert new cylinder head bolts and tighten them in the sequence shown in Fig. 1.3 to the specified torque. Note that the bolts must be tightened to an initial torque then angle-tightened in stages (photos).
44 Refit the crankcase ventilation tube with a new gasket, and tighten the bolts. Refit the hose to the camshaft housing and tighten the clips (photo).
45 Refit the front coolant and thermostat housing to the cylinder head using a new O-ring seal. Insert and tighten the bolts.
46 Refit the cooling fan hub bracket to the block. Insert and tighten the bolts.
47 Smear some oil on the sealing ring of the new oil filter then screw it onto the oil pump housing hand tight only.
48 Refit the rear timing belt cover. Insert and tighten the bolts.
49 Apply silicon grease or equivalent to the surfaces of the water pump in contact with the block. Fit a new rubber O-ring.
50 Locate the water pump in the block with the timing cover projections correctly seated. Insert the securing bolts and washers loosely.
51 Locate the sprocket on the front of the camshaft and engage the peg. Insert the bolt. Hold the camshaft stationary and tighten the bolt to the specified torque. An open-ended spanner may be used on the flats provided if required (photos).
52 Refit the spacer, Woodruff key and sprocket to the front of the crankshaft. Temporarily engage the timing belt with the crankshaft, camshaft and water pump sprockets.
53 Locate the crankshaft pulley/vibration damper on the crankshaft sprocket and insert the bolts. Insert the centre bolt.
54 Hold the flywheel/driveplate stationary using the method described in Section 9, paragraph 12. Tighten first the outer bolts, then the centre bolt to the specified torque (photos). Note that the centre bolt must be tightened to an initial torque then angle-tightened.
55 Disconnect the timing belt and align the timing marks on the camshaft sprocket and crankshaft pulley with the pointers on the rear cover. Reconnect the belt without disturbing the sprockets and apply some tension by moving the water pump clockwise (photo).
56 Ideally the tension gauge specified by GM (KM-510-A) should be used to adjust the timing belt tension. If this is available, proceed as follows.
57 Turn the water pump clockwise to apply moderate tension to the belt then tighten the bolts. Rotate the crankshaft half a turn clockwise to tension the belt between the camshaft and crankshaft sprockets. Fit the tension gauge between the camshaft and water pump sprockets and check that the reading is as given in the Specifications.
58 If adjustment is necessary move the water pump clockwise to increase or anti-clockwise to decrease the tension. Rotate the crankshaft through one full turn and repeat the test.

59 If the tension gauge is not available, an approximate setting may be made by checking if it is possible to twist the belt through 90° with the thumb and finger (photo).
60 With the adjustment correct, tighten the water pump bolts to the specified torque (Chapter 2), and recheck the timing mark alignment.
61 Insert and tighten the bolt securing the water pump section of the timing cover to the oil pump housing.
62 Refit the two timing belt covers.
63 Refit the cooling fan pulley. Insert and tighten the screws.
64 Refit the camshaft cover together with a new cork gasket. Insert and tighten the bolts.
65 On fuel injection models refit the auxiliary air valve bracket to the camshaft housing together with a new gasket. Insert and tighten the bolts.
66 Reconnect the crankcase ventilation hose to the camshaft cover.
67 Insert the engine oil dipstick.
68 Insert and tighten the oil pressure switch.
69 Using a block of wood, fit a new oil seal in the rear of the camshaft housing. Smear a little grease on the oil seal lips.

17 Engine ancillaries – refitting

Refer to Section 8 and refit the listed components, with reference to the Chapters indicated where necessary.

18 Engine – refitting

Refitting the engine is a reversal of the removal procedure given in Section 6, but in addition note the following points:

(a) Lightly grease the gearbox input shaft or torque converter spigot as applicable
(b) On automatic transmission models, check that the torque converter is fully engaged with the transmission oil pump with reference to Chapter 6 Section 14
(c) Refill the engine with the specified quantity and grade of oil
(d) On manual gearbox models, adjust the clutch cable with reference to Chapter 5
(e) Adjust the tension of the power steering pump, alternator/fan, and air conditioning compressor drivebelts as described in Chapters 10, 2 and 11 respectively
(f) Adjust the accelerator cable, and where necessary, the automatic transmission kickdown cable and the cruise control cable as described in Chapters 3, 6 and 13 (as applicable)
(g) Refill the cooling system as described in Chapter 2

19   Engine – initial start-up after major overhaul or repair

1   Make sure that the battery is fully charged and that all lubricants, coolant and fuel are replenished.
2   Double check all fittings and connections.
3   Remove the spark plugs and the negative (No. 1) wiring from the ignition coil. Turn the engine over on the starter motor until the oil pressure warning light is extinguished, or until oil pressure is recorded on the gauge. This will ensure that the engine is not starved of oil during the critical few minutes running after initial start-up. The fuel system will also be primed during this operation.
4   Reconnect the ignition coil wiring and refit the spark plugs and leads. Start the engine.
5   As soon as the engine fires and runs, keep it going at a fast tickover only (no faster) and bring it up to normal working temperature.
6   As the engine warms up there will be odd smells and some smoke from parts getting hot and burning off oil deposits. The signs to look for are leaks of water or oil, which will be obvious if serious. Check also the exhaust pipe and manifold connections as these do not always find their exact gas tight position until the warmth and vibration have acted on them, and it is almost certain that they will need tightening further. This should be done, of course, with the engine stopped.
7   When normal running temperature has been reached, adjust the engine idle speed as described in Chapter 3.
8   Stop the engine and wait a few minutes to see if any lubricant or coolant is dripping out when the engine is stationary.
9   During the initial period that the engine is running it is not unusual for the hydraulic valve lifters to be noisy, but this should gradually disappear, certainly within a few miles driving on the road.
10   After reaching normal temperature the engine should be stopped, and the cylinder head bolts angle-tightened by the specified amount in the sequence given in Fig. 1.3. It is not necessary to re-tighten the bolts.
11   If many new internal components have been fitted, it will be beneficial to change the engine oil and oil filter after the first 1000 km (600 miles).

20   Fault diagnosis – engine

Symptom	Reason(s)
Engine fails to start	Discharged battery
	Loose battery connection
	Loose or broken ignition leads
	Moisture on spark plugs, distributor cap, or HT leads
	Incorrect spark plug gaps
	Cracked distributor cap or rotor
	Other ignition system fault
	Dirt or water in fuel
	Empty fuel tank
	Faulty fuel pump
	Other fuel system fault
	Faulty starter motor
	Low cylinder compressions
Engine idles erratically	Intake manifold air leak
	Leaking cylinder head gasket
	Worn rocker arms or faulty hydraulic lifters
	Worn camshaft lobes
	Faulty fuel pump
	Loose crankcase ventilation hoses
	Idle adjustment incorrect
	Uneven cylinder compressions
Engine misfires	Spark plugs worn or incorrectly gapped
	Dirt or water in fuel
	Burnt out valve
	Leaking cylinder head gasket
	Distributor cap cracked
	Uneven cylinder compressions
	Worn carburettor (where applicable)
	Ignition system fault
Engine stalls	Idle adjustment incorrect
	Intake manifold air leak
	Ignition system fault
Excessive oil consumption	Worn pistons, cylinder bores or piston rings
	Valve guides and valve stem seals worn
	Oil leaks
Engine backfires	Idle adjustment incorrect
	Ignition system fault
	Intake manifold air leak
	Sticking valve

Chapter 2 Cooling system

Contents

Specifications

System type .... Pressurised, with downflow radiator, belt-driven thermo-viscous cooling fan, centrifugal water pump driven by timing belt, thermostat, expansion tank either remote or built into radiator header tank

General

Pressure cap opening pressure.. 1.2 to 1.3 bar (17.4 to 18.9 lbf/in^2)
System nominal boiling temperature... 125°C (257°F)

Thermostat

Opening commences .... 92°C (198°F)
Fully open .... 107°C (225°F)

Coolant

Type .... Ethylene glycol based antifreeze, to GM spec GME L 6368, and soft water (Duckhams Universal Antifreeze and Summer Coolant)
Capacity... 6.4 litres (11.3 pints)

Torque wrench settings

	Nm	lbf ft
Water pump..	25	19
Temperature gauge sender unit	10	7
Thermostat housing cover...........................	15	11
Cooling fan pulley.......................................	8	6
Thermo-viscous cooling fan	50	37

1 General description

The cooling system comprises a downflow radiator, belt-driven thermo-viscous cooling fan, timing belt-driven water pump, thermostat, and expansion tank. The expansion tank is either incorporated in the radiator header tank or of the plastic type located on the right-hand side of the engine compartment.

The system functions as follows. Cold water from the water pump is forced around the cylinder block and head, then through a bypass hose back to the inlet side of the water pump. Additional circulation occurs through the car heater matrix. When the engine reaches a predetermined temperature, the thermostat commences to open and the coolant then circulates through the radiator to provide extra cooling. The thermo-viscous cooling fan is controlled by the temperature of air behind the radiator. When the predetermined temperature is reached,

an internal valve opens and allows a fluid drive system to turn the fan blades. At lower temperatures the drive is reduced accordingly. The fan is therefore only operated when required, and compared with direct drive type fans, represents a considerable improvement in fuel economy, drivebelt wear and fan noise.

2 Routine maintenance

1 Carry out the following procedures at the intervals given in *Routine Maintenance* at the front of this manual.

Check coolant level

2 With the engine cold, check that the coolant is approximately at the

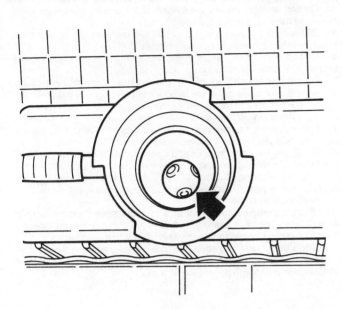

Fig. 2.1 Coolant cold level plate in the radiator filler neck (Sec 2)

2.3 Topping up the coolant level with antifreeze

'cold' level mark. On models with a remote expansion tank, this is marked on the outside of the tank, but on other models the radiator pressure cap must be removed. In the latter case a cold level plate is provided on some models, or alternatively the level must be 50.0 mm (2.0 in) below the top edge of the filler neck.

3   Top up the level as necessary. If possible the antifreeze specific gravity should be checked before adding the additional coolant, so that adjustment may be made to the antifreeze concentration (photo).

4   If regular topping-up is required, the system should be checked for leaks.

5   Do not add cold water to an overheated engine whilst it is still hot, since this may result in a cracked cylinder head or block.

6   Refit the pressure cap on completion.

Check cooling system for leaks

7   Inspect all the coolant hoses for condition and security.

8   Check for signs of leakage from the radiator, water pump, expansion tank (where applicable), and the thermostat cover.

Check cooling fan/alternator drivebelt

9   Examine the full length of the drivebelt for wear, damage and deterioration.

10   Check the drivebelt tension with reference to Section 13.

Renew coolant

11   Drain and flush the cooling system as described in Sections 3 and 4.

12   Fill the system with new antifreeze mixture as described in Section 5.

3   Cooling system – draining

1   Unscrew the filler cap from the expansion tank or radiator (as applicable). If the engine is hot, place a thick cloth over the cap before removing it slowly, otherwise there is a danger of scalding.

2   Place a suitable container beneath the right-hand side of the radiator.

3   Loosen the clip and disconnect the bottom hose from the radiator. Drain the coolant into the container.

4   Dispose of the old coolant, or keep it in a covered container if it is to be re-used.

5.3 Temperature sensor on the thermostat housing

4   Cooling system – flushing

1   Flushing should not be necessary unless periodic renewal of the coolant has been neglected, or unless plain water has been used as a coolant. In either case the coolant will appear rusty and dark in colour. Flushing is then required and should be carried out as follows.

2   Drain the system as described in the previous Section.

3   Start by flushing the expansion tank where fitted. The heater may be flushed by disconnecting the hoses on the bulkhead and then inserting a garden hose.

4   Flush the radiator by inserting the garden hose into the top of the radiator and run the water until it runs clear from the bottom outlet. If, after a reasonable period the water still does not run clear, the radiator may be flushed with a good proprietary cleaning agent such as Holts Radflush or Holts Speedflush.

5   Reverse flush the engine by removing the thermostat (Section 9) and inserting the garden hose until water flows clear from the bottom hose. Also unscrew the cylinder block drain plug located on the front left-hand side of the engine, and allow the water to run clear.

6   In severe cases of contamination the radiator should be removed, inverted and flushed in the reverse direction to normal flow. Shake the radiator gently while doing this to dislodge any deposits.

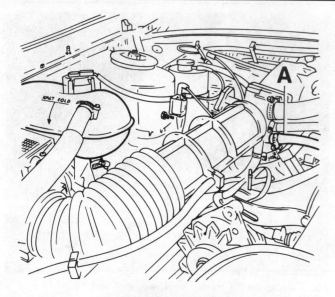

Fig. 2.2 On fuel injection engines disconnect hose (A) when filling the system (Sec 5)

5   Cooling system – filling

1   Reconnect the hoses and tighten the clips. Refit and tighten the cylinder block drain plug.

2   On carburettor engines, disconnect the warm air duct to provide access to the thermostat housing.

3   Disconnect the wiring and unscrew the temperature sensor from the top of the thermostat housing (photo).

4   On fuel injection engines, also disconnect the coolant hose from the bottom of the throttle housing.

5   Pour the specified coolant into the radiator or expansion tank (as applicable) until it runs out of the temperature sensor hole, then refit and tighten the sensor and reconnect the wiring.

6   Refit the warm air duct on carburettor engines.

7   On fuel injection engines, continue to add coolant until it runs out of the throttle housing hose, then reconnect the hose.

8   On all engines, continue to add coolant until it reaches the 'cold' level mark. On the radiator this is either indicated by a level plate in the filler neck or by being 50.0 mm (2.0 in) below the top edge of the filler neck. On the remote expansion tank a cold level mark is provided.

9   Refit the filler cap.

10   Start the engine and run it at a fast idle speed until it reaches normal operating temperature, indicated by the thermostat opening and the top hose becoming noticeably hotter when touched.

11   Stop the engine and allow it to cool for two or three hours, then recheck the coolant level and if necessary top up to the cold level described in paragraph 8. Refit the filler cap.

6   Antifreeze mixture – general

Warning: *Antifreeze mixture is poisonous. Keep it out of reach of children and pets. Wash splashes off skin and clothing with plenty of water. Wash splashes off vehicle paintwork, too, to avoid discoloration*

1   The antifreeze/water mixture must be renewed every two years to preserve its anti-corrosive properties. The engine must not be run with plain water as a coolant, except in an emergency situation when the ambient temperature is well above freezing.

7.1   Top hose connection

7.2A   Remove the clips ...

7.2B   ... release the engine wiring harness ...

7.2C   ... and remove the cooling fan shroud

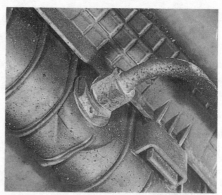

7.3   Automatic transmission fluid union connection to the radiator

7.5 Radiator rubber mounting and clip (arrowed)

7.6 Removing the radiator

9.3 Top hose connection to the thermostat housing cover

9.4 Removing the thermostat and cover

11.3 Removing the thermo-viscous cooling fan

2   The mixture should be made up from clean water with a low lime content (preferably rain water), and a good quality ethylene glycol based antifreeze which contains a corrosion inhibitor and is suitable for use in 'mixed metal' (aluminium and iron) engines.

3   The proportions of antifreeze to water required will depend on the manufacturer's recommendations, but the mixture must be adequate to give protection down to approximately -30°C (-22°F).

4   Before filling with fresh antifreeze, drain and if necessary flush the cooling system as described in Sections 3 and 4.

5   The strength of the antifreeze already in the cooling system can be checked with an instrument similar to a battery hydrometer. Most garages should possess such an instrument, or one may be purchased from an accessory shop.

7 Radiator – removal and refitting

1   Drain the cooling system as described in Section 3. Disconnect the top hose (photo).

2   Pull out the upper clips and release the cooling fan shroud from the slots in the bottom of the radiator. The shroud may now be positioned over the cooling fan blades, however for additional working room unclip the engine wiring harness and completely remove the shroud (photos).

3   On automatic transmission models, place a container beneath the radiator, then unscrew the union nuts and disconnect the fluid cooler pipes from the radiator (photo). Drain the fluid and plug the pipes to prevent entry of dust and dirt.

4   Where applicable disconnect the expansion tank hose from the right-hand side of the radiator.

5   Squeeze together and remove the spring clips retaining the rubber mountings on each side of the radiator (photo).

6   Lift the radiator straight up from the side and bottom mountings, and withdraw it from the engine compartment (photo).

7   Check the side and bottom rubber mountings and renew them if necessary. If a new radiator is being fitted, transfer the side mountings to the new unit.

8   Refitting is a reversal of removal. Refill the cooling system as described in Section 5. On automatic transmission models, tighten the fluid cooler unions to the torque setting given in Chapter 6, and also top up the transmission fluid level.

8 Radiator – inspection and repair

1   If the radiator has been removed because of suspected blockage, reverse-flush it as described in Section 4.

2   Clean dirt and debris from the radiator fins, using an air jet or water and a soft brush. Be careful not to damage the fins, or cut your fingers.

3   A radiator specialist can perform a 'flow test' on the radiator to establish whether an internal blockage exists.

4   A leaking radiator must be referred to a specialist for permanent repair. Do not attempt to weld or solder a leaking radiator, as damage to the plastic parts may result.

5   In an emergency, minor leaks from the radiator can be cured by using a radiator sealant such as Holts Radweld with the radiator still *in situ*.

9 Thermostat – removal and refitting

1   Drain the cooling system as described in Section 3.

2   On carburettor engines, disconnect the warm air duct to provide access to the thermostat housing.

3   Loosen the clip and disconnect the top hose from the thermostat housing cover (photo).

4   Mark the cover in relation to the housing, then unscrew the bolts

12.9   Removing the water pump

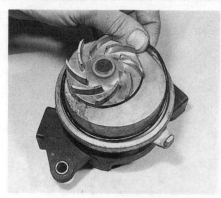

12.10   Water pump rubber O-ring removal

12.11A   Twisting the timing cover section from the plate (arrowed) on the water pump

12.11B   Water pump with timing cover section removed

13.4   Checking the cooling fan/alternator drivebelt tension

and remove the cover and thermostat (photo).
5   Prise the rubber O-ring from the cover.
6   It is not recommended that the thermostat be separated from the cover, as they are supplied new as one unit.
7   Clean the mating faces of the cover and housing, and obtain a new rubber O-ring.
8   Refitting is a reversal of removal. Refill the cooling system as described in Section 5.

10   Thermostat – testing

1   A rough test of the thermostat may be made by suspending it with a piece of string in a saucepan full of water. Bring the water to the boil and check that the thermostat opens. If not, renew it.
2   If a thermometer is available, the precise opening temperature of the thermostat may be determined and compared with that given in the Specifications.
3   A thermostat which fails to close as the water cools must also be renewed.

11   Thermo-viscous cooling fan – removal and refitting

1   On carburettor engines disconnect the warm air duct and move it to one side.
2   If required, the cooling fan shroud may be removed. Pull out the upper clips, unclip the wiring harness, and remove the shroud.
3   Using two open-ended spanners hold the hub stationary then unscrew the fan nut noting that it has a **left-hand** thread. Remove the cooling fan (photo).
4   Refitting is a reversal of removal.

12   Water pump – removal and refitting

1   Remove the thermo-viscous cooling fan (Section 11) and the alternator/fan drivebelt (Section 13).
2   Remove the radiator (Section 7).
3   Remove the drivebelt pulley from the cooling fan hub (four screws).
4   Unclip and remove the timing belt covers.
5   Turn the engine with a spanner on the crankshaft pulley bolt until the mark on the camshaft sprocket is aligned with the pointer on the top of the rear timing belt cover. Also align the notch in the crankshaft pulley with the pointer on the lower part of the rear timing belt cover.
6   Using an Allen key loosen the three bolts securing the water pump to the block.
7   Unscrew and remove the bolt securing the water pump section of the timing cover to the oil pump housing.
8   Rotate the water pump body anti-clockwise. Release the timing belt from the water pump sprocket and tie it loosely to one side.
9   Unscrew and remove the three securing bolts and washers, and withdraw the water pump from the block (photo).
10   Prise the rubber O-ring from the groove in the water pump (photo).
11   If a new water pump is being fitted, transfer the timing cover section to the new pump. To do this, engage the two cut-outs and twist off the timing cover section (photos).Similarly fit the cover to the new water pump.
12   Commence refitting by smearing silicon grease or equivalent to the surfaces of the water pump in contact with the block. If this precaution is not taken the water pump may seize in the block.
13   Apply the grease to the rubber O-ring and locate it in the groove.
14   Locate the water pump in the block with the timing cover projections correctly seated. Insert the securing bolts and washers loosely.
15   Engage the timing belt with the water pump sprocket. Turn the water pump clockwise to tension it. Complete the tensioning procedure with reference to Chapter 1, making sure that the timing marks are correctly aligned. Tighten the water pump securing bolts to the specified torque.

16   Insert and tighten the bolt securing the timing cover to the oil pump housing.
17   Refit the timing belt covers.
18   Refit the drivebelt pulley to the cooling fan hub and tighten the screws.
19   Refit the radiator (Section 7).
20   Refit the alternator/fan drivebelt (Section 13) and the thermo-viscous cooling fan (Section 11).

13   Cooling fan/alternator drivebelt – renewal and adjustment

1   Where fitted remove the power steering pump drivebelt with reference to Chapter 10.
2   Disconnect the warm air duct (carburettor engines) or throttle housing air duct (fuel injection engines) to provide access to the alternator.
3   Loosen the alternator pivot and adjustment link bolts, swivel the alternator towards the engine, and slip the drivebelt off the alternator, cooling fan, and crankshaft pulleys. Ease the drivebelt over the cooling fan blades.
4   Locate the new drivebelt on the pulleys, then lever out the alternator to tension it. It will help if the adjustment link bolt is initially slightly tightened so that the alternator remains in its tensioned position. With correct adjustment the drivebelt should move approximately 13.0 mm (0.5 in) under firm finger or thumb pressure mid-way between the alternator and crankshaft pulleys (photo).
5   Tighten the alternator pivot and adjustment link bolts.

14   Expansion tank – removal and refitting

1   Drain the cooling system as described in Section 3.
2   Remove the filler cap.
3   Loosen the clip and disconnect the radiator de-gas hose.
4   Unclip the expansion tank from the front suspension tower.
5   Loosen the clip and disconnect the supply hose.
6   Withdraw the expansion tank from the engine compartment.
7   Refitting is a reversal of removal. Refill the cooling system with reference to Section 5.

15   Temperature gauge sender unit – removal and refitting

1   The temperature gauge sender unit is located on the thermostat housing. If the engine is hot, allow it to cool before attempting to remove the unit.
2   Remove the filler cap from the radiator or expansion tank to release any remaining pressure, then refit the cap to help reduce the loss of coolant.
3   Disconnect the wiring from the terminal on the sender unit.
4   Unscrew and remove the sender unit, and temporarily plug the aperture with a suitable rubber or cork bung.
5   Refitting is a reversal of removal. Top up the cooling system if necessary.

16   Fault diagnosis – cooling system

Symptom	Reason(s)
Overheating	Low coolant level
	Radiator blocked
	Thermostat sticking shut
	Faulty thermo-viscous cooling fan
	Retarded ignition timing
	Slack cooling fan drivebelt
Overcooling	Thermostat sticking open
Loss of coolant	Damaged or perished hose
	Radiator leaking
	Pressure cap defective
	Blown cylinder head gasket
	Cracked cylinder block or head

Chapter 3 Fuel and exhaust systems

For modifications, and information applicable to later models, see Supplement at end of manual

Contents

Specifications

General
System type:
18SV engine	Rear fuel tank, mechanical fuel pump, downdraught carburettor
18SEH engine	Rear fuel tank, electric fuel pump, Bosch L3 Jetronic fuel injection
20SE engine	Rear fuel tank, electric fuel pump, Bosch Motronic ML4 fuel injection

Fuel tank capacity:
Saloon	75 litres (16.5 gallons)
Estate	70 litres (15.4 gallons)

Air cleaner element
18SV engine	Champion U512
18SEH and 20SE engines	Champion U507

Fuel filter
18SEH and 20SE engines	Champion L201

Carburettor
Type	Pierburg 2E3
Float level setting	28 to 30 mm (1.10 to 1.18 in)
Accelerator pump delivery:	
Manual gearbox models	1.20 to 1.40 cm^3
Automatic transmission models	0.85 to 1.05 cm^3
Throttle valve gap:	
Manual gearbox models	0.95 to 1.05 mm (0.030 to 0.040 in)
Automatic transmission models	1.15 to 1.25 mm (0.045 to 0.050 in)
Choke valve gap:	
'Small' gap	2.0 to 2.3 mm (0.08 to 0.09 in)
'Large' gap	3.0 to 3.3 mm (0.12 to 0.13 in)
Fast idle cam adjustment	0.7 to 1.1 mm (0.028 to 0.044 in)
Choke valve forced opening:	
Manual gearbox models	1.5 to 3.5 mm (0.06 to 0.13 in)
Automatic transmission models	3.0 to 5.0 mm (0.12 to 0.20 in)
Idle speed:	
Manual gearbox models	850 to 900 rpm
Automatic transmission models	750 to 800 rpm
Fast idle speed	1900 to 2300 rpm
CO at idle	0.5 to 1.0%
Main jet:	
Primary	X107.5
Secondary	Z132.5

Carburettor (continued)

Idle Jet..	137.5
Full load enrichment...	90
Needle valve..	1.5
Air correction jet:	
Primary..	110
Secondary..	90

Fuel injection system

Fuel pump flow capacity .... 120 litres/hour
Fuel pump operating pressure (engine idling at specified speed):
    Pressure regulator vacuum hose connected:
        L3 Jetronic system .... 2.0 to 2.2 bars
        Motronic ML4 system... 2.3 to 2.7 bars
    Pressure regulator vacuum hose disconnected and plugged:
        L3 Jetronic system .... 2.3 to 2.7 bars
        Motronic ML4 system... 3.1 to 3.3 bars
Coolant temperature sensor resistance............................ 4800 to 6600 ohms at 0°C
    2200 to 2800 ohms at 20°C
    1000 to 1400 ohms at 40°C
    270 to 380 ohms at 80°C

	Manual gearbox	Automatic transmission (selector in P)
Idling speed:		
18SEH engine	850 to 900 rpm	850 to 900 rpm
20SE engine	720 to 780 rpm	720 to 780 rpm
CO at idle...	0.4 to 1.0%	

Torque wrench settings

	Nm	lbf ft
Inlet manifold	25	19
Exhaust manifold	25	19

1   General description

The fuel system consists of a rear-mounted fuel tank, a mechanical or electric fuel pump, and a downdraught carburettor or Bosch fuel injection system. A fuel feed and return system is fitted to prevent excessive fuel temperatures, and on some models a compensation tank (photo) is fitted to the inlet hose to even out fuel pump pulses.

The exhaust system is in three sections, and a twin downpipe is fitted to all models.

The use of unleaded fuel is permitted in all models. Details of ignition timing adjustments necessary are given in Chapter 4.

2   Routine maintenance

1   Carry out the following procedures at the intervals given in *Routine maintenance* at the front of this manual.
2   Renew the air cleaner element with reference to Section 4.
3   Check and adjust the idling speed and mixture with reference to Section 14 or 23 as applicable.
4   Renew the fuel filter on fuel injection engines with reference to Section 7. On carburettor models, a fuel strainer is incorporated in the carburettor fuel inlet pipe (see Section 16, paragraph 4), this must be cleaned at regular intervals to prevent possible blockage which could lead to fuel starvation problems.
5   Examine the fuel lines by first raising the vehicle and supporting it on axle stands.
6   Examine all fuel lines for security, damage and deterioration. Also check for signs of leakage.
7   Lower the vehicle to the ground.
8   Lubricate the throttle controls and cables using one or two drops of engine oil. Check the accelerator cable for correct adjustment.

3   Tamperproof adjustment screws – general

Certain adjustment points (where applicable) in the fuel system are protected by 'tamperproof' caps. The purpose of such tamperproofing is to discourage, and also to detect, adjustment by unqualified personnel. In some EC countries (though not yet in the UK) it is an offence to drive a vehicle with missing or broken tamperproof caps.

Before disturbing a tamperproof cap, satisfy yourself that you will not be breaking local or national anti-pollution regulations by doing so. Fit a new cap when adjustment is complete when this is required by law.

Do not break tamperproof caps on a vehicle which is still under warranty.

4   Air cleaner and element – removal and refitting

Carburettor models

1   Disconnect the air inlet duct and warm air tube from the air cleaner.
2   Unscrew the three mounting nuts, lift the air cleaner from the carburettor, and disconnect the vacuum hose for the inlet air temperature control.
3   Remove the air cleaner gasket.
4   Remove the cover from the air cleaner, and remove the element.
5   Wipe clean the inside of the body and cover. Examine the gasket and renew it if necessary. Obtain a new element.
6   To check the operation of the inlet air temperature control, apply

1.1   Compensation tank fitted in the fuel line (arrowed)

4.8   Air cleaner cover spring clip

4.9   Removing the air cleaner element

5.3   Removing the fuel pump (carburettor models)

6.1A   Tank-mounted fuel pump (1) and fuel gauge sender unit (2)

6.1B   Remote-mounted fuel pump

6.4   Bridging the fuel pump relay base terminals

vacuum to the temperature switch on the bottom of the air cleaner. The flap in the inlet tube should uncover the warm air port and close the cold air port.

7   Refitting is a reversal of removal.

Fuel injection models

8   Release the spring clips securing the cover to the air cleaner body (photo).

9   Lift the cover and remove the element (photo).

10   Wipe clean the inside of the body and cover. Obtain a new element.

11   If necessary, unbolt and remove the body. Disconnect the air inlet duct where applicable.

12   Refitting is a reversal of removal.

---

5   Fuel pump (carburettor models) – removal, testing and refitting

1   The fuel pump is located on the front right-hand side of the camshaft housing.

2   Identify the fuel inlet and outlet hoses, then slacken their clips and disconnect them from the pump. Plug both hoses to prevent fuel leakage.

3   Unscrew the mounting nuts and withdraw the pump from the studs on the camshaft housing. Recover the spacer/gasket (photo).

4   To test the pump operation, refit the fuel inlet hose to the pump inlet nozzle and hold a rag near the outlet. Operate the plunger by hand and check that a strong jet of fuel is ejected from the outlet nozzle.

5   Clean the contact faces of the pump and camshaft housing.

6   Refitting is a reversal of removal, but fit a new spacer/gasket.

---

6   Fuel pump (fuel injection models) – testing, removal and refitting

1   Depending on the model the fuel pump may be fitted inside the fuel

tank, or mounted separately just in front of the fuel tank (photos).

2   To check its delivery, disconnect the fuel feed hose at the fuel distribution rail in the engine compartment and direct it into a calibrated container of at least 5 litres capacity.

3   Remove the relay cover from the right-hand rear corner of the engine compartment. Pull out the fuel pump relay and slide the base from the bracket.

4   Using a bridging wire, connect the terminals 30 and 87B together for a period of exactly one minute (photo).

5   Check that 1.6 to 2.4 litres of fuel have been collected in the container. If this is not the case, the fuel filter may be blocked or the fuel pump is faulty.

6   To remove the fuel pump, chock the front wheels, jack up the rear of the car and support it on axle stands.

7   On the remote-mounted fuel pump type, disconnect the wiring, then fit hose clamps to both hoses and disconnect them. Unscrew the clamp bolt and withdraw the fuel pump.

8   On the tank-mounted type remove the filler cap and syphon or pump out the fuel. Disconnect the wiring plug, then fit hose clamps to the feed and return hoses and disconnect them. Unscrew the bolts and remove the fuel pump. Recover the gasket.

9   Refitting is a reversal of removal. On the tank-mounted type fit a new gasket, and apply locking fluid to the bolts before inserting and tightening them progressively.

---

7   Fuel filter (fuel injection models) – renewal

1   Chock the front wheels, then jack up the rear of the car and support it on axle stands.

2   If available fit hose clamps to the fuel filter inlet and outlet hoses.

3   Unscrew the mounting clamp bolt(s) from the underbody.

4   The fuel inside the filter remains under pressure even with the ignition switched off, so wrap some cloth rags around both ends of the filter to absorb spilled fuel. If hose clamps are not used, position a container beneath the filter.

5   Loosen the clips and disconnect the filter from the hoses.
6   Fit the new filter using a reversal of the removal procedure, but make sure that the arrow on the filter faces the direction of flow of the fuel from the fuel tank to the engine.

8   Fuel tank – removal and refitting

Note: *For safety, the fuel tank must always be removed in a well-ventilated area, never over a pit.*

1   Disconnect the battery negative lead.
2   Remove the tank filler cap, and if possible syphon or pump out all of the fuel (there is no drain plug).
3   Chock the front wheels, then jack up the rear of the vehicle and support it on axle stands.
4   Disconnect the wiring from the fuel gauge sender unit and, if fitted in the fuel tank, the fuel pump.
5   The fuel remains pressurized within the fuel lines even with the ignition switched off, so position a suitable container beneath the fuel tank to catch the spilled fuel.
6   Identify the fuel feed and return hoses for position and if available fit hose clamps to them. Loosen the clips, disconnect the hoses, and plug the open ends.
7   On fuel injection models, disconnect the vent pipe.
8   On models equipped with a pneumatic rear suspension levelling system, unclip the pressure line from the edge of the fuel tank.
9   Support the fuel tank using a block of wood and a trolley jack.
10   Unbolt the two retaining straps from the underbody (photo).
11   Slowly lower the fuel tank while removing the filler neck from the rubber sleeve in the side panel.
12   Remove the rubber sleeve from the side panel.
13   Note the location of the vent lines then disconnect them.
14   Remove the fuel gauge sender unit, and where applicable the fuel pump (Sections 9 and 6).
15   Loosen the hose clips and remove the filler neck, vent container, and hose.
16   Drain any remaining fuel from the tank.
17   If the tank is contaminated with sediment or water, swill it out with clean fuel. If the tank leaks or is damaged, it should be repaired by specialists or alternatively renewed. **Do not** under any circumstances solder or weld a fuel tank.
18   Examine the vent lines, hose and hose clips for damage and renew if necessary.
19   Refitting is a reversal of removal, but note the following additional points:

(a)   *Make sure that the vent lines and hoses are not twisted or trapped*
(b)   *Refit the rubber sleeve with the 'U' marking at the bottom*
(c)   *Do not tighten the filler hose bottom clip until the filler neck is correctly positioned*

9   Fuel gauge sender unit – removal and refitting

1   Disconnect the battery negative lead.
2   Remove the tank filler cap, and if possible syphon or pump out all of the fuel.
3   Chock the front wheels, then jack up the rear of the car and support it on axle stands. Disconnect the wiring from the fuel gauge sender unit.
4   Where the sender unit also incorporates the fuel feed and return hoses, identify the hoses for position then loosen the clips and disconnect them. Be prepared for some loss of fuel.
5   Where a bayonet-type metal ring is fitted use two crossed screwdrivers to turn it anti-clockwise. Where bolts are fitted, unscrew the bolts. Remove the metal ring and the sender unit.
6   Remove the O-ring seal or gasket.
7   Clean the contact faces of the sender unit and fuel tank.
8   Where applicable apply a little multi-purpose grease to the new

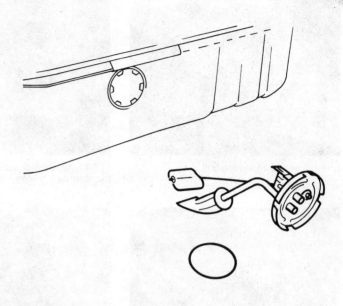

Fig. 3.1 Fuel gauge sender unit removal (Sec 9)

O-ring seal and locate it in the sender unit groove.
9   Fit the sender unit to the tank with the pick-up tube facing downwards. Use a new gasket where fitted.
10   Where a bayonet-type metal ring is fitted, tighten the ring fully clockwise.
11   Where bolts are fitted, apply locking fluid to their threads then insert and tighten them in diagonal sequence.
12   Refit the hoses and wiring, and reconnect the battery negative lead. Lower the car to the ground.
13   Refill the tank with fuel and refit the filler cap.

10   Diaphragm damper (fuel injection engines) – removal and refitting

1   Chock the front wheels, then jack up the rear of the car and support it on axle stands.
2   Fit hose clamps each side of the diaphragm damper.
3   Loosen the clips and disconnect the hoses. The fuel is under pressure, so wrap a cloth rag around the first hose disconnected to absorb the fuel.
4   Unscrew the mounting nut and remove the diaphragm damper.
5   Refitting is a reversal of removal.

11   Accelerator cable – removal, refitting and adjustment

1   On carburettor models, remove the air cleaner (Section 4), then open the throttle by hand and unhook the inner cable from the grooved cam.
2   On fuel injection models, release and remove the small spring clip, and disconnect the inner cable ball end from the lever on the throttle housing (photos).
3   Slide the outer cable bush from the support bracket (photo).
4   Working inside the car, disconnect the inner cable from the accelerator pedal.
5   Release the grommet from the bulkhead and pull the cable into the engine compartment.
6   Refitting is a reversal of removal. Adjust the cable by selecting the appropriate position of the spring clip behind the outer cable bush, to give just a barely-perceptible amount of slack in the inner cable with the accelerator pedal released.

8.10 Fuel tank mounting bolt

11.2A Accelerator cable connection to the throttle housing

11.2B Disconnecting the accelerator inner cable

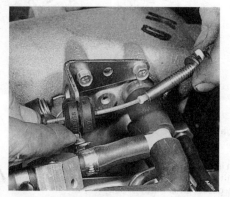

11.3 Releasing the accelerator outer cable bush

12.2 Accelerator pedal and bracket

14.4 Idle speed adjustment screw (1) and idle mixture adjustment screw (2) under tamperproof cap

16.19A Choke drive lever (1) engages with loop (2)

16.19B Automatic choke cover alignment marks (arrowed)

18.3 Fast idle adjustment screw under tamperproof cap (arrowed)

12 Accelerator pedal – removal and refitting

1 Disconnect the accelerator cable from the pedal with reference to Section 11.
2 Prise the spring clip from the inner end of the pivot rod, and remove the bushes, washers and return spring (photo).
3 Remove the pedal from the bracket.
4 Refitting is a reversal of removal, but adjust the cable as described in Section 11.

13 Carburettor – description

The carburettor is a Pierburg 2E3 incorporating a coolant temperature and electrically controlled automatic choke. It is of twin-barrel construction with progressively-operated throttle valves. The primary throttle valve is opened mechanically, but the secondary throttle is opened by vacuum developed in both venturis.

Primary and secondary transition systems, and a part load enrichment valve, ensure efficient operation under all speed and load conditions. An idle cut-off valve stops the supply of fuel to the idle circuit when the ignition is switched off.

14 Carburettor – idle speed and mixture adjustments

1 A tachometer (rev counter) and an exhaust gas analyser (CO meter) are required for accurate adjustment.
2 Adjustment should be made with the air cleaner fitted, the accelerator cable correctly adjusted, and the engine at normal operating temperature. Ensure the adjustment screw is not touching the fast idle cam; on models equipped with automatic transmission, position the selector lever in the 'P' position.
3 Connect the tachometer and exhaust gas analyser to the engine in accordance with the manufacturers' instructions. Start the engine and allow it to idle.
4 Read the idle speed on the tachometer and compare it with the

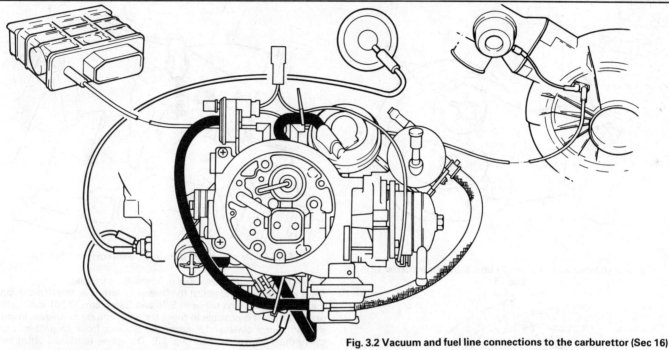

Fig. 3.2 Vacuum and fuel line connections to the carburettor (Sec 16)

value given in the Specifications. If adjustment is necessary, turn the idle speed adjustment screw as required (photo).

5   Check that the CO content is as given in the Specifications. If not, prise off the tamperproof cap and turn the idle mixture adjustment screw as required.

6   If necessary, repeat the procedure given in paragraph 4.

7   Switch off the engine and disconnect the tachometer and exhaust gas analyser.

15 Carburettor – removal and refitting

1   Disconnect the battery negative lead.

2   Remove the air cleaner as described in Section 4.

3   Drain the cooling system (Chapter 2) or alternatively fit hose clamps to the automatic choke coolant hoses.

4   Loosen the clips and disconnect the coolant hoses from the automatic choke cover.

5   Loosen the clips and disconnect the fuel supply and, if fitted, the return hose(s).

6   Disconnect the accelerator cable (Section 11).

7   Disconnect the wiring from the idle cut-off valve, the thermo time valve, and the automatic choke.

8   Note the location of the vacuum hoses, then disconnect them.

9   Unscrew the securing nuts then lift the carburettor off its studs. Recover the gasket.

10   Refitting is a reversal of removal, but if necessary use a new gasket. Adjust the accelerator cable as described in Section 11. Refill the cooling system (Chapter 2) and refit the air cleaner (Section 4).

16 Carburettor – overhaul

1   With the carburettor removed from the vehicle, drain the fuel from the float chamber and vapour separator. Clean the outside of the carburettor.

2   Remove the hoses and wires from the carburettor, making identifying marks or notes to avoid confusion on reassembly.

3   Access to the jets and float chamber is obtained by removing the top half of the carburettor, which is secured by five screws. Blow through the jets and drillings with compressed air, or air from a foot-pump – *do not probe them with wire. If it is wished to remove the jets, unscrew them carefully with well-fitting tools.*

4   Remove the fuel strainer from the inlet pipe by hooking it out with a small screwdriver.

5   Clean any foreign matter from the float chamber. Renew the inlet needle valve if wear is evident, or if a high mileage has been covered.

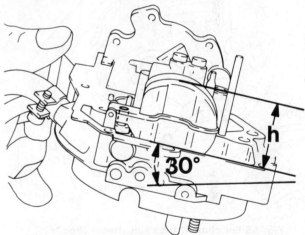

Fig. 3.3 Float level checking dimension (Sec 16)

h = 28 to 30 mm (1.10 to 1.18 in)

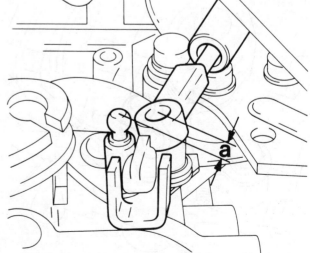

Fig. 3.4 Rest position of vacuum pullrod (Sec 16)

a = 0.5 to 2.0 mm (0.02 to 0.08 in)

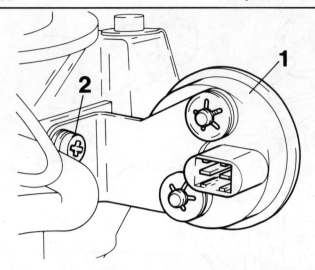

Fig. 3.5 Thermo time valve (1) and mounting screw (2) (Sec 16)

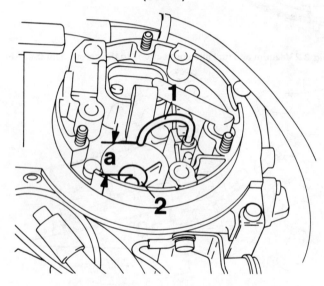

Fig. 3.6 Enrichment tube adjustment (Sec 16)

a = 24 to 26 mm (0.95 to 1.02 in)
1   Enrichment tube
2   Venturi

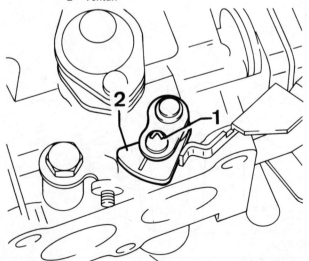

Fig. 3.7 Accelerator pump adjustment bolt (1) and cam (2) (Sec 16)

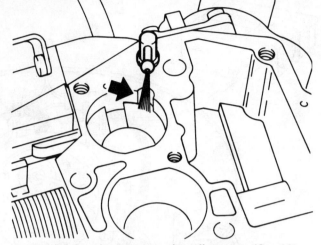

Fig. 3.8 Accelerator pump jet adjustment (Sec 16)

Renew the float if it is punctured or otherwise damaged.

6   It is not possible to adjust the float level setting as this depends on the float weight being between 5.75 and 5.95 grams (0.201 and 0.210 oz). However, it is possible to check the initial setting as follows. Invert the carburettor cover and measure the distance from the joint face to the furthest edge of the float (Fig. 3.3). The spring-tensioned ball in the needle valve should not be depressed during the check. The distance should be as given in the Specifications.

7   Renew the diaphragms in the part load enrichment valve and in the accelerator pump. Renew the inlet pipe fuel strainer. Obtain an overhaul kit of gaskets.

8   To remove the 2nd stage vacuum unit, prise the pullrod from the lever ball and remove the bracket screws. When refitting the unit, the rest position of the pullrod must be between 0.5 and 2.0 mm (0.02 and 0.08 in) away from the lever ball as shown in Fig. 3.4. This ensures that the pullrod is pre-tensioned when reconnected.

9   The thermo time valve may be removed by removing the bracket screw (Fig. 3.5).

10   Reassemble the carburettor in the reverse order to dismantling using new gaskets and seals. Lubricate linkages with a little oil.

11   Refer to Fig. 3.6 and check that the distance between the enrichment tube and the venturi is between 24 and 26 mm (0.95 and 1.02 in). Also check that the tube is vertically over the centre of the venturi.

12   The accelerator pump delivery may be checked as follows but the fuel level must be maintained at the correct level in the float chamber. On automatic transmission models, adjust the dashpot upwards first (Section 17). Turn the automatic choke cam clear of the fast idle adjustment screw. Position the carburettor over a suitable container, then open and close the throttle valve ten times at a rate of approximately one second per stroke, waiting approximately three seconds in between each stroke. Divide the quantity of fuel collected by ten, and compare with the amount given in the Specifications. If adjustment is necessary, referring to Fig. 3.7, slacken the bolt and reposition the cam as required, noting that rotating the cam clockwise will increase the pump delivery, and rotating it anti-clockwise will decrease the pump delivery.

13   Check that the accelerator pump jet directs the fuel towards the recess as shown in Fig. 3.8. If not, it will be necessary to remove the carburettor cover to move the jet.

14   Refer to Fig. 3.9 and check that the 2nd stage linkage clearances are as shown, with the 1st stage throttle valve in its idle position. If necessary, bend the fork to correct.

15   Invert the carburettor and position the fast idle adjustment screw on the highest level of the cam. Using a twistdrill check that the clearance between the primary throttle valve and the barrel is as given in the Specifications for the throttle valve gap. This provides an initial setting for the fast idle speed. Adjust the fast idle adjustment screw if necessary.

16   To check the choke valve gap, first ensure that the pulldown diaphragm is not leaking, then disconnect the vacuum pipe from the diaphragm. Fully close the choke valve, and position the adjusting screw on the highest step of the fast idle cam. Using a small screwdriver, push in the pulldown diaphragm rod to the first pressure point. With the rod in this position, use a twistdrill to check the 'small' choke

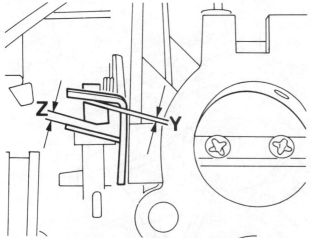

Fig. 3.9 2nd stage linkage clearances (Sec 16)

Y = 0.6 to 1.0 mm (0.024 to 0.039 in)
Z = 0.2 to 0.6 mm (0.008 to 0.024 in)

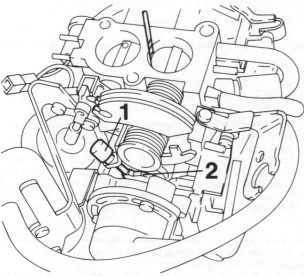

Fig. 3.10 Checking the throttle valve gap (Sec 16)

1 Fast idle adjustment screw
2 Stepped plate

Fig. 3.11 Checking the choke valve gap (Sec 16)

1 Pulldown diaphragm rod
2 Pulldown unit adjustment screw

A Twistdrill checking choke valve gap

Fig. 3.12 Checking fast idle cam adjustment (Sec 16)

1 Fast idle stepped cam
2 Adjusting lever
3 Choke lever
4 Fast idle speed adjustment screw

valve gap between the choke valve and bore (Fig. 3.11). If necessary, adjust the gap by rotating the adjustment screw on the pulldown unit. Once the 'small' choke valve gap is correct, push the pulldown rod fully into the diaphragm, then repeat the measuring procedure and check the 'large' choke valve gap. Again, if necessary adjust the gap by rotating the adjustment screw on the pulldown unit.

17   Once the choke valve gap is correctly adjusted, check the fast idle cam adjustment as follows. Referring to Fig. 3.12, open the throttle valve, press the choke lever lightly in the direction of the arrow, then close the throttle valve again; the adjustment screw should now be positioned on the second step of the cam. Using a twistdrill, check the clearances between the choke valve and bore. If necessary, adjust the fast idle clearance by carefully bending the lever (Fig.3.13), taking care not to damage the return springs.

18   Next check the choke valve forced opening as follows. Referring to Fig. 3.14, rotate the choke lever in the direction of the arrow until it abuts its stop. Retain the lever in this position using an elastic band, then fully open the throttle valve and measure the choke valve forced opening (dimension 'B'). If adjustment is necessary, either carefully increase the gap using a screwdriver, or close the gap using a pair of pointed-nose pliers. Once the gap is correctly set, remove the rubber band from the choke lever.

19   Refit the choke cover to the carburettor, ensuring the lever is correctly engaged with the cover spring loop, and align the marks provided (photos).

Fig. 3.13 Adjust the fast idle cam setting by bending the lever, taking care not to damage the return springs – arrowed (Sec 16)

1 Fast idle stepped cam
2 Adjusting lever

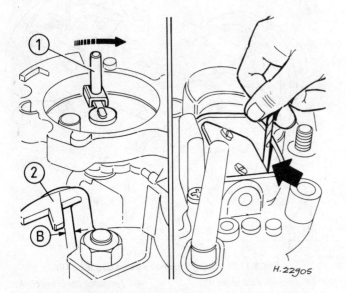

**Fig. 3.14 Checking the choke valve forced opening with a twistdrill –
arrowed (Sec 16)**

1   Choke lever   B   Choke valve forced opening
2   Adjustment segment   dimension

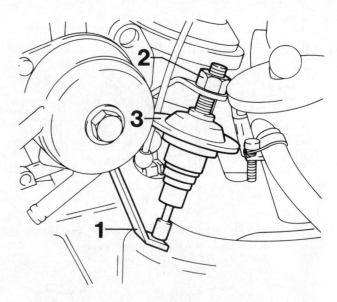

**Fig. 3.15 Throttle valve dashpot on automatic transmission models
(Sec 17)**

1   Throttle lever   3   Dashpot
2   Adjusting nut

17   Carburettor throttle valve dashpot (automatic transmission models) – adjustment

1   Adjust the idle speed and mixture as described in Section 14.
2   With the throttle lever in the idle position, loosen the locknut on the dashpot and adjust the unit until the gap between the end of the plunger and the throttle lever is 0.05 mm (0.002 in). From this position turn the dashpot **down** $2\frac{1}{2}$ turns, then tighten the locknut.

18   Carburettor – fast idle speed adjustment

1   The engine must be at operating temperature and the idle speed and mixture must be correctly adjusted.
2   Position the fast idle adjustment screw on the second highest step of the fast idle cam. Connect a tachometer to the engine in accordance with the manufacturer's instructions. Make sure that the choke plate is fully open.
3   Start the engine without touching the throttle pedal and compare the engine speed with that given in the Specifications. If adjustment is necessary remove the tamperproof cap from the head of the fast idle screw by crushing it with pliers, and adjust by means of the screw (photo).
4   When adjustment is correct, stop the engine and disconnect the tachometer.

19   Carburettor thermotime valve – checking

1   Remove the air cleaner (Section 4).
2   Disconnect the wiring plug from the thermo time valve. Switch on the ignition, and use a voltmeter to check that the current supply is at least 11.5 volts.
3   Using an ohmmeter, check that the resistance across the time valve terminals is 6.0 ± 1.5 ohms at an ambient temperature of between 20 and 30°C (68 to 86°F).

4   Disconnect the vacuum hoses, then apply vacuum to the port nearest the carburettor. With the wiring still disconnected the valve should be open.
5   Reconnect the wiring and continue to apply the vacuum with the ignition switched on. From the point of reconnection, the valve should close after four to ten seconds at an ambient temperature of 20°C (68°F). Renew the valve if this is not the case.
6   Switch off the ignition and refit the air cleaner.

20   Inlet manifold preheater element (carburettor models) – removal, checking and refitting

1   The preheater element is located underneath the inlet manifold.

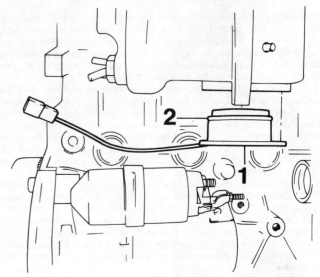

**Fig. 3.16 Inlet manifold preheater element (1) and O-ring
seal (2) (Sec 20)**

23.2 Adjusting the idle speed (L3 Jetronic system)

23.4A Idle mixture screw location (arrowed) (L3 Jetronic system)

23.4B Adjusting the idle mixture (Motronic system)

24.1 Disconnecting throttle valve switch wiring

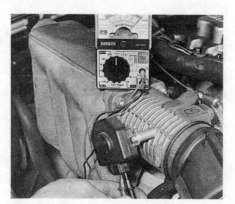

24.2 Checking the resistance of the throttle valve switch

25.1 Throttle valve switch

First disconnect the wiring.

2   Remove the screws and withdraw the element from the inlet manifold. Remove the O-ring seal.

3   Using an ohmmeter check that the resistance across the element wire terminals is approximately 1.5 ohms.

4   Refitting is a reversal of removal, but use a new O-ring seal.

21 Fuel injection system – description

1.8 models are fitted with a Bosch L3 Jetronic fuel injection system but 2.0 models are fitted with a Bosch Motronic ML4 engine management system. Both systems function is a similar manner although the Motronic system is more advanced including an idle speed adjuster unit, a control unit fully integrated into the ignition system, and a self diagnosis system. The latter system communicates any faults by means of a flashing code signal when activated by a service mechanic.

The main components of the system are:

(a) A **control unit** which determines the length of the injection stroke from information sent to it from the various engine sensors

(b) **Fuel injectors** to supply suitably atomised fuel to the cylinders

(c) An **air flow sensor** to monitor the volume of air entering the engine

(d) An **electrically operated fuel pump**

(e) A **fuel pump control relay** incorporating double contacts one of which is operated by the ignition pulse. This ensures that the fuel pump does not operate unless the engine is turning.

In addition, and essential to the system, are a fuel filter, throttle valve switch, fuel pressure regulator, coolant temperature sensor, an auxiliary air valve (L3 system only), an idle speed adjuster (Motronic system only), and an intake air temperature sensor (Motronic system only).

22 Fuel injection system – precautions

The fuel injection system is normally trouble-free. Avoid damage to the electrical components by observing the following precautions.

(a) *Do not disconnect the battery with the engine running*

(b) *Do not use a boost charger as a starting aid*

(c) *Do not disconnect or reconnect wiring plugs with the ignition switched on*

(d) *Remove the control unit if the temperature will exceed 80°C (176°F), as for example in a paint drying oven*

(e) *Before performing a cylinder compression test, unplug the control relay to disable the fuel pump*

(f) *Any faults registered on the Motronic self-diagnosis system will be deleted when the battery is disconnected*

23 Fuel injection system – idle speed and mixture adjustment

Note: *On the Motronic system it is only possible to adjust the idle mixture, as the idle speed is controlled by the idle speed adjuster*

1   Run the engine to normal operating temperature, then switch it off and connect a tachometer to it in accordance with the manufacturer's instructions.

2   Allow the engine to idle and compare the idle speed with that given in the Specifications. If adjustment is necessary locate the adjusting screw on the throttle housing (L3 system only) and turn it as required (photo).

3   Stop the engine and connect an exhaust gas analyser in accordance with the manufacturer's instructions.

4   With the engine idling at the specified speed, read the CO level and

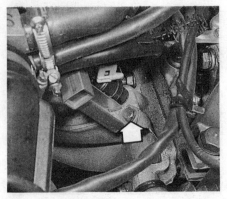

25.6 Fuel distribution rail mounting bolt (arrowed)

25.8 Disconnecting the brake servo vacuum pipe

25.11 Checking the resistance of an injector

25.13 Disconnecting the air duct from the airflow sensor

25.18 Coolant temperature sensor for the fuel injection system (arrowed)

25.25A Loosen the clips ...

compare it with that specified. If adjustment is necessary turn the screw located on the side of the airflow sensor clockwise to enrich the mixture or anti-clockwise to weaken it (photos).
5   Readjust the idle speed if necessary.

24 Fuel injection system throttle valve switch – checking and adjustment

1   Disconnect the wiring plug from the throttle valve switch (photo).
2   Connect an ohmmeter between the centre terminal (18) on the switch and each of the outer terminals in turn (2 and 3) (photo). The resistance between terminals 2 and 18 should be zero, and between terminals 3 and 18 infinity.
3   To adjust the switch on the L3 Jetronic system, loosen the two screws, turn the switch clockwise, then turn it slowly anti-clockwise until the microswitch is heard to click. Tighten the screws with the switch in this position.
4   To adjust the switch on the Motronic system, loosen the two screws and turn the switch clockwise then slowly anti-clockwise to the point where resistance is felt. Tighten the screws with the switch in this position. Slowly open the throttle and check that the switch is heard to click as the throttle opens.

25 Bosch L3 Jetronic fuel injection system components – removal and refitting

Note: *It is not possible to repair the main components of the fuel injection*

system. *In the event of a fault, it is best to have the fault isolated by a GM dealer or other competent specialist who will have the necessary test equipment. With the problem diagnosed, there is no reason why the defective component cannot be renewed by following the instructions in this Section.*

Throttle valve switch

1   Disconnect the wiring plug from the switch (photo).
2   Remove the two mounting screws and pull the switch off the throttle valve spindle.
3   Refitting is a reversal of removal, but adjust the switch as described in Section 24.

Fuel injectors

4   Disconnect the battery negative lead.
5   Disconnect the wiring plugs from the injectors.
6   Unscrew the four bolts retaining the fuel distribution rail to the inlet manifold (photo).
7   Using a screwdriver, prise out the clips holding the injectors to the distribution rail.
8   Unscrew the union nut and disconnect the brake servo vacuum pipe from the inlet manifold (photo).
9   Remove the bracket for the fuel feed pipe.
10   Place some cloth rags around the injectors to absorb spilled fuel, then ease the distribution rail from the injectors and pull the injectors from the inlet manifold.
11   Connect an ohmmeter across the injector terminals and check that the resistance is 16.0 ± 1.0 ohms (photo).
12   Refitting is a reversal of removal, but if necessary renew the injector sealing rings.

Airflow sensor and control unit

13   Loosen the clip and disconnect the air duct from the airflow sensor

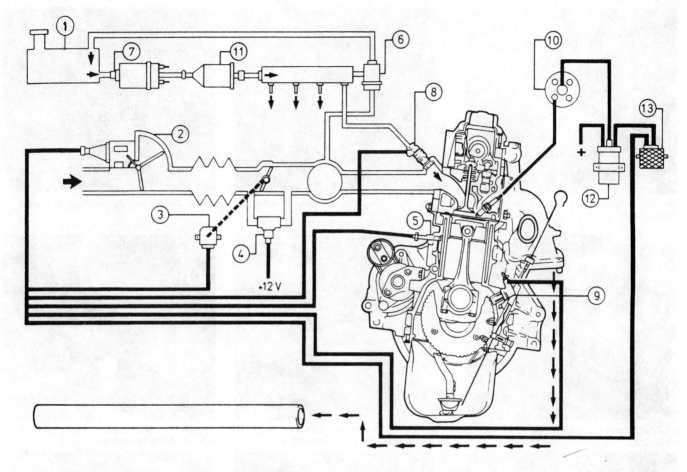

Fig. 3.17 Bosch L3 Jetronic fuel injection system layout (Sec 21)

1 Fuel tank	4 Auxiliary air valve	8 Injector	11 Fuel filter
2 Airflow sensor and control	5 Coolant temperature sensor	9 Inductive pulse sensor	12 Ignition coil
unit	6 Fuel pressure regulator	10 Distributor cap	13 Ignition trigger box
3 Throttle valve switch	7 Fuel pump		

(photo). Disconnect the wiring multi-plug.

14   Release the spring clips and lift the airflow sensor and cover from the air cleaner body.

15   Wipe clean the sensor air valve and check it for free movement.

16   The control unit is located inside the sensor cover, which may be removed by extracting the four screws.

17   Refitting is a reversal of removal.

Coolant temperature sensor

18   The coolant temperature sensor is located by the alternator on the side of the block (photo).

19   Drain the cooling system (Chapter 2).

20   Disconnect the wiring plug and unscrew the sensor.

21   To test the sensor, connect an ohmmeter across the two terminals and compare the resistance with the valves given in the Specifications.

22   Refitting is a reversal of removal. Refill the cooling system with reference to Chapter 2.

Auxiliary air valve

23   The auxiliary air valve is bolted to the side of the camshaft housing.

24   Disconnect the wiring plug from the valve.

25   Loosen the hose clips and disconnect the air hoses (photo).

26   Unbolt and remove the valve (photo).

27   The function of the valve may be checked by looking through the hose connecting stubs. When cold the valve should be slightly open. As the valve is heated (achieved by connecting a 12 volt supply to its terminals) the regulator disc should move round and block the hole.

28   Refitting is a reversal of removal.

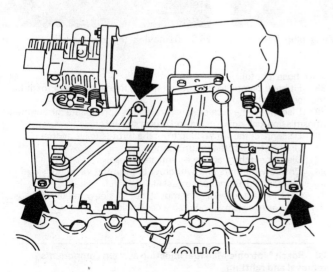

Fig. 3.18 Fuel distribution rail mounting bolts (Sec 25)

25.25B ... and disconnect the auxiliary air valve hoses

25.26 Removing the auxiliary air valve

25.32 Fuel pressure regulator (arrowed)

25.37A Disconnecting the air inlet duct ...

25.37B ... and auxiliary air valve hose from the throttle valve housing

25.38A Throttle valve housing bottom coolant hose (arrowed)

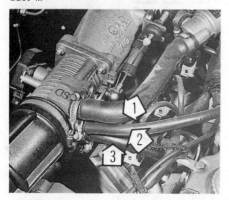

25.38B Hose connections to the throttle valve housing
1 Idle speed adjuster hose
2 Crankcase ventilation hose
3 Coolant hose

26.4 Disconnecting wiring plug from an injector

26.6 Removing the injector clips

Control relay

29 The control relay is located in the left-hand rear corner of the engine compartment. Unplugging the relay disables the fuel pump.
30 Lift off the cover and pull the relay from the terminal socket.
31 Refit in the reverse order to removal.

Fuel pressure regulator

32 The fuel pressure regulator is located between injectors 3 and 4 (photo).
33 Place cloth rag around the regulator to absorb spilled fuel.
34 Disconnect the fuel and vacuum hoses and remove the regulator.
35 Refitting is a reversal of removal.

Throttle valve housing

36 Disconnect the battery negative lead.
37 Loosen the clips and disconnect the air inlet duct and auxiliary air

valve hose (photo).
38 Fit hose clamps to the coolant hoses, then disconnect them from the housing (photos).
39 Disconnect the accelerator cable, and as appropriate the automatic transmission kick-down cable and cruise control cable.
40 Disconnect the wiring plug from the throttle valve switch.
41 Unhook the throttle return spring.
42 Disconnect the crankcase ventilation hose.
43 Unscrew the nuts and withdraw the throttle valve housing from the inlet manifold. Remove the gasket.
44 Refitting is a reversal of removal, but fit a new gasket and adjust the cables as necessary. Top up the coolant level.

---

26 Bosch Motronic ML4 fuel injection system components – removal and refitting

---

Refer to the preliminary note given in Section 25.

26.7 Disconnecting the brake servo vacuum pipe

26.9 Removing injector from the inlet manifold

26.10 Refitting the injector clips

26.12 Disconnecting the wiring multi-plug from the airflow sensor

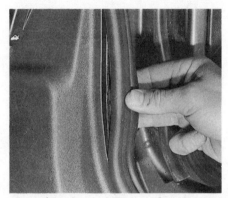

26.17 Pull back the rubber moulding and remove the trim panel

26.18 Control unit and upper mounting screws

26.19A Pull back the spring clip ...

26.19B ... and disconnect the wiring multi-plug

26.22 Disconnecting the wiring plug from the idle speed adjuster

26.24 Checking the resistance of the idle speed adjuster

27.1 Cruise control system motor (arrowed)

27.2 Clutch (1) and brake (2) pedal switches (Photo taken using a mirror)

28.3 Disconnecting Motronic idle speed adjuster hose from the inlet manifold

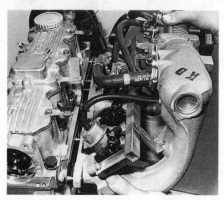

28.6A Removing the inlet manifold

28.6B Inlet manifold gasket on the cylinder head

28.8 Tightening the inlet manifold nuts

29.2A Exhaust downpipe and gasket

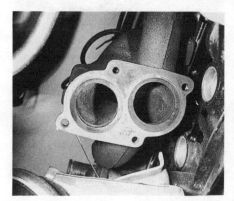

29.2B Exhaust manifold flange

29.3 Removing the exhaust manifold

29.5 Tightening the exhaust manifold nuts

Throttle valve switch

1   Refer to Section 25 paragraphs 1 to 3.

Fuel injectors

2   Disconnect the battery negative lead.
3   Disconnect the wiring plug from the idle speed adjuster. Disconnect the hoses and remove the adjuster.
4   Disconnect the wiring plugs from the injectors (photo).
5   Unscrew the four bolts retaining the fuel distribution rail to the inlet manifold.
6   Using a screwdriver, prise out the clips holding the injectors to the distribution rail (photo).
7   Unscrew the union nut and disconnect the brake servo vacuum pipe from the inlet manifold (photo).
8   Remove the bracket for the fuel feed pipe.

9   Place some cloth rags around the injectors to absorb spilled fuel, then ease the distribution rail from the injectors and pull the injectors from the inlet manifold (photo). Test the injectors as described in Section 25.
10   Refitting is a reversal of removal but, if necessary, renew the injector sealing rings (photo).

Airflow sensor

11   Loosen the clip and disconnect the air duct from the airflow sensor.
12   Disconnect the wiring multi-plug (photo).
13   Release the spring clips and lift the airflow sensor and cover from the air cleaner body.
14   If necessary unbolt the sensor from the cover.
15   Wipe clean the sensor air valve and check it for free movement.
16   Refitting is a reversal of removal.

30.4A Exhaust front mounting clamp

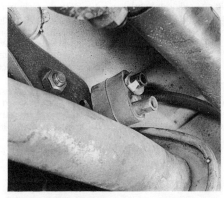

30.4B Intermediate exhaust mounting with exhaust fitted

30.4C Intermediate exhaust mounting rubber with exhaust removed

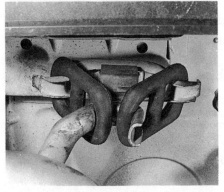

30.4D Rear exhaust mounting rubber rings

30.6A Exhaust downpipe to intermediate section flange

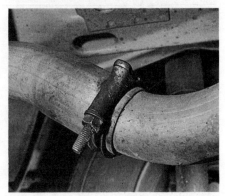

30.6B Intermediate to rear section clamp

Control unit

17 Pull back the rubber moulding and remove the trim panel from the right-hand side of the driver's footwell (photo).
18 Remove the three mounting screws (photo).
19 Pull back the spring clip and disconnect the wiring multi-plug (photos). Withdraw the control unit.
20 Refitting is a reversal of removal.

Coolant temperature sensor

21 Refer to Section 25, paragraphs 18 to 22.

Idle speed adjuster

22 Disconnect the wiring plug from the rear of the adjuster (photo).
23 Loosen the clips and disconnect the air hoses.
24 Connect an ohmmeter across the adjuster terminals and check that the resistance is 8 ohms (photo).
25 Refitting is a reversal of removal.

Control relay

26 Refer to Section 25, paragraphs 29 to 31.

Fuel pressure regulator

27 Refer to Section 25, paragraphs 32 to 35.

Throttle valve housing

28 The procedure is basically as given in Section 25, paragraphs 36 to 44, except for the disconnection of the auxiliary air valve hose.

27 Cruise control system – general

Cruise control is optional on some models. It consists of an electronically controlled motor (photo) which operates the throttle valve by means of a cable. By depressing the switch on the end of the left-hand steering column stalk at a given speed above 25 mph, the system automatically maintains the speed by opening or closing the throttle

valve as required. The system is switched off if the speed drops below 25 mph, or if the clutch or brake pedal is depressed, however the previously selected speed is still held in the system memory until such time as the engine is switched off. The brake and clutch pedals are fitted with control switches (photo).

28 Inlet manifold – removal and refitting

1 The manifold may be removed with or without the carburettor or fuel injection components. First remove the air cleaner (carburettor models) or disconnect the air inlet duct from the throttle housing (fuel injection models).
2 Drain the cooling system (Chapter 2).
3 Disconnect all crankcase ventilation, coolant, fuel and air hoses (photo).
4 Disconnect all electrical wires.
5 Disconnect the throttle control cable(s) as previously described.
6 Progressively unscrew the nuts then withdraw the inlet manifold from the studs on the cylinder head. Remove the gasket (photos).
7 Clean the mating faces of the inlet manifold and cylinder head.
8 Refitting is a reversal of removal but use a new gasket and tighten the mounting nuts to the specified torque (photo).

29 Exhaust manifold – removal and refitting

1 Disconnect the HT cables from the spark plugs and ignition coil.
2 Unscrew the bolts securing the exhaust downpipe to the exhaust manifold, lower the downpipe and recover the joint (photos).
3 Progressively unscrew the nuts, then withdraw the exhaust manifold from the studs on the cylinder head (photo).Remove the gasket.

4   Clean the mating faces of the exhaust manifold and cylinder head.
5   Refitting is a reversal of removal, but use a new gasket and tighten the mounting nuts to the specified torque (photo).

30   Exhaust system – removal and refitting

1   The exhaust system is in three sections, each with its own silencer, except for the front pipe on carburettor models which is plain.
2   To remove the complete system, position the car over an inspection pit, or raise the car and support it on axle stands.
3   Unscrew the bolts securing the exhaust downpipe to the manifold, lower the downpipe and recover the joint.

4   With the help of an assistant, unbolt the front mounting clamp and unhook the rubber mountings. The intermediate mounting rubbers are retained with metal clips (photo).On some models the front mounting is of rubber instead of a clamp.
5   Lower the exhaust system to the ground.
6   Separate the sections by unbolting the flange and removing the clamp (photos).
7   Refitting is a reversal of removal, but fit a new manifold gasket. Tighten the manifold bolts with the exhaust system loose in the front clamp, then tighten the clamp.
8   Holts Flexiwrap and Holts Gun Gum exhaust repair systems can be used for effective repairs to exhaust pipes and silencer boxes, including ends and bends. Holts Flexiwrap is an MOT approved permanent exhaust repair.

31   Fault diagnosis – fuel and exhaust systems

Symptom	Reason(s)
Excessive fuel consumption	Air cleaner element choked
	Fuel leakage
	Mixture adjustment incorrect
	Automatic choke defective
Insufficient fuel supply or weak mixture	Faulty fuel pump
	Mixture adjustment incorrect
	Air leak on induction component
	Fuel filter blocked
Difficult starting	Automatic choke defective

Chapter 4 Ignition system

For modifications, and information applicable to later models, see Supplement at end of manual

Contents

Specifications

System type
1.8 engines..	MSTS – i (Microprocessor Spark Timing System – inductive)
2.0 engines..	Integrated with Bosch Motronic ML4 engine management system

General
Ignition control unit (1.8 engines):	
Carburettor engine code..	CB
Fuel injection engine code..	CC
Ignition coil:	
Make..	Bosch
Primary resistance (1.8 engine only)..	0.68 to 0.76 ohms
Secondary resistance (1.8 engine only)	7.0 to 8.4 ohms
Inductive impulse sensor resistance	0.5 to 1.6 k ohms
HT leads resistance	9 to 20 k ohms
Distributor rotor arm rotation	Anti-clockwise
Firing order	1-3-4-2 (No 1 at timing belt end of engine)

Ignition timing (1.8 engines)

Engine code/rpm:	A*	B*	C*
18SV/2000..	12° to 17° BTDC	7° to 12° BTDC	34° to 41° BTDC
18SEH/1800...	14° to 18° BTDC	9° to 13° BTDC	44° to 48° BTDC

*A = Octane rating 98 RON
B = Octane rating 95 RON
C = With vacuum hose or throttle valve switch reconnected

Spark plugs
Type	Champion RN7YCC or RN7YC
Electrode gap:	
RN7YCC	0.8 mm (0.032 in)
RN7YC	0.7 mm (0.028 in)

HT leads
HT leads	Champion LS-11 (boxed set)

Torque wrench settings
	Nm	lbf ft
Spark plugs	20	15

1 General description and precautions

To achieve optimum performance from an engine, and to meet stringent exhaust emission requirements, it is essential that the fuel/air mixture in the combustion chamber is ignited at exactly the right time relative to engine speed and load. The ignition system provides the spark necessary to ignite the mixture, and automatically varies the instant at which ignition occurs according to the engine requirements.

The ignition system consists of a primary low tension (LT) circuit and a secondary high tension (HT) circuit. When the ignition is switched on, current is fed to the coil primary windings and a magnetic field is established. At the required point of ignition, the primary circuit is interrupted electronically by the sensor disc attached to the crankshaft. The magnetic field collapses and a secondary high tension voltage is induced in the secondary windings. This HT voltage is fed via the distributor rotor arm to the relevant spark plug. After delivering the spark the primary circuit is re-energised and the cycle is repeated.

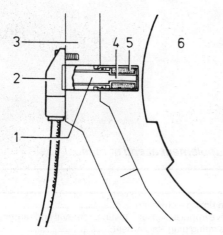

Fig. 4.1 Inductive impulse sensor in the 1.8 litre engine (Sec 1)

1	Permanent magnet	4	Soft iron case
2	Housing	5	Coil
3	Cylinder block	6	Sensor disc

The ignition timing is controlled by a microprocessor within the control unit. On 1.8 models, the control unit is located in the right-hand rear corner of the engine compartment, and on carburettor models has a vacuum hose connected to it. On 2.0 models, the control unit is integral with the Motronic engine management control unit located on the right-hand side of the driver's footwell. The control unit receives information on engine speed, load and temperature and from this determines the correct ignition timing.

Note: *When working on the ignition system, remember that the high tension voltage can be considerably higher than on a conventional system, and in certain circumstances could prove fatal.*

2 Routine maintenance

1   Carry out the following procedures at the intervals given in *Routine maintenance* at the front of this manual.
2   Clean or renew the spark plugs with reference to Section 9.
3   Clean and check the distributor cap, rotor arm, HT leads and ignition coil with reference to the appropriate Section.

3 Distributor cap and rotor arm – removal and refitting

1   Access to the distributor is not easy since it is located on the rear of the camshaft housing near the bulkhead.
2   On carburettor engines remove the air cleaner assembly (Chapter 3).
3   Unscrew the distributor cap retaining screws and withdraw the cap (photo). Disconnect the HT leads from the spark plugs and ignition coil. The leads should already be marked for location, but if not, attach identification tags to them.
4   Remove the condensation seal from the rotor arm (photo).
5   Note the position of the rotor arm, then use an Allen key to unscrew the two bolts. Remove the rotor arm from the backplate (photos).
6   Pull the backplate out of the oil seal (photo).
7   To ensure correct refitting, mark the end of the camshaft with a dab of paint in the direction the rotor arm was pointing.
8   Examine the cap and rotor arm for signs of arcing which will show up as thin black lines of carbon. Clean any build-up of carbon from the metal segments, but do not remove any metal as this will increase the gap the HT spark has to jump. Check that the carbon brush inside the cap is free to move against the spring tension (photo).
9   Refitting is a reversal of removal, but apply a little sealing compound under the bolt heads of the backing plate before tightening them.

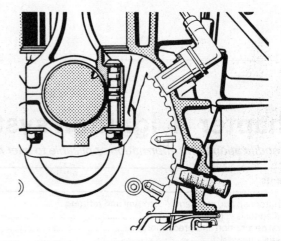

Fig. 4.2 Inductive impulse sensor on the 2.0 litre engine (Sec 1)

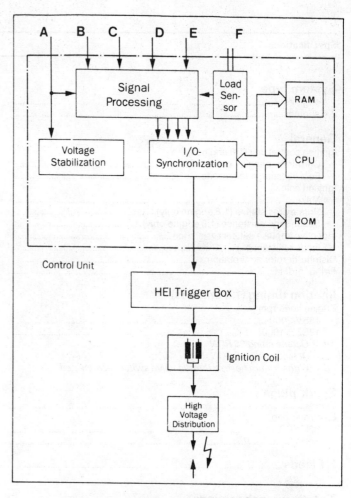

Fig. 4.3 Ignition system components on the 1.8 litre carburettor engine (Sec 1)

A	Battery voltage	CPU	Control processing unit
B	Resistance coding		(microprocessor)
	(octane rating)	RAM	Random access memory
C	Coolant temperature	ROM	Read only memory
D	Engine speed		(programme memory)
E	Throttle valve switch	I/O	Input/output
	position		
F	Intake manifold vacuum		

3.3   Removing the distributor cap (engine removed for clarity)

3.4   Condensation seal removal

3.5A   Unscrew the bolts ...

3.5B   ... and remove the rotor arm

3.6   Removing the backplate

3.8   View inside the distributor cap

5.1   Octane rating plug (arrowed)

6.1   Ignition coil

6.2   Disconnecting the coil HT lead (arrowed)

4   Ignition timing – checking

1   Checking of the ignition timing is not possible on the 2.0 litre engine fitted with the Motronic engine management system. On the 1.8 litre engine the ignition timing can be checked as described in the following paragraphs, although no adjustment is possible since this is carried out automatically by the electronic control unit. The procedure may be used if a fault is suspected or if any of the ignition components have been renewed.

2   Run the engine to normal operating temperature, then switch off.

3   On carburettor versions disconnect the vacuum hose from the electronic control unit located in the right-hand rear corner of the engine compartment.

4   On fuel injection versions disconnect the plug from the throttle valve switch and connect together terminals 18, 3 and 2 inside the plug with bridging wires.

5   Connect a tachometer and stroboscopic timing light to the engine (No. 1 cylinder at front).

6   Check that the octane rating plug near the brake vacuum servo is set to the 98 octane number with the number '98' on the same side as the black plastic clip. If it is set to 95, unclip the plug and turn it round.

7   Start the engine and run it at the specified speed.

8   Point the timing light to the left-hand side of the crankshaft pulley and check that the notch in the pulley appears in line with the pointer on the rear timing cover.

9   Stop the engine. Refit the throttle valve switch plug or the control unit vacuum hose as applicable.

10   If the ignition timing is now checked again, the increased advance

should be as given in the Specifications. There are no additional marks on the crankshaft pulley, however some timing lights may have a facility for setting the advance reading obtained in paragraph 8 to the specified amount then reading the increased advance after completing the procedure given in paragraph 9. Alternatively the crankshaft pulley may be marked with the degree settings.

11   With the engine stopped disconnect the tachometer and timing light.

12   If necessary, reset the octane rating plug to the required position.

5   Octane rating plug – adjustment

1   All models are fitted with an octane rating plug located in the right-hand rear corner of the engine compartment, near the brake servo unit (photo).

2   The plug is colour-coded according to the engine fitted, as follows.

Engine code	Colour
18SV	To June 1987: Brown From June to December 1987: Green From December 1987: Brown
18SEH	To June 1987: Brown From June to December 1987: White From December 1987: Brown
20SE	To June 1987: (Manual) White, (Automatic) Brown From June 1987: Violet (Manual and Automatic)

3   The plug may be set for either leaded fuel (98 RON) or unleaded fuel (95 RON), and the plug is designed so that the chosen setting is always visible. To reset the plug, release the clip then separate the plug, turn it through half a turn, and reconnect.

4   When changing from the 98 RON to the 95 RON setting, the ignition timing is retarded by 5° by means of two resistors located inside the plug.

6   Ignition coil – testing, removal and refitting

Note: *Test procedures only apply to 1.8 engines*

1   The ignition coil is mounted on the left-hand side of the engine compartment, to the rear of the battery (photo).

2   With the ignition switched off, disconnect the HT and LT leads (photo), and examine the coil tower for signs of arcing which will be

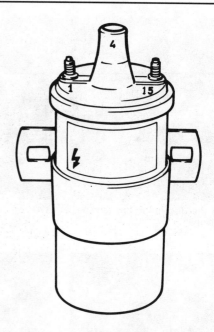

Fig. 4.4 Ignition coil terminal numbers (Sec 6)

indicated by thin lines of carbon. Remove the plastic cap for a more thorough investigation.

3   To check the primary windings, connect an ohmmeter between terminals 1 and 15 and compare the reading with the resistance given in the Specifications.

4   To check the secondary windings, connect the ohmmeter between terminals 1 (-) and 4 (HT), and again compare with the specified resistance.

5   Renew the coil if the winding resistances are incorrect or if there are signs of arcing.

6   With all leads disconnected the coil may be removed by unbolting the bracket from the inner wing panel. Note the location of the radio interference suppressor beneath one of the bolts.

7   Refitting is a reversal of removal.

7   Inductive impulse sensor – testing, removal and refitting

1   The inductive impulse sensor is located on the front left-hand side of the cylinder block.

2   To test the sensor disconnect the wiring plug on the top of the engine and connect an ohmmeter across the two terminals leading to the sensor. The resistance should be as shown in the Specifications. If not, the sensor is faulty.

7.4A   Unscrew the bolt ...

7.4B   ... and withdraw the inductive impulse sensor

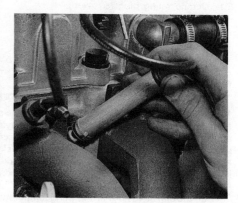

9.2   Disconnecting an HT lead from a spark plug

9.11A Fitting a spark plug

9.11B Tightening a spark plug to the correct torque setting

3 The resistance may also be checked at the control unit by disconnecting the multi-plug. The terminal numbers are 11 and 12 on 1.8 models, and 23 and 25 on 2.0 models.
4 To remove the sensor, use an Allen key to unscrew the retaining bolt, and withdraw the sensor from the cylinder block (photos).
5 Disconnect the wiring plug and unclip the cable from the timing belt cover.
6 Refitting is a reversal of removal.

8 Ignition control unit (1.8 models) – removal and refitting

1 The ignition control unit is located in the right-hand rear corner of the engine compartment. First disconnect the battery negative lead.
2 Lift the bonnet weatherstrip and plastic cover from the bulkhead on the right-hand side.
3 Disconnect the multi-plug.
4 On carburettor models, disconnect the vacuum hose.
5 Unscrew the mounting bolts and withdraw the control unit.
6 Refitting is a reversal of removal.

9 Spark plugs – removal, servicing and refitting

1 The correct functioning of the spark plugs is vital for the correct running and efficiency of the engine. It is essential that the plugs fitted are appropriate for the engine, and the suitable type is specified at the beginning of this chapter. If this type is used and the engine is in good condition, the spark plugs should not need attention between scheduled replacement intervals. Spark plug cleaning is rarely necessary and should not be attempted unless specialised equipment is available as damage can easily be caused to the firing ends.
2 On carburettor models, remove the air cleaner (Chapter 3).
3 Identify the HT leads for position, then disconnect them from the spark plugs. The lead ends are fitted with special sleeves which completely cover the spark plugs (photo).
4 Using a spark plug spanner, unscrew the spark plugs from the cylinder head.
5 Examination of the spark plugs will give a good indication of the condition of the engine.
6 If the insulator nose of the spark plug is clean and white, with no deposits, this is indicative of a weak mixture, or too hot a plug (a hot plug transfers heat away from the electrode slowly - a cold plug transfers heat away quickly). The recommended plugs are detailed in the Specifications at the beginning of this Chapter.

7 If the top and insulator nose is covered with hard black-looking deposits, then this is indicative that the mixture is too rich. Should the plug be black and oily, then it is likely that the engine is fairly worn, as well as the mixture being too rich.
8 If the insulator nose is covered with light tan to greyish brown deposits, then the mixture is correct, and it is likely that the engine is in good condition.
9 The spark plug gap is of considerable importance, because if it is either too large or too small the size of the spark and its efficiency will be seriously impaired. The spark plug gap should be set to the figure given in the Specifications.
10 To set it, measure the gap with a feeler gauge and then bend open, or close, the outer plug electrode until the correct gap is achieved. The centre electrode should never be bent as this may crack the insulation and cause plug failure, if nothing worse.
11 To fit the plugs, screw each plug in by hand (photos). Tighten the plugs to the specified torque. If a torque wrench is not available tighten them hand tight onto their seating and then tighten further by approximately $\frac{1}{8}$ of a turn.
12 When reconnecting the HT leads, make sure that they are refitted in their correct order.
13 Refit the air cleaner on carburettor models.

10 HT leads – general

1 The HT leads require no routine attention other than being kept clean and wiped over regularly. When attending to the spark plugs, it is a good idea to remove each plug lead in turn from the distributor cap. Water can find its way into the joints giving rise to a white corrosive deposit which must be carefully removed from the end of each cable and the terminal sockets in the distributor cap.
2 The HT leads fitted as original equipment are of the resistor type and may be checked using an ohmmeter. The resistance of each lead should be as shown in the Specifications. Renew all the HT leads if the resistance is excessive.

11 Fault diagnosis – ignition system

Since the ignition primary circuit is controlled electronically, it is relatively trouble-free compared to other systems. Any faults occurring in the primary circuit are most likely to be caused by broken or disconnected leads or bad contact caused by corrosion. However the high tension circuit is of conventional type, and the associated faults are covered in the following paragraphs. There are two main symptoms indicating ignition faults. Either the engine will not start or fire, or the engine is difficult to start and misfires.

Engine fails to start

1   If the starter motor fails to turn the engine, check the battery and starter motor with reference to Chapter 12.
2   Disconnect an HT lead from any spark plug and hold the end of the cable approximately 5 mm (0.2 in) away from the cylinder head using *well-insulated pliers.* While an assistant spins the engine on the starter motor check that a regular blue spark occurs. If so, remove and re-gap the spark plugs as described in Section 9.
3   If no spark occurs, disconnect the main feed HT lead from the distributor cap and check for a spark as in paragraph 2. If sparks now occur, check the distributor cap, rotor arm, and HT leads as described in Sections 3 and 10.
4   If no sparks occur check the resistance of the main feed HT lead as described in Section 10, and renew as necessary. Should the lead be serviceable, check that all wiring and multi-plugs are secure in the low tension circuit.
5   Check the ignition coil as described in Section 6.
6   If the above checks reveal no faults but there is still no spark, the control unit must be suspect. Consult a GM dealer for further testing, or test by substitution.

Engine misfires

7   If the engine misfires regularly, run it at a fast idling speed. Pull off each of the plug HT leads in turn and listen to the note of the engine. *Hold the plug leads with a well- insulated pair of pliers as protection against a shock from the HT supply.*
8   No difference in engine running will be noticed when the lead from the defective circuit is removed. Removing the lead from one of the good cylinders will accentuate the misfire.
9   Remove the plug lead from the end of the defective plug and hold it about 5 mm (0.2 in) away from the cylinder head. Restart the engine. If the sparking is fairly strong and regular, the fault must lie in the spark plug.
10   The plug may be loose, the insulation may be cracked, or the points may have burnt away giving too wide a gap for the spark to jump. Worse still, one of the points may have broken off. Either renew the plug or reset the gap, and then test it.
11   If there is no spark at the end of the plug lead, or if it is weak and intermittent, check the HT lead from the distributor to the plug. If the insulation is cracked or perished, or if its resistance is incorrect, renew the lead. Check the connection at the distributor cap.
12   If there is still no spark, examine the distributor cap carefully for tracking. This can be recognised by a very thin black line running between two or more electrodes, or between an electrode and some other part of the distributor. These lines are paths which now conduct electricity across the cap thus letting it run to earth. The only answer is a new distributor cap. Tracking will also occur if the inside or outside of the distributor cap is damp. If this is evident use a proprietary moisture dispersant, such as Holts Wet Start. To prevent the problem recurring, Holts Damp Start can be used to provide a sealing coat, so excluding any further moisture from the ignition system.

In extreme difficulty, Holts Cold Start will help to start a car when only a very poor spark occurs.

Chapter 5 Clutch

Contents

Specifications

General
Clutch type .... Single dry plate, diaphragm spring pressure plate
Actuation.. Cable

Friction plate
Diameter .... 216 mm (8.5 in)
Total lining thickness (new)... 9.0±1.0 mm (0.354±0.04 in)
Maximum lateral run-out.. 0.4 mm (0.016 in)

Adjustment
Clutch pedal stroke .... 142 + 7 mm (5.59 + 0.28 in)

Torque wrench settings

	Nm	lbf ft
Clutch cover (pressure plate)	15	11

---

1 General description

All models with manual transmission have a single dry plate, diaphragm spring clutch. The clutch cover is bolted to the rear face of the flywheel.

The friction plate is located between the flywheel and the pressure plate and slides on splines on the gearbox input shaft. When the clutch is engaged, the diaphragm spring forces the pressure plate onto the friction plate which in turn is forced against the flywheel. Drive is then transmitted from the flywheel, through the friction plate to the gearbox input shaft. On disengaging the clutch, the pressure plate is lifted from the friction plate, and drive to the gearbox is then disconnected.

The clutch is operated by a foot pedal suspended under the facia, and a cable connected to the clutch release lever on the gearbox. Depressing the pedal causes the release lever to move the release bearing against the fingers of the diaphragm spring in the clutch cover. The spring is sandwiched between two rings which act as fulcrums. As the centre of the spring is moved in, the periphery moves out to lift the pressure plate and disengage the clutch. The reverse takes place when the pedal is released.

As the friction plate linings wear, the foot pedal will rise progressively relative to its original position, and it is therefore necessary to periodically adjust the height and stroke of the pedal.

2 Routine maintenance

1   Carry out the following procedure at the intervals given in *Routine Maintenance* at the front of this manual.

Check clutch pedal adjustment
2   With the clutch pedal in the at-rest position, use a tape measure to measure the distance from the centre of the pedal pad to the base of the steering wheel rim (furthest point from the pedal). Note the measurement as (A).
3   Fully depress the clutch pedal and repeat the procedure given in paragraph 2. Note the measurement as (B).
4   Subtract measurement (A) from measurement (B) to calculate the clutch pedal stroke. This should be as shown in the Specifications at the start of this Chapter.
5   If adjustment is necessary, apply the handbrake, jack up the front of the vehicle and support it on axle stands. Loosen the locknut on the clutch cable end fitting (photos) and turn the adjustment nut clockwise to increase the dimension difference, or anti-clockwise to reduce it. Tighten the locknut and recheck the dimension difference. Lower the vehicle to the ground.
6   Note that with correct adjustment the clutch pedal will be slightly higher in relation to the brake pedal. The adjustment is incorrect if both pedals are at the same height and it is likely that the clutch will not fully release.

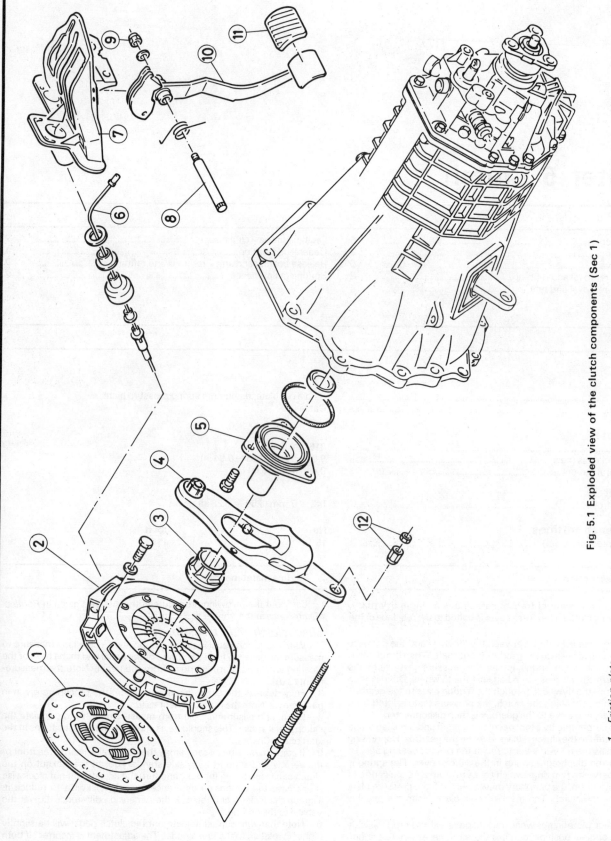

Fig. 5.1 Exploded view of the clutch components (Sec 1)

1 Friction plate
2 Clutch cover and pressure
   plate
3 Release bearing

4 Release arm
5 Guide sleeve
6 Clutch cable
7 Pedal bracket

8 Pedal shaft
9 Nut
10 Clutch pedal

11 Front pad
12 Cable adjustment nut and
    locknut

2.5A Adjusting the clutch cable

2.5B On some models there is no counterbalance weight on the release arm, and the adjustment nut acts directly on the arm

3.2 Measuring the position of the clutch cable adjustment nut and locknut

3.3 Clutch cable adjustment nut (1) and locknut (2)

3.4 Removing the clutch cable end fitting from the release lever

3.7 Clutch cable at the bulkhead

5.2 Clutch cover and flywheel marked in relation to each other

5.4 Removing the friction plate

7 As the clutch linings wear, the clutch pedal rest position will progressively move upwards, making periodic adjustment necessary at the specified intervals.

3 Clutch cable – removal and refitting

1 Apply the handbrake. Jack up the front of the vehicle and support it on axle stands.
2 Using a steel rule, measure the distance from the locknut to the end of the threaded cable fitting (photo). This will provide an initial setting when refitting the cable.
3 Unscrew and remove the locknut, and the adjustment nut noting that the inner end of the adjustment nut is ball-shaped (photo).
4 Remove the end fitting from the release lever, and remove both the

inner and outer cables from the hole in the clutch housing (photo).
5 Working inside the vehicle, reach up behind the facia and disengage the inner cable from the curved upper section of the clutch pedal.
6 Where necessary, unbolt the cable clip from the steering gear.
7 Withdraw the clutch cable from the bulkhead and remove it from the engine compartment (photo).
8 Refitting is a reversal of removal, but make sure that the cable is correctly located in the clutch pedal, bulkhead, and clutch housing. Initially adjust the cable to the setting noted in paragraph 2, but finally check the pedal adjustment as described in Section 2.

4 Clutch pedal – removal and refitting

1 Disconnect the clutch cable from the pedal with reference to Section 3.

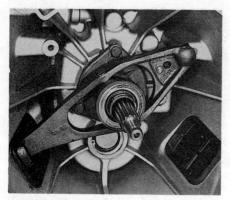

7.1   View of the clutch release bearing and arm inside the clutch housing

7.2   Forward pointing arrow on the clutch housing grommet

7.3   Disengaging the clutch release arm from the ball-pin

2   Working inside the vehicle, disconnect the wiring from the brake stop-lamp switch, unhook the brake pedal return spring and disconnect the servo pushrod from the brake pedal.

3   Loosen the nut on the end of the pedal shaft. Unhook the clutch pedal return spring.

4   Unscrew the nuts holding the pedal bracket to the bulkhead, and turn the bracket around the steering column to allow removal of the pedal shaft. Note that on later models, it may be necessary to remove the steering column to allow the pedal bracket to be slid off its retaining studs. The column can be removed as described in Chapter 10, Section 22, noting that it is not necessary to remove the steering wheel or the lock cylinder; the column can be removed with these items still in position.

5   Remove the pedal location clips, then unscrew the nut, remove the washer and withdraw the shaft until the clutch pedal can be removed from the bracket. Recover the pedal thrustwashers.

6   Refitting is a reversal of removal, but lubricate the shaft with grease. Adjust the clutch cable as described in Section 3, then check the clutch pedal adjustment as described in Section 2.

5   Clutch – removal

1   Remove the gearbox as described in Chapter 6.

2   Mark the clutch cover in relation to the flywheel (photo).

3   Unscrew, in a diagonal progressive manner, the bolts securing the clutch cover to the flywheel. Care should be exercised to unscrew the bolts evenly otherwise there is a risk of distorting the diaphragm spring. To avoid this, GM dealers use a special tool, shown in Fig. 5.2, to depress the diaphragm spring, and the pressure plate is then held in this position with special clips while the bolts are unscrewed. Removal of the clips and the subsequent fitting of them to the new cover requires the use of a press. However, provided that the bolts are unscrewed evenly, no distortion should occur.

4   Lift the cover from the flywheel and remove the friction plate, noting which way round the latter is fitted (photo).

6   Clutch – inspection

1   Examine the surfaces of the pressure plate and flywheel for scoring. If this is only light the parts may be re-used, but if scoring is excessive renew both the pressure plate and flywheel.

2   If the pressure plate has any blue discoloured areas, the clutch has been overheated at some time and renewal is necessary.

3   Examine the clutch cover for loose components and for distortion of the diaphragm spring.

4   Renew the friction plate if the linings are worn down to, or near the rivets. If the linings appear oil stained, the cause of the oil leak must be found and rectified. This is most likely to be a failed gearbox input shaft oil seal or crankshaft rear oil seal. Check the friction plate hub and centre splines for wear.

5   Spin the release bearing in the clutch housing and check it for roughness. If any excessive movement or roughness is evident, renew the release bearing as described in Section 7.

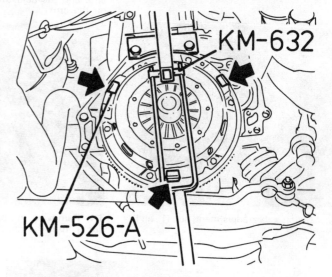

Fig. 5.2 GM tool used to depress the diaphragm spring (Sec 5)

Arrows indicate where pressure plate retaining clips are fitted

7   Release bearing and arm – removal and refitting

1   With the gearbox removed in order to provide access to the clutch, attention can be given to the release bearing located in the clutch housing (photo).

2   Prise the rubber grommet from the clutch housing, and remove it from the end of the release arm. Note the arrow pointing forwards (photo).

3   Pull the release arm slightly out of the clutch housing hole until the socket and spring are disengaged from the ball pin (photo, then slide the bearing and arm from the guide sleeve inside the clutch housing.

4   Separate the bearing from the rollers on the release arm (photo). If necessary, remove the circlip and balance weight (photo).

5   Clean the release arm, release bearing and guide sleeve. Note however, if the release bearing is to be re-used, do not allow any solvent to enter it.

6   Apply a little high melting-point grease to the ball pin, socket, guide sleeve and bearing collar contact faces.

7   Refitting is a reversal of removal. When fitted, the release arm should be held firmly in contact with the ball pin. If this is not the case, press the fork-shaped spring against the release arm to give it extra tension (photo).

8   Clutch – refitting

1   Wipe clean the pressure plate and flywheel faces with a clean cloth.

7.4A Separating the bearing from the release arm

7.4B Release arm balance weight and retaining circlip

7.7 Fork-shaped spring on the release arm

8.3 Fitting the clutch friction disc and cover

8.4 Centralising the clutch friction disc with the special tool

8.5 Tightening the clutch cover bolts

During the refitting procedure take care not to allow oil or grease onto the linings or friction faces.

2   Locate the friction plate on the flywheel with the raised hub facing outwards. The word 'GETRIEBESEITE' on the hub must also face outwards.

3   Fit the cover and insert the bolts loosely (photo). Align the previously-made marks if the original cover is being refitted.

4   The friction plate must now be centralised so that when the gearbox is refitted, the input shaft will press through the friction plate splines, and enter the spigot bearing in the end of the crankshaft. Ideally a universal clutch centralising tool should be used (photo),or if available an old gearbox input shaft. Alternatively a bar or wooden mandrel may be used, although the degree of accuracy in this instance will depend on how accurate the tool dimensions are.

5   Make sure that the centralising tool is located correctly in the friction plate and spigot bearing, then tighten the clutch cover bolts in a diagonal progressive manner to the specified torque (photo).Remove the tool.

6   Refit the gearbox as described in Chapter 6.

9   Fault diagnosis – clutch

Symptom	Reason(s)
Judder when taking up drive	Worn friction disc linings or contamination with oil Worn splines on friction disc or gearbox input shaft Engine/gearbox mountings loose or deteriorated
Clutch drag (failure to disengage)	Friction disc sticking on input shaft spline Crankshaft spigot bearing seizing Clutch pedal adjustment incorrect
Clutch slip (engine speed increases without increasing road speed)	Friction disc linings worn or contaminated with oil Weak or broken diaphragm spring
Noise when depressing clutch pedal (engine stopped)	Worn diaphragm spring Pedal shaft dry
Noise when depressing clutch pedal (engine running)	Dry or worn release bearing

Chapter 6 Manual gearbox and automatic transmission

For modifications, and information applicable to later models, see Supplement at end of manual

Contents

Specifications

Type

Type	Five forward speeds and reverse, synchromesh on all forward and reverse gears
Designation	R25

Ratios

1st	4.044 : 1
2nd	2.264 : 1
3rd	1.434 : 1
4th	1.000 : 1
5th	0.842 : 1
Reverse	3.748 : 1

Lubricant

Type/specification	Gear oil, GM type 19 40 761 (90 297 261) (Duckhams Hypoid 75W/90S)
Capacity	1.2 litres (2.1 pints)

Torque wrench settings

	Nm	lbf ft
Front cover	20	15
Release bearing guide sleeve	22	16
Output flange	180	133
Gearbox-to-engine bolts:		
Normal shank	75	55
Reduced diameter shank	60	44
Rear crossmember	45	33
Rear casing	22	16
Filler/drain plugs	30	22
Reversing lamp switch	20	15
Detent plate	10	7

Automatic transmission

Type

Type	Aisin-Warner four forward speeds and one reverse, 4th gear lock-up clutch
Designation	AW 03-71 L

Ratios
1st...	2.45 : 1
2nd..	1.45 : 1
3rd...	1.00 : 1
4th...	0.69 : 1
Reverse..	2.22 : 1

Lubricant
Type/specification...	Dexron II type ATF (Duckhams Uni-Matic or D-Matic)
Capacity:	
From dry	6.3 litres (11.1 pints) approx
Drain and refill only	2.5 litres (4.4 pints) approx
After removing sump	3.3 litres (5.8 pints) approx

Torque wrench settings
	Nm	lbf ft
Transmission sump and filter...	5	4
Solenoid valve	13	10
Torque converter to driveplate	30	22
Rear crossmember	45	33
Drain plug	20	15
Transmission to engine:		
M10 bolts...	35	26
M12 bolts...	55	41
Inhibitor switch	22	16
Fluid coolant lines..	35	26

1 General description

The manual gearbox fitted is of five-speed type with synchromesh on all gears including reverse. All gears, including the reverse idler gear, are in constant mesh with those on the laygear. Gear engagement is by locking the corresponding gear to the mainshaft with the synchro unit sliding sleeves. As the gears are engaged, the synchro-rings match the speed of the mainshaft with that of the gear being selected in order to ensure smooth engagement.

The automatic transmission of four-speed type. In 4th gear the torque converter is locked by access of an internal clutch, thereby eliminating any slip. With the selector lever in Drive (D) it is possible to select either a three or four-speed sequence by pressing the button on the lever. It is also possible to select speeds '1' and '2' separately. The transmission incorporates the normal kickdown facility to enable greater acceleration in all the gears, but in addition a kickdown switch is provided on the accelerator pedal specifically to shift from 4th to 3rd gear.

2 Routine maintenance

Check manual gearbox oil level

1   Carry out the following procedures at the intervals given in *Routine maintenance* at the front of this manual.
2   Either position the vehicle over an inspection pit, or jack up the front and rear of the vehicle and support it on axle stands. The vehicle must be

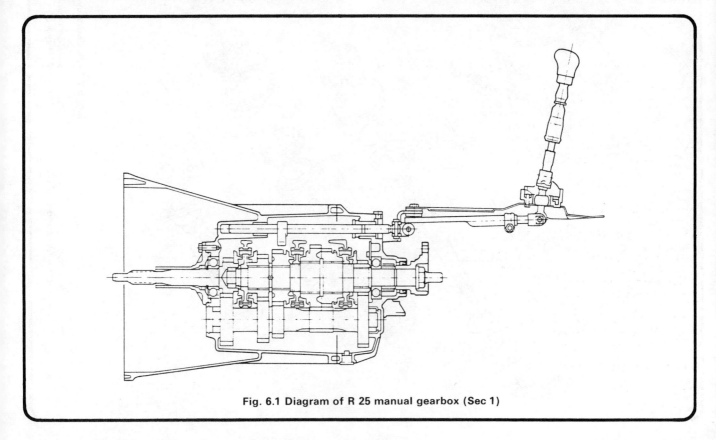

Fig. 6.1 Diagram of R 25 manual gearbox (Sec 1)

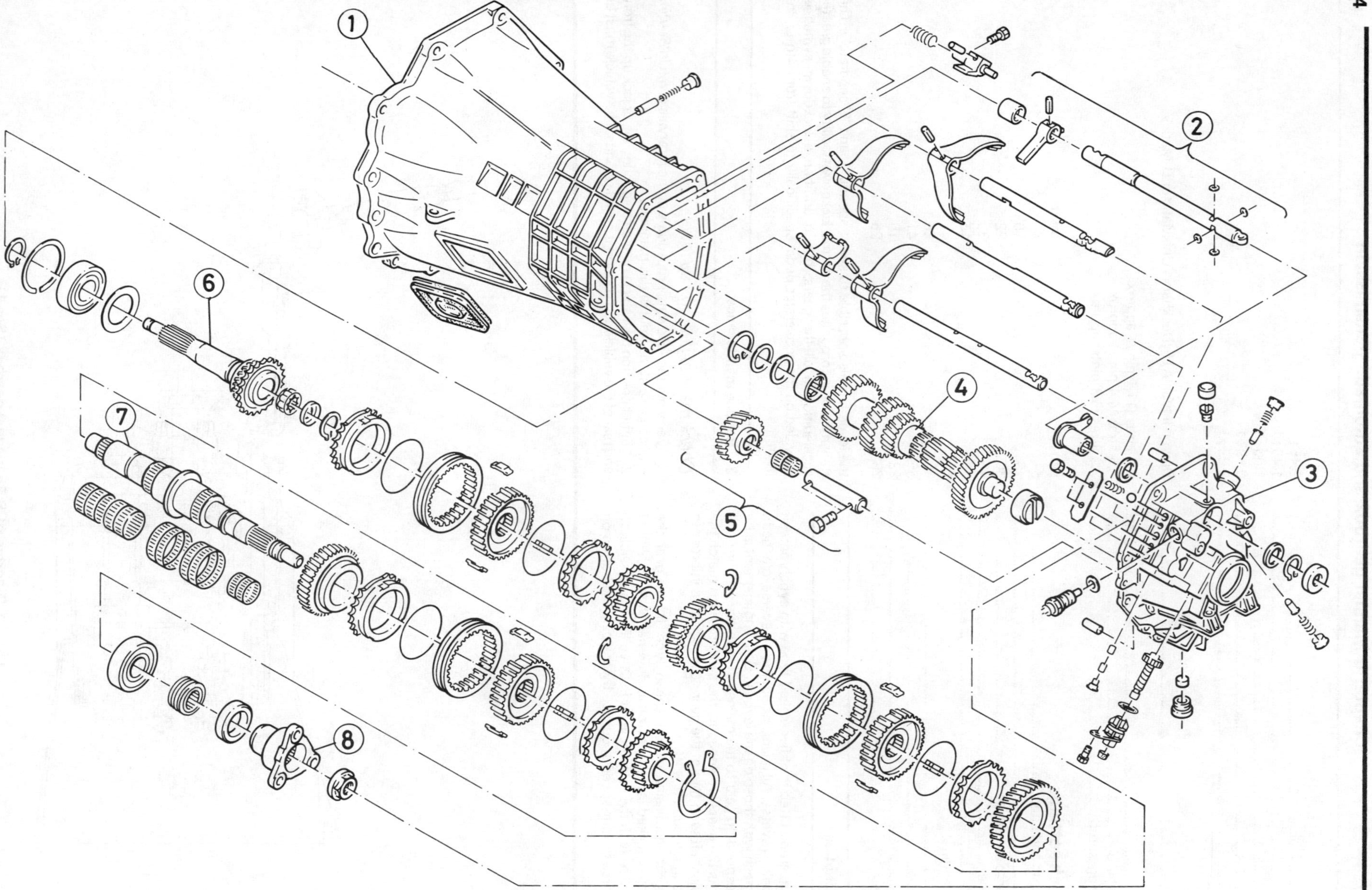

Fig. 6.2 Exploded view of manual gearbox inner parts (Sec 1)

1 Main casing
2 Selector forks and shafts
3 Rear casing
4 Laygear
5 Reverse idler gear
6 Input shaft
7 Mainshaft
8 Output flange

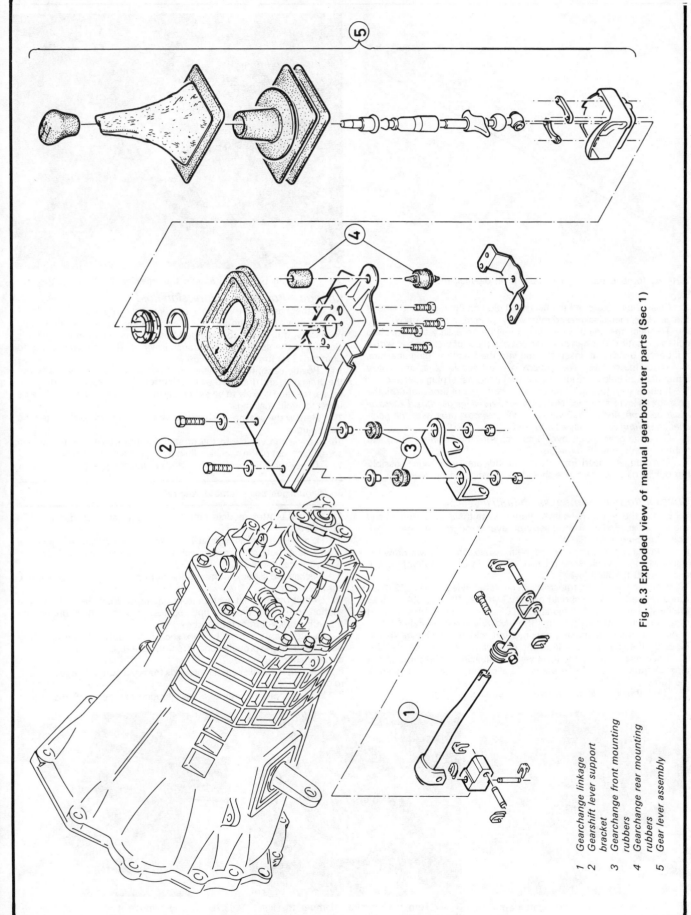

Fig. 6.3 Exploded view of manual gearbox outer parts (Sec 1)

1 Gearchange linkage
2 Gearshift lever support bracket
3 Gearchange front mounting rubbers
4 Gearchange rear mounting rubbers
5 Gear lever assembly

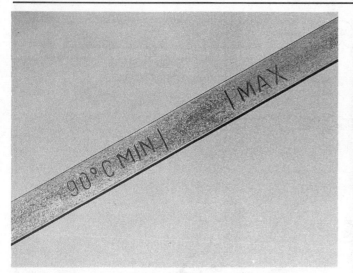

2.10 Automatic transmission fluid level dipstick markings

2.11 Topping up the automatic transmission fluid

level.

3 Clean the area around the filler/level plug on the right-hand side of the gearbox, then slacken and remove the plug from the gearbox.

4 To check the gearbox oil level, it will be necessary to fabricate a suitable dipstick. This can be made out of a piece of welding rod with a right-angle bend in it. Insert the rod into the filler/level plug aperture, and check the oil level. The gearbox oil level should be approximately 9 mm (0.36 in) below the lower edge of the filler/level plug aperture.

5 If necessary, top-up using the specified type of lubricant until the gearbox oil level is correct. **Note:** *Do not overfill the gearbox. Excess oil must be syphoned or drained out of the gearbox, otherwise the gear-change shifting action may be impaired.*

6 Once the gearbox oil level is correct, refit the filler/level plug and tighten it to the specified torque.

7 The frequent need for topping-up indicates a leakage, possibly through an oil seal. The cause should be investigated and rectified.

Check automatic transmission fluid level

8 Ensure the vehicle is on level ground. With the engine running and the brakes applied, move the selector lever through all the gear positions, finishing in 'P' (Park).

9 With the engine still idling and the transmission in 'P', withdraw the transmission dipstick, wipe it clean, then re-insert it and withdraw it again. Read the fluid level.

10 With the engine and transmission hot (after at least 20 km/13 miles running) the fluid level should be between the MIN and MAX marks on the side of the dipstick marked '90°C' (photo). The quantity of fluid required to raise the level from MIN to MAX is approximately 0.6 litre (1 pint). With the engine and transmission cold, the fluid level should be up to the line on the side of the dipstick marked '20°C'.

11 If necessary top up the level with the specified fluid through the dipstick tube (photo). Take care not to allow any dust or dirt to enter the tube.

12 Refit the dipstick and switch off the engine.

Change automatic transmission fluid

13 Either position the vehicle over an inspection pit or jack up the front of the vehicle and support it on axle stands. Although not strictly necessary, it is also recommended that the transmission fluid filter is cleaned at the same time the transmission fluid is renewed. Refer to Chapter 13 for further information.

14 Position a container beneath the transmission sump then unscrew the drain plug and drain all the fluid. **Caution:** If the vehicle has just been in use, the fluid is likely to be extremely hot, and care must therefore be taken to avoid scalding.

15 Renew the sealing washer if necessary, then refit and tighten the drain plug.

16 Lower the vehicle to the ground. Fill the transmission with the correct amount of the specified fluid through the dipstick tube.

17 Check the fluid level as described previously.

---

3 Manual gearbox – removal and refitting

1 On carburettor models remove the air cleaner as described in Chapter 3.

2 Position the vehicle over an inspection pit, or alternatively drive the front wheels onto car ramps or jack it up and support it on axle stands. Apply the handbrake.

3 Slacken the slider joint nut on the front propeller shaft section one complete turn.

4 Unbolt the exhaust system front downpipe from the intermediate section, mounting bracket, and exhaust manifold. Also unbolt the mounting bracket from the gearbox.

5 Using a conventional, or Torx socket, as applicable, unscrew the bolts securing the propeller shaft front flexible disc joint to the gearbox output flange.

6 Lever the propeller shaft rearwards from the output flange and tie it to one side (photo).

7 Where applicable, remove the vibration damper from the output

3.6 Removing the propeller shaft from the output flange

3.7A Turn the vibration damper to align the cut-outs ...

3.7B ... and remove it

3.9   Disconnecting the wiring from the reversing lamp switch

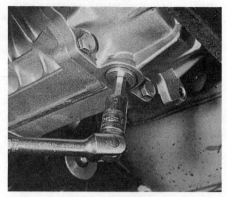

3.10   Removing the oil drain plug

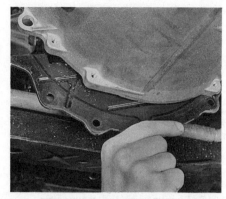

3.13   Removing the gearbox front cover plate

3.15A   Gearchange linkage connection to the gear lever

3.15B   Removing the pin from the gearchange linkage

3.16   Unbolting the gear lever bracket

3.20   Place a piece of wood between the sump and front crossmember

3.24A   Rear crossmember and exhaust mounting bracket

3.24B   Gearchange linkage connection to the gearbox

flange by turning it so that the special cut-outs are aligned with the flange extremities (photos).

8   Disconnect the speedometer cable and tie it to one side.

9   Disconnect the wiring from the reversing lamp switch (photo).

10   Position a container beneath the gearbox, then using an Allen key, unscrew the drain plug and drain the oil (photo). Refit the drain plug on completion.

11   Measure the distance from the clutch cable locknut to the end of the threaded cable fitting, and record this to provide an initial setting when refitting the cable.

12   Unscrew the locknut and adjustment nut, and remove the clutch cable from the release lever and clutch housing. Tie the cable to one side.

13   Unbolt the cover plate from the front of the gearbox (photo).

14   Unscrew and remove the two lower gearbox-to-engine bolts.

15   Reach up over the propeller shaft and disconnect the gearchange linkage from the bottom of the gear lever. To do this, extract the spring clip from one end of the pivot pin and withdraw the pin (photos).

16   Unscrew the two bolts securing the gear lever bracket to the rear of the gearbox (photo).

17   For additional working room, unbolt and remove the underbody crossmember located behind the gearbox.

18   Support the gearbox on a trolley jack.

19   Unbolt the rear mounting crossmember from the underbody.

20   Position a thin piece of wood beneath the engine sump on the front crossmember (photo).

21   Lower the gearbox until the engine sump rests on the piece of wood.

22   Unscrew and remove the remaining gearbox-to-engine bolts.

23   With the help of an assistant, lift the gearbox rearwards from the engine, then withdraw it from under the car. Take care not to allow the weight of the gearbox to bear on the input shaft while it is still engaged with the clutch friction disc.

24   If necessary, extract the spring clip, remove the pin, and disconnect the gearchange linkage from the gearshift lever shaft on the gearbox. Also unbolt and remove the crossmember and exhaust mounting bracket (photos).

25   Refitting is a reversal of removal. Check that the clutch release arm and bearing are correctly fitted, and lightly grease the input shaft splines.

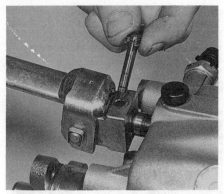

3.24C   Disconnecting the gearchange linkage

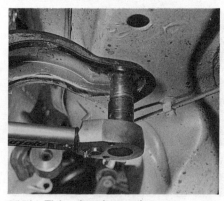

3.25A   Tightening the gearbox rear mounting crossmember bolts

3.25B   Tightening the underbody crossmember bolts

3.25C   Tightening the propeller shaft front flexible disc joint Torx bolts

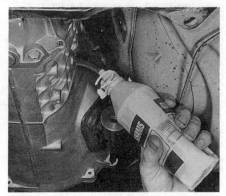

3.25D   Filling the gearbox with oil

3.25E   Tightening the gearbox filler plug

4.3   Removing the reversing lamp switch

4.4   Removing the speedometer drive pinion and housing

4.6A   Fit the tool ...

To help engage the input shaft and clutch friction disc splines, select 4th gear and slowly turn the output flange. Note also that the friction disc must be centralised as described in Chapter 5 in order for the gearbox input shaft to enter the crankshaft spigot bearing. Check and if necessary adjust the clutch cable. Tighten all nuts and bolts to the specified torque. Before inserting the crossmember bolts, apply locking fluid to their threads. Finally fill the gearbox with the specified grade and quantity of oil, and tighten the filler plug on completion (photos).

4   Manual gearbox – dismantling into major assemblies

1   Clean the exterior of the gearbox.
2   Remove the clutch release bearing and arm with reference to Chapter 5.
3   Unscrew and remove the reversing lamp switch (photo).
4   Unscrew the bolt and withdraw the speedometer drive pinion and

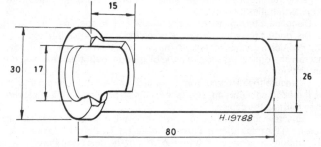

Fig. 6.4 Dimensions (mm) of the special tool for removing the detent caps (Sec 4)

housing (photo).
5   It is now necessary to remove the gearshift lever shaft detent pin which is retained by a special cap pressed into the gearbox casing. The

4.6B ... and remove the cap ...

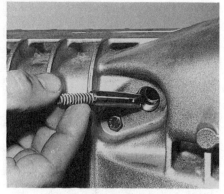

4.6C ... spring and detent pin

4.7 Removing the clutch bearing guide sleeve

4.8 Input shaft bearing inner circlip

4.9A Loosening the output flange nut

4.9B Removing the output flange

4.10 Removing the reverse idler gear shaft retaining bolt

4.12 Pressing the input shaft through the bearing

4.13 Removing the detent plate

GM tool for doing this is numbered KM-630-1, and is used in conjunction with a slide hammer. If it is not possible to obtain this tool, then a substitute tool must be made to the dimensions shown in Fig. 6.4. The claw should be welded to the pipe as brazing would not be strong enough.

6   Use the tool to remove the cap, then extract the spring and detent pin (photos).

7   Inside the clutch bellhousing, unscrew the bolts and remove the clutch bearing guide sleeve over the input shaft (photo).

8   Using circlip pliers extract the inner circlip retaining the input shaft bearing (photo).

9   Hold the output flange stationary by bolting a length of metal bar to it, then unscrew the flange nut using a 32.0 mm socket. Remove the flange with a suitable puller (photos).

10   Unscrew and remove the reverse idler gear shaft retaining bolt (photo).

11   Unscrew the bolts retaining the rear casing to the main casing.

12   The input shaft must now be pressed through the bearing in the

main casing in order to withdraw the rear casing and gears. A suitable three-legged puller may be used to do this, by bolting the legs to the main casing (photo).

13   Unscrew the bolts and remove the detent plate from the rear casing (photo).

14   Extract the detent springs followed by the detent balls (photo). A pencil magnet is ideal for removing the detent balls.

15   Using a pin punch, drive the roll pins from the selector forks while supporting the shafts with a block of wood.

16   Note the position of the selector forks and shafts, and if necessary identify them.

17   Pull out the selector shafts and disengage the selector forks from the synchro sleeves. Turn the gearshift lever shaft as necessary to move the selector finger to one side.

18   Unscrew the reverse idler gear shaft bolt. Withdraw the shaft until the reverse idler gear can be removed (photos). Remove the needle roller bearings.

19   Squeeze together the circlip retaining the mainshaft bearing in the

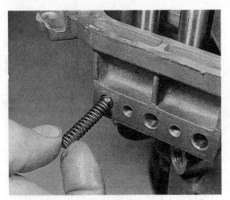

4.14   Removing the detent springs and balls

4.18A   Remove the bolt ...

4.18B   ... and withdraw the reverse idler gear and shaft

4.19   Mainshaft bearing circlip held in the compressed position with a bent piece of metal rod (arrowed)

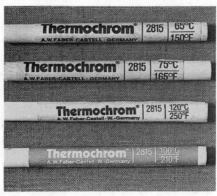

4.20   Selection of thermocolour pencils

4.21   Removing the mainshaft from the rear casing

4.22   The laygear

4.23   Separating the input shaft from the mainshaft

6.2   Speedometer drive gear on the mainshaft splines

rear casing, and hold it in the compressed position using a bent piece of metal rod (photo).
20   The casing must now be heated to 100°C (212°F) in order to remove the mainshaft bearing and gears. An industrial, or paint stripper, hot air blower should be used, and it is recommended that thermocolour pencils (photo) are used so that the correct temperature may be gauged.
21   When the correct temperature is reached, carefully tap the mainshaft from the casing and withdraw the gear cluster as an assembly (photo).
22   Separate the laygear from the input shaft and mainshaft (photo).
23   Separate the input shaft from the mainshaft (photo).

5   Manual gearbox – inspection

1   Clean all the components, however take care not to lose the interlocking pins from the rear casing.

2   Examine each component for general wear, distortion, slackness of fit, and damage to machined faces and threads.
3   Examine the gears for excessive wear and chipping of the teeth. Renew them as necessary.
4   Examine the bearings and bushes for wear and renew as necessary.
5   Renew all oil seals and the six synchro rings as a matter of course.
6   Examine the synchro units and selector forks for excessive wear. In particular check the ends of the forks where they rub against the grooves in the synchro sleeves, and if possible compare them with new forks to determine the wear that has occurred.
7   It may well be worth costing the total price of parts necessary to overhaul the gearbox, and comparing this with the price of a reconditioned gearbox which may, in addition, be guaranteed.

6   Manual gearbox mainshaft – dismantling and reassembly

1   Remove the 4th synchro-ring from the 3rd/4th synchro unit. Identify

6.3 Circlip retaining 3rd/4th synchro unit (arrowed)

6.4 Removing the 3rd/4th synchro unit and 3rd speed gear

6.6A Remove the retaining ring (arrowed) ...

6.6B ... and the two thrustwasher halves

6.7A Removing the 2nd speed gear ...

6.7B ... 2nd synchro-ring ...

6.7C ... and needle roller bearing

6.8 Circlip retaining the 1st/2nd synchro unit (arrowed)

6.9 Removing the 1st/2nd synchro unit and 1st speed gear

the ring for position.
2   Slide the speedometer drive gear from the rear of the mainshaft (photo).
3   Using circlip pliers extract the circlip from the front of the mainshaft (photo).
4   Using a puller, remove the 3rd/4th dsynchro unit and 3rd speed gear together (photo). Also remove the 3rd speed gear needle roller bearing.
5   Separate the 3rd/4th synchro unit from the 3rd speed gear and remove the 3rd synchro-ring. Identify the synchro-ring for position.
6   Remove the retaining ring then release the two thrustwasher halves (photos).
7   Remove the 2nd speed gear and the 2nd synchro-ring. Also remove the 2nd speed gear needle roller bearing (photos).
8   Using circlip pliers extract the circlip retaining the 1st/2nd synchro unit (photo).
9   Using a puller, remove the 1st/2nd synchro unit and 1st speed gear together (photo). Also remove the needle roller bearing.

10   Separate the 1st/2nd synchro unit from the 1st speed gear and remove the 1st synchro-ring. Identify the ring for position.
11   Using a puller, remove the ball bearing from the rear of the mainshaft (photo).
12   Remove the bearing retaining circlip (photo).
13   Remove the 5th speed gear, 5th synchro-ring and the split needle roller bearing (photos).
14   Using circlip pliers, extract the circlip retaining the 5th/reverse synchro unit (photo).
15   Using a puller remove the reverse gear together with the 5th/reverse synchro unit from the rear of the mainshaft (photo). Separate the gear from the synchro unit and recover the reverse synchro-ring.
16   Remove the split roller bearing from the mainshaft (photo).
17   If necessary the synchro units may be dismantled as follows, however keep all parts identified for location to ensure correct assembly.
18   Prise the springs from each side of the synchro unit (photo).
19   Mark the synchro-hub and sleeve in relation to each other, then

6.11   Removing the mainshaft rear bearing

6.12   Rear bearing circlip removal

6.13A   Removing the 5th speed gear ...

6.13B   ... 5th synchro-ring ...

6.13C   ... and needle roller bearing

6.14   5th/reverse synchro unit retaining circlip removal

6.15   Removing the reverse gear and 5th/reverse synchro unit

6.16   Mainshaft completely dismantled

6.18   Spring removal from the synchro unit

slide off the sleeve and recover the sliding keys.
20   Clean all the components, examine them for wear and damage, and renew them as necessary.
21   Commence reassembly by assembling the synchro units as follows. Slide the sleeve onto the hub, aligning the previously-made marks. The notches in the sleeve must be aligned with the sliding key slots and on the same side as the hub raised collar (photo).
22   Insert the sliding keys in the slots, then fit the springs so that the hooked ends are both located in the same key but with the free ends facing in opposite directions (photos). Note that the spring for the 4th synchro-ring is interfaced by approximately 10.0 mm (0.39 in).
23   Locate the reverse gear split roller bearing on the mainshaft, followed by the reverse gear and the reverse synchro-ring (photos).
24   Using a hot air blower, heat the 5th/reverse synchro unit (no grooves on the sleeve) to approximately 100°C (212°F). Immediately press the synchro unit onto the mainshaft splines using a puller, making sure that the sliding keys engage with the slots in the synchro-ring (photos).

25   Fit the retaining circlip in its groove.
26   Fit the 5th gear split needle roller bearing, 5th synchro-ring and the 5th speed gear (photo). Make sure that the slots in the synchro-ring engage with the sliding keys.
27   Locate the bearing retaining circlip over the 5th speed gear. Alternatively the circlip may be held in its compressed position with a piece of bent wire at this stage (photo).
28   Using a puller, press the bearing onto the mainshaft with its closed side against the gear (photo).
29   Fit the 1st gear needle roller bearing, followed by the 1st speed gear, and the 1st synchro-ring (photos).
30   Using the hot air blower, heat the 1st/2nd synchro unit (one groove on the sleeve) to approximately 100°C (212°F). Immediately press the synchro unit onto the mainshaft splines using a puller, making sure that the sliding keys engage with the slots in the synchro-ring. The identification groove on the sleeve should be towards the front end of the mainshaft (photos).
31   Fit the retaining circlip in its groove.

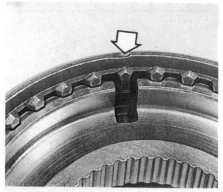

6.21 The notches on the sleeve must align with the key slots

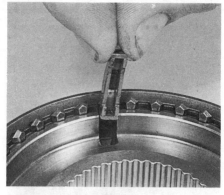

6.22A Insert the sliding keys ...

6.22B ... and fit the springs (arrowed)

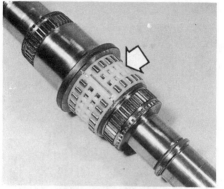

6.23A Fit the split roller bearing ...

6.23B ... reverse gear ...

6.23C ... and reverse synchro-ring

6.24A Heat the 5th/reverse synchro unit ...

6.24B ... and pull it onto the mainshaft splines

6.26 Fitting the 5th synchro-ring

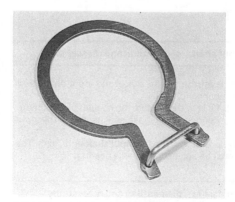

6.27 Rear mainshaft bearing circlip held in its compressed position

6.28 Using a puller to press the bearing into position

6.29A Fitting the 1st speed gear ...

6.29B ... and 1st synchro-ring

6.30A Single groove identification on the 1st/2nd synchro unit (arrowed)

6.30B Fitting the 1st/2nd synchro unit

6.34A Fitting the 3rd speed gear ...

6.34B ... and 3rd synchro-ring

6.35A Double groove identification on the 3rd/4th synchro unit (arrowed)

6.35B Fitting the 3rd/4th synchro unit

7.1 Input shaft oil seal and roller bearing

32   Fit the 2nd gear needle roller bearing, followed by the 2nd synchro-ring and the 2nd speed gear. Make sure that the slots in the synchro-ring engage with the sliding keys.
33   Fit the two thrustwasher halves and retain with the ring.
34   Fit the 3rd gear needle roller bearing, followed by the 3rd speed gear and the 3rd synchro-ring (photos).
35   Using the hot air blower, heat the 3rd/4th synchro unit (two grooves on the sleeve) to approximately 100°C (212°F). Immediately press the synchro unit onto the mainshaft splines using a puller, making sure that the sliding keys engage with the slots in the synchro-ring. The identification grooves on the sleeve should be towards the front end of the mainshaft (photos).
36   Fit the retaining circlip in its groove.
37   Locate the 4th synchro-ring in the 3rd/4th synchro unit with the cut-outs aligned with the sliding keys.
38   Slide the speedometer drivegear onto the rear of the mainshaft.

7 Manual gearbox input shaft – dismantling and reassembly

1   Using a screwdriver lever the oil seal out of the input shaft, then remove the needle roller bearing (photo).
2   Clean the recess and, if it is to be re-used, the needle roller bearing.
3   Pack the needle roller bearing with grease and insert it in the input shaft recess.
4   Fit the new oil seal by pressing it into the input shaft until flush. The closed side of the seal must be against the needle bearing.

8 Manual gearbox rear casing – dismantling and reassembly

1   Using the tool previously described in Section 4, paragraph 5,

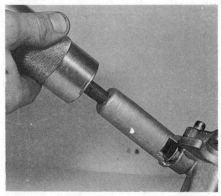

8.1A Using the special tool to pull out the cap

8.1B Remove the cap ...

8.1C ... spring ...

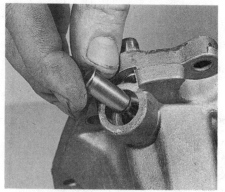

8.1D ... and plunger

8.2 Selector shaft bores

8.3 Gearshift lever shaft oil seal

8.5 Laygear roller bearing

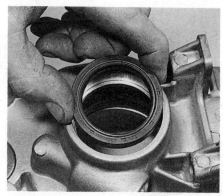

8.6 Output flange oil seal removal

8.9A Refitting the plungers, springs and caps

8.9B Carefully drive the caps into the casing

8.9C Rocker arms with plungers in position

8.11 Fitting an output flange oil seal

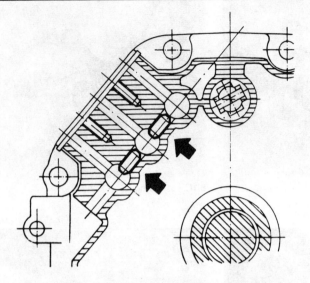

Fig. 6.5 Interlocking pin location (Sec 8)

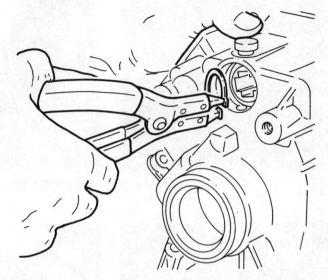

Fig. 6.6 Extracting the rocker arm circlip (Sec 8)

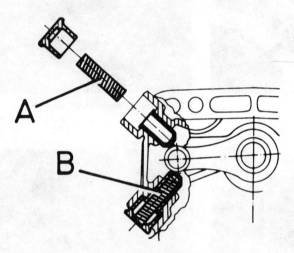

Fig. 6.7 Detent spring locations (Sec 8)

A   *Short (blue)*   B   *Long (green)*

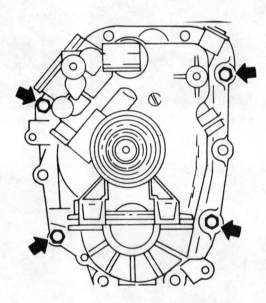

Fig. 6.8 Insert only the bolts indicated when checking the laygear endfloat (Sec 9)

remove the special caps, springs and plungers for the gearshift lever shaft rocker arm (photos). Note the location of the springs as they are of different lengths. The short spring is coloured blue and the long spring green.

2   Extract the interlocking pins located between the selector shaft bores using a pencil magnet (photo). There is no need to remove the end cap.

3   Using a screwdriver, lever out the gearshift lever shaft oil seal (photo).

4   Extract the circlip, then withdraw the rocker arm from inside the casing noting the location of any spacers.

5   Remove the laygear roller bearing using a suitable puller (photo). If necessary heat the casing around the bearing before removing it.

6   Lever the output flange oil seal from the casing (photo).

7   Clean all the components and renew them as necessary.

8   Commence reassembly by inserting the rocker arm, together with any spacers into the casing. Fit any outer spacers followed by the circlip.

9   Refit the plungers, springs, and caps. Use a mallet to drive the caps fully into the casing, and make sure that the springs are in their correct locations (photos).

10   Using a metal tube drive the laygear roller bearing into the casing until flush. The slot under the bearing should face the recess in the casing.

11   Press in a new output flange oil seal into the casing (photo).
12   Press a new gearshift lever shaft oil seal into the casing.

---

9 Manual gearbox main casing – dismantling and reassembly

1   Unscrew the bolt near the gearshift lever shaft detent hole, then from inside the casing, remove the reverse gear block, spring, and shaft (photos).

2   If necessary, extract the gearshift lever shaft guide bearing using a suitable puller (photo).

3   Using circlip pliers extract the laygear roller bearing retaining circlip (photos). If it is tight, tap the bearing inwards slightly. Remove the shims and drive out the bearing from the inside using metal tubing.

4   Using metal tubing drive out the input shaft bearing from the inside of the casing (photo).

5   Clean all the components and renew them as necessary.

6   If the main casing or laygear are renewed, carry out the following

9.1A Reverse gear block bolt

9.1B Reverse gear block inside the casing

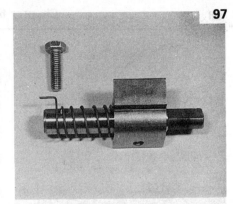

9.1C Reverse gear block components

9.2 Gearshift lever shaft guide bearing (arrowed)

9.3A Laygear roller bearing circlip

9.3B Inner view of laygear roller bearing (arrowed) and input shaft bearing

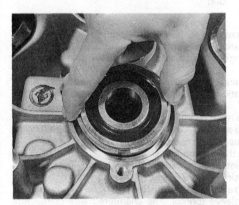

9.4 Input shaft bearing removal

9.10 Dial test indicator with probe on 5th gear

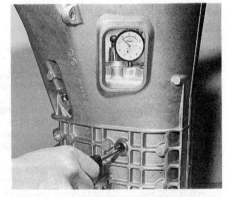

9.11 Checking the laygear endfloat

9.13 Fitting the laygear roller bearing shims

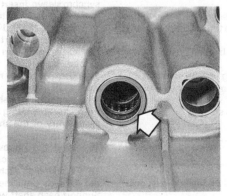

9.14 Fitted gearshift lever shaft guide bearing

10.1 Input shaft, mainshaft and laygear

10.3   Lowering the gear cluster into the rear casing

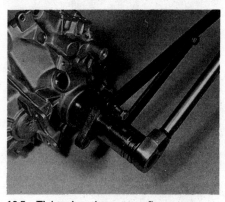

10.5   Tightening the output flange nut

10.6   Fitting the reverse idler gear. Note identification groove position (arrowed)

10.8   Inserting the interlocking pins

10.9   5th/reverse selector fork installed

10.11   1st/2nd selector fork, shaft and dog

procedure to determine the shims necessary for the laygear roller bearing.

7   Place the rear casing on the bench and fit the laygear in it with the 5th gear uppermost.

8   Temporarily refit the laygear roller bearing to the main casing without any shims. With the circlip in place, tap the bearing outwards so that it contacts the circlip.

9   Locate the main casing on the rear casing, and insert the bolts shown in Fig. 6.8. Tighten the bolts to 25 Nm (18 lbf ft).

10   Using a metal bar across the clutch bellhousing mount a dial test indicator with its probe on the 5th gear of the laygear (photo). Zero the indicator.

11   Insert a screwdriver through the oil drain plug hole and move the laygear upwards (photo). Record the amount of endfloat, then deduct from this 0.20 mm (0.008 in) to determine the shim thickness necessary at the laygear roller bearing. The final endfloat should be between 0.15 and 0.25 mm (0.006 and 0.010 in), and shims are available in 1.7, 1.8, 2.0, 2.1 and 2.2 mm thicknesses.

12   Remove the laygear.

13   Fit the laygear roller bearing to the main casing together with the correct shims (photo). With the circlip in place, tap the bearing outwards so that it contacts the shims.

14   Drive in the new gearshift lever shaft guide bearing flush with the casing (photo).

15   Refit the reverse gear block, shaft and spring making sure that the short end of the spring is in the casing and the long end on the block. Insert and tighten the bolt.

16   The input shaft bearing is not refitted at this stage.

10   Manual gearbox – reassembly

1   Assemble the input shaft to the mainshaft, then mesh the laygear with them (photo).

2   Mount the rear casing in a vice, and heat the casing around the bearing seat to approximately 100°C (212°F).

3   Lower the gear cluster as an assembly into the casing making sure that the mainshaft bearing is fully entered (photo).

4   Locate the retaining circlip in its groove and remove the bent piece of metal rod.

5   Slide the output flange onto the mainshaft splines and screw on the nut. Hold the flange stationary and tighten the nut to the specified torque (photo).

6   Locate the needle roller bearings in the reverse idler gear, position the gear on the casing and insert the shaft. Note that the identification groove on the gear must face forwards (photo).

7   Insert and tighten the reverse idler shaft bolt.

8   Grease the two interlocking pins and insert them between the selector shaft bores using a pencil magnet if necessary (photo).

9   Engage the 5th/reverse selector fork with the groove in the 5th/reverse synchro sleeve (photo). The chamfered side of the fork should be against the casing.

10   Check that all the synchro sleeves are in neutral.

11   Engage the 1st/2nd selector fork with the groove in the 1st/2nd synchro sleeve. Insert the 1st/2nd selector shaft through the fork into the rear casing then locate the selector dog on the shaft (photo).

12   Engage the 3rd/4th selector fork with the groove in the 3rd/4th synchro sleeve. Insert the 3rd/4th selector shaft through the fork into the rear casing and turn it until the selector finger cut-outs are aligned (photo).

13   Grease the four rollers and locate them on the pins on the gearshift lever shaft (photo).

14   Insert the gearshift lever shaft complete with selector finger into the rocker arm. Using a screwdriver, turn the rocker arm as necessary to assist entry of the shaft and to allow the selector finger to enter the cut-outs (photo).

15   Insert the 5th/reverse selector shaft through the 5th/reverse selector fork into the rear casing (photo).

16   Working on each selector shaft in turn, align the holes and drive in the roll pins until they protrude by approximately 1.0 mm (0.04 in). Support each shaft with a block of wood while driving in the roll pins (photos).

17   Insert the detent balls and springs in the rear casing.

10.12   3rd/4th selector fork and shaft

10.13   Gearshift lever shaft

10.14   Inserting the gearshift lever shaft

10.15   Inserting the 5th/reverse selector shaft

10.16A   Inserting the roll pins

10.16B   Selector shafts with roll pins fitted

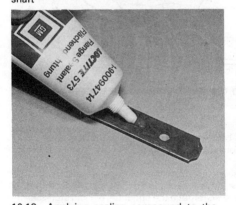

10.18   Applying sealing compound to the detent plate

10.20   Applying sealing compound to the rear casing

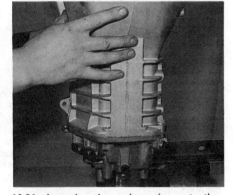

10.21   Lowering the main casing onto the rear casing

18   Apply a little sealing compound to the detent plate (photo), then fit it over the springs, insert the bolts, and tighten them to the specified torque.

19   Engage 4th gear but check that the remaining synchro-rings are not jammed on their respective gear cones. If necessary, free the rings with a screwdriver.

20   Apply sealing compound to the mating face of the rear casing (photo).

21   Carefully lower the main casing onto the rear casing making sure that the selector shafts and laygear enter their respective holes (photo).

22   A tool must now be obtained or made in order to fit the input shaft bearing. It is not permissible to simply drive the bearing into position, since the input shaft would be forced against the mainshaft and damage may also occur to the synchro-rings. It would also be impossible to refit the bearing circlip. The tool shown (photo) was found to be effective as it carries out the same functions as the GM tool No KM-461 used by GM dealers. It is made from metal tubing cut to form a clamp for gripping the input shaft. The two side bolts are then used to press the bearing into the casing, using metal blocks to prevent damage to the bearing.

23   Before fitting the bearing, heat the casing around the bearing seat to approximately 100°C (212°F).

24   Locate the bearing (fitted with circlip) over the input shaft and use the special tool to press it into the casing (photos). Check that the inner circlip groove is visible on the input shaft.

25   Remove the tool, then fit the inner circlip to the input shaft.

26   Select neutral. Turn the input shaft to confirm that the synchro-rings are not jammed on their cones.

27   Insert the casing bolts and tighten them progressively to the specified torque (photo).

28   Insert the front reverse idler gear shaft retaining bolt and tighten to the specified torque.

29   Remove the rubber O-ring from the clutch bearing guide sleeve and also lever out the oil seal. Clean the seating and drive in a new oil seal using metal tubing or a suitable size socket. The closed side of the oil seal must be inside the sleeve. Fit a new rubber O-ring (photos).

30   Smear the oil seal lip with grease, then refit the clutch release bearing guide sleeve taking care not to damage the seal on the input shaft splines. Insert the bolts and tighten to the specified torque (photo).

10.22 Tool for refitting the input shaft bearing

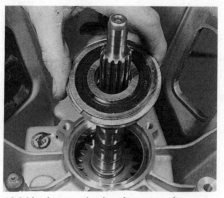

10.24A Locate the bearing over the input shaft

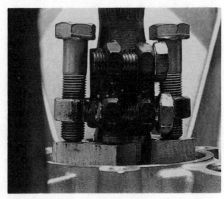

10.24B Side view of the special tool in use

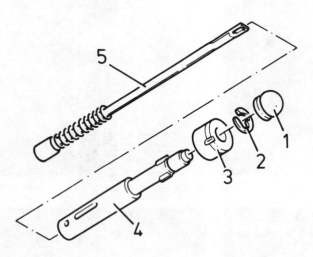

Fig. 6.9 Gearshift lever components (Sec 11)

1 Grommet	4 Shift finger tube
2 Lockwasher	5 Cable retainer and spring
3 Grommet	

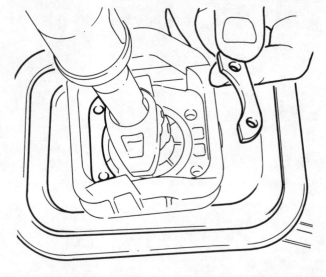

Fig. 6.10 Locating the threaded plates in the shift housing (Sec 11)

31   Insert the gearshift lever shaft detent pin and spring, making sure that the pin roller is horizontal. Drive the cap into the casing with a mallet.
32   Refit the speedometer drive pinion and housing. Insert and tighten the bolt.
33   Insert and tighten the reversing lamp switch (photo).
34   Refit the clutch release bearing and arm with reference to Chapter 5.

11 Manual gearbox gearshift lever — removal, overhaul and refitting

1   Apply the handbrake. Jack up the front of the vehicle and support it on axle stands.
2   Reach up over the propeller shaft and disconnect the gearchange linkage from the bottom of the gear lever. To do this, extract the spring clip from one end of the pivot pin and withdraw the pin.
3   Unscrew the four bolts securing the gear lever to the bracket (photo).
4   Working inside the vehicle, prise the gaiter from the centre console surround (photo). Lift the gaiter so that it is inside out then untie the cord and remove the gaiter.
5   Remove the two screws and withdraw the centre console surround (photo).
6   Cut the strap retaining the rubber bellows on the gear lever. Release the bellows from the lower plate and gear lever (photo).
7   Lift out the gearshift lever assembly, and mount it in a vice.

8   Prise the two half-bushes from the bottom of the gear lever.
9   Remove the bottom foam ring and tap the gear lever out using a mallet.
10   Remove the retaining ring from the housing.
11   Using a pin punch, drive the roll pin from the shift finger tube, then tap off the shift finger. Also remove the upper roll pin and stop sleeve.
12   If necessary remove the gear lever knob by cutting it with a hacksaw taking care not to damage the lever.
13   Remove the reverse gear block by prising off the retainer.
14   Using circlip pliers, extract the spring clip then withdraw the tube, grommet, lock washer, lower grommet and shift finger tube.
15   Remove the cable retainer and spring.
16   Clean all the components and examine them for wear and damage. Renew them as necessary and obtain a new gear lever knob.
17   Commence reassembly by fitting the spring to the retainer.
18   Insert the retainer in the shift finger tube.
19   Push on the grommet with its open groove uppermost, then fit the spring clip and upper grommet.
20   Assemble the shift finger tube to the gearshift lever tube with its groove aligned with the lug. Fit the retainer.
21   Where fitted, position the O-ring on the gearshift lever tube, then insert the reverse gear block.
22   Push up the cable retainer and attach to the lug.
23   Fit the stop sleeve and drive in the roll pin. The upper, long finger should point to the right.
24   Fit the shift finger and drive in the roll pin. Make sure that the stop moves freely.
25   Locate the retaining ring on the gear lever ball, then locate the assembly in the housing.

10.24C Top view of the special tool in use

10.27 Tightening the casing bolts

10.29A Insert the oil seal ...

10.29B ... and drive it into the clutch bearing guide sleeve

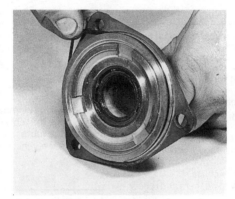

10.29C Fitting a new rubber O-ring

10.30 Tightening the clutch release bearing guide sleeve bolts

10.33 Tightening the reversing lamp switch

11.3 Gear lever housing retaining bolts (arrowed)

11.4 Removing the gear lever gaiter

11.5 Removing the centre console surround

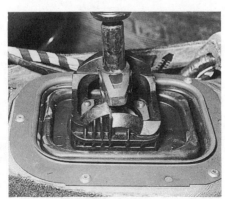

11.6 Gearshift lever assembly (with centre console removed)

12.4 Gearshift lever support bracket

26   Press the two half bushes into the bottom of the gear lever.
27   Heat the new gear lever knob to approximately 70°C (158°F) then drive it on the gear lever in its correct position using a block of wood and a mallet.
28   Apply a little grease to the threaded plates and locate them in the shift housing.
29   Stick the foam spacer under the housing with a little grease.
30   Locate the gearshift lever assembly in the vehicle and align the bolt holes.
31   Working under the vehicle, insert and tighten the four bolts.
32   Refit the gearchange linkage pivot pin and retain with the spring clip.
33   Refit the gear lever rubber bellows using a new strap. It will help to dip the bellows in soapy water.
34   Refit the centre console surround and gaiter.
35   Lower the vehicle to the ground.

12   Manual gearbox gearshift lever support bracket – removal and refitting

1   Apply the handbrake. Jack up the front of the vehicle and support it on axle stands.
2   Reach up over the propeller shaft and disconnect the gearchange linkage from the gear lever by extracting a spring clip and withdrawing the pin.
3   Unscrew the four bolts securing the gear lever to the bracket.
4   Unbolt the rear mounting bracket from the underbody, and the front of the support bracket from the gearbox (photo).
5   Withdraw the support bracket from under the vehicle.
6   Unbolt and remove the rubber mountings. Examine them and renew them as necessary.
7   Refitting is a reversal of removal. If the threaded plates on top of the gear lever assembly have become displaced, gain access to them with reference to Section 11.

13   Manual gearbox gearchange linkage – adjustment

Adjustment is only possible using GM tool No KM-631

1   Apply the handbrake. Jack up the front of the vehicle and support it on axle stands. Position the gear lever in neutral.
2   Loosen the clamp bolt on the gearchange linkage.
3   Working inside the vehicle, prise the gaiter from the centre console surround and lift it up. Remove the two screws and withdraw the centre console surround. Release the rubber bellows and fold upwards.
4   Fit the tool No KM-631 into the housing while depressing the gear lever to the right.
5   Using a spanner on the flats provided, turn the linkage clockwise (as viewed from the driving position) up to the stop.

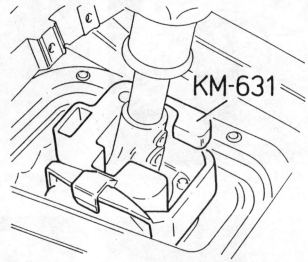

Fig. 6.11 Tool KM-631 for holding the gear lever for linkage adjustment (Sec 13)

6   Tighten the clamp bolt.
7   Remove the tool and check for correct gear selection.
8   Refit the rubber bellows, centre console surround, and gaiter.
9   Lower the vehicle to the ground.

14   Automatic transmission – removal and refitting

1   Disconnect the battery negative lead.
2   Move the selector lever to position 'N'.
3   Pull the fluid level dipstick from its tube.
4   Unbolt the dipstick tube from the bracket, then cut the strap and pull the filler tube from the receiver tube.
5   Unclip the cooling fan shroud from the radiator.
6   Disconnect the kickdown cable from the throttle lever, then compress the outer cable and detach it from the bracket. On carburettor models first remove the air cleaner as described in Chapter 3.
7   Disconnect the inhibitor switch plug located on the bulkhead, and cut the wiring strap from the filler tube.
8   Unbolt the exhaust system front downpipe from the intermediate section mounting bracket, and exhaust manifold. Also unbolt the mounting bracket and heat shield.
9   Slacken the slider joint nut on the front propeller shaft section one complete turn.
10   Using a conventional or Torx socket as applicable, unscrew the bolts securing the propeller shaft front flexible disc joint to the transmission output flange. Lever the propeller shaft rearwards from the output

14.11   Speedometer cable connection

14.12   Selector rod connection to the transmission lever

14.13   Fluid drain plug (arrowed)

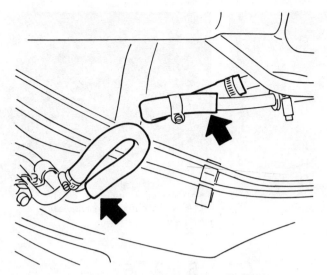

Fig. 6.12 Disconnect the transmission fluid hoses at diagonally opposite ends then reconnect them as shown (Sec 14)

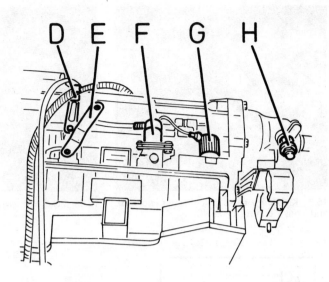

Fig. 6.13 Components to transfer to the new transmission (Sec 14)

D   Cable retainer   G   Kickdown switch
E   Selector lever   H   Speedometer drive gear
F   Solenoid valve

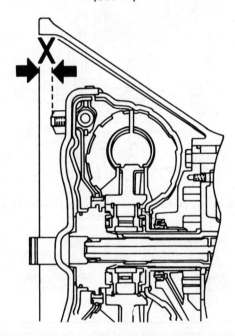

Fig. 6.14 With the torque converter fully engaged, dimension 'X' should be approximately 14.25 mm (0.56 in) (Sec 14)

flange and tie it to one side.
11   Unscrew the knurled nut, and disconnect the speedometer cable from the transmission (photo).
12   Disconnect the selector rod from the transmission lever by releasing the spring clip and pivot pin (photo).
13   Position a container beneath the transmission sump, unscrew the drain plug and drain the fluid (photo). Refit and tighten the drain plug on completion.
14   Loosen the clips and disconnect the flexible rubber fluid hoses at the underbody connection. To ensure correct refitment and to prevent the entry of dust and dirt, disconnect the hoses only at diagonally opposite ends then fold them back onto the adjacent pipes.
15   Unscrew the bolts securing the front brackets to the engine.
16   Unbolt the transmission front cover and front brackets.
17   Unscrew the bolts securing the torque converter to the driveplate. To gain access to all the bolts, turn the engine with a spanner on the crankshaft pulley bolt.

18   Lever the torque converter away from the driveplate.
19   Support the transmission on a trolley jack.
20   Unscrew the two lower bolts securing the transmission to the engine.
21   Unbolt the rear mounting crossmember from the underbody, then lower the transmission slightly.
22   Disconnect the wiring plugs for the solenoid valve and kickdown switch.
23   Unscrew the remaining bolts securing the transmission to the engine.
24   With the help of an assistant, lower the transmission and withdraw it from the engine, making sure that the torque converter remains fully engaged with the fluid pump.
25   If a new transmission is being fitted, the following parts must be transferred from the old unit:
   Rear mounting crossmember
   Fluid lines
   Inhibitor switch and wiring
   Cable retainer
   Selector lever
   Solenoid valve
   Kickdown switch
   Speedometer drive gear
26   Refitting is a reversal of the removal procedure but note the following additional points:

(a)   *Before offering the transmission to the engine, check that the torque converter is fully engaged. The dimension shown in Fig. 6.14 must be as stated*
(b)   *Apply a little grease to the torque converter centre pin*
(c)   *Apply locking fluid to the threads of the rear mounting crossmember bolts before inserting and tightening them*
(d)   *Tighten all nuts and bolts to the specified torque*
(e)   *Adjust the kickdown cable (Section 16), and selector lever linkage (Section 17)*
(f)   *Fill the transmission with the specified fluid (Section 2)*

---

15   Automatic transmission kickdown cable – renewal

---

1   On carburettor models remove the air cleaner (Chapter 3), then remove the spring clip and detent spring. Disconnect the outer cable

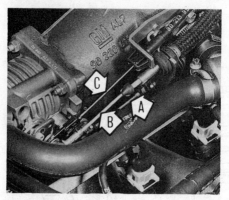

15.2 Kickdown cable (A), throttle cable (B), and cruise control cable (C)

16.8 Kickdown switch (arrowed)

18.1A Prise out the gear indicator panel ...

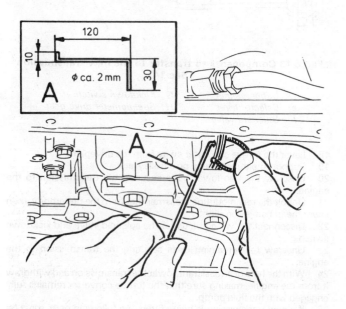

Fig. 6.15 Using a piece of wire (A) to turn the curved disc (Sec 15)

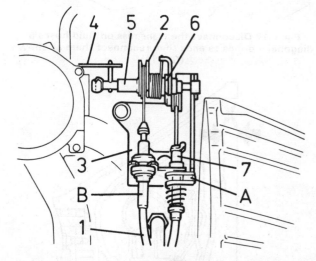

Fig. 6.16 Upper kickdown cable connection on carburettor models (Sec 16)

1 Accelerator cable	6 Lever
2 Cam	7 Kickdown cable
3 Bracket	
4 Throttle valve lever	A Spring clip
5 Shaft	B Ferrule

from the segment disc and remove the safety clip if necessary.

2   On fuel injection models, disconnect the inner cable from the ball socket. Compress the plastic bracket and remove the outer cable from the bracket (photo).

3   Cut the transmission fluid filler tube retaining strap.

4   Jack up the front of the vehicle and support it on axle stands.

5   Position a container beneath the transmission sump then unscrew the drain plug and drain the fluid. Refit and tighten the plug on completion.

6   Unbolt and remove the transmission sump and remove the joint and filler tube.

7   Make a piece of wire to the dimensions shown in Fig. 6.15. Using the wire turn the curved disc until the cable can be disconnected.

8   Release and remove the kickdown cable.

9   Attach the new cable to the transmission fluid filler tube with a strap.

10   Apply a little grease to the cable seal.

11   Connect the cable to the curved disc using the piece of wire. Check that the cable moves the disc easily.

12   Adjust the cable with reference to Section 16 and reconnect the upper end of the cable.

13   Refit the transmission sump using a new joint and filler tube O-ring and tighten the sump bolts.

14   On carburettor models, refit the air cleaner.

15   Lower the vehicle to the ground.

16   Refill the transmission with the specified quantity of fluid as described in Section 2.

16   Automatic transmission kickdown cable – adjustment

Carburettor models

1   Remove the air cleaner (Chapter 3).

2   Refer to Fig. 6.16 and release the spring clip (A).

3   Release the accelerator cable adjustment, then pull the ferrule (B) until the throttle lever (4) rests against the throttle stop without parts (5) and (6) turning against each other. Secure the ferrule in this position.

4   Adjust the accelerator pedal so that it is free of any play in the idle position.

5   Have an assistant slowly depress the accelerator pedal until the kickdown switch is fully depressed. Refit the spring clip (A).

6   Refit the air cleaner (Chapter 3).

Fuel injection models

7   Refer to Fig. 6.17 and release the safety clip (B).

8   Have an assistant depress the accelerator pedal until it just touches the kickdown switch (photo).

9   Pull the ferrule (6) until the throttle lever rests against the full throttle stop, then refit the spring clip (B).

10   With the accelerator pedal in the idle position, adjust it so that there is no free play.

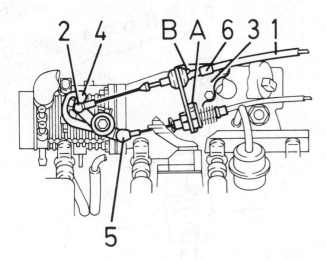

Fig. 6.17 Upper kickdown cable connection on fuel injection models (Sec 16)

1	Accelerator cable	5	Kickdown cable
2	Ball socket	6	Ferrule
3	Bracket	A	Spring clip
4	Throttle valve lever	B	Safety clip

11   Release the spring clip (A).

12   Have an assistant slowly depress the accelerator pedal until the kickdown switch is fully depressed. Refit the spring clip (A).

17   Automatic transmission selector lever linkage – adjustment

1   Position the vehicle over an inspection pit, or alternatively jack up the front end and support it on axle stands.

2   Move the selector lever to position 'N'.

3   Disconnect the linkage rod from the lever on the transmission by releasing the spring clip and pivot pin.

4   Check that the transmission lever is in position 'N' (third notch from rear).

5   Move the linkage rod rearwards to push the selector lever against the front of the 'N' position, then locate the adjustment fork on the transmission lever. Check the alignment of the holes and if necessary turn the fork until the holes are exactly aligned.

6   From this position turn the adjustment fork one complete turn clockwise onto the linkage rod.

7   Refit the spring clip and pivot pin.

8   Check that the selector lever operates correctly. Also check that the inhibitor switch functions correctly. With the selector lever in positions R, D, 2 and 1 it should not be possible to operate the starter motor.

18   Automatic transmission selector lever – removal and refitting

1   Using a small screwdriver prise out the gear indicator panel and

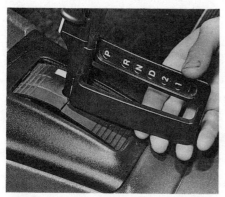

18.1B   ... and remove it from the selector lever

18.2   Removing the slot cover

18.3A   Remove the screw ...

18.3B   ... and release the surround panel from the centre console

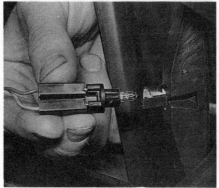

18.4   Removing the bulbholder

18.9A   Right-hand view of selector lever

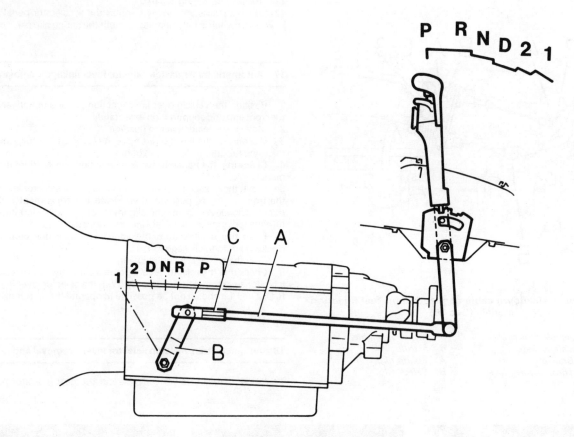

Fig. 6.18 Selector lever linkage (Sec 17)

A   Selector rod   B   Transmission lever   C   Adjustment fork

remove it from the selector lever (photos).
2   Lift out the slot cover (photo).
3   Remove the front mounting screw and release the surround panel from the rear location holes (photos).
4   Pull out the bulbholder and remove the surround panel (photo).
5   Position a block of wood on the right-hand side of the selector lever (Fig. 6.19).
6   Jack up the front of the vehicle and support it on axle stands.
7   Disconnect the linkage rod from the lever on the transmission by releasing the spring clip and pivot pin.

8   Unscrew the nut and disconnect the linkage from the selector lever shaft. Recover the corrugated washer and rubber ring. Remove the block of wood.
9   Disconnect the wiring plug, then slide the selector lever sideways from the bearing and remove it (photos).
10   If necessary disconnect the wiring from the bulbholder and pull out the bulb (photo).
11   Refitting is a reversal of removal, but adjust the linkage as described in Section 17.

18.9B   Left-hand view of selector lever

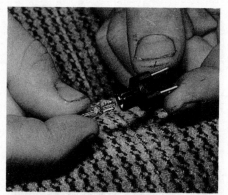

18.10   Separating the bulb from the bulbholder

19.5   Fluid cooler pipes

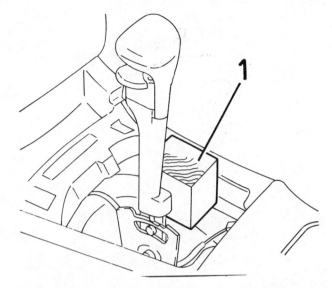

Fig. 6.19 Selector lever supported with a block of wood
(Sec 18)

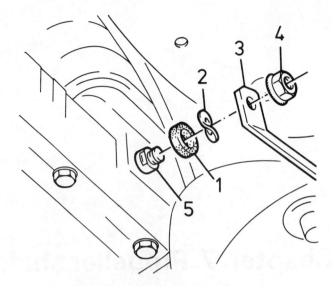

Fig. 6.20 Linkage to selector lever components (Sec 18)

1	Rubber ring	4	Locknut
2	Corrugated washer	5	Selector lever shaft
3	Linkage		

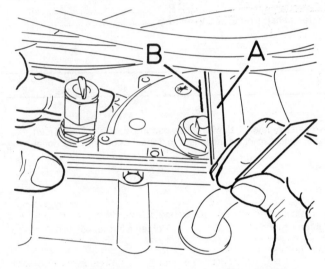

Fig. 6.21 Aligning the inhibitor switch (Sec 19)

A   Straight edge   B   Alignment mark

19   Inhibitor switch – removal and refitting

1   Move the selector lever to position "N".
2   Disconnect the inhibitor switch plug located on the bulkhead. Cut the strap holding the wiring to the filler tube.
3   Jack up the front of the vehicle and support it on axle stands.
4   Release the wiring from the underbody and from the clip on the transmission.
5   Disconnect the fluid cooler pipes from the transmission (photo). Plug the open ends to prevent entry of dust and dirt.
6   Unscrew the locknut from the front connector on the switch. Move the connector aside and plug it.
7   Unscrew the rear bolt. Bend the locktab and unscrew the nut.
8   Withdraw the inhibitor switch from the transmission.
9   Refitting is a reversal of removal, however before tightening the rear bolt, the switch must be correctly aligned as follows. Position a steel rule or length of bar on the rear flat of the switch shaft. With the transmission in Neutral align the line on the switch with the rule then tighten the switch to the specified torque.

20   Fault diagnosis – manual gearbox and automatic transmission

Symptom	Reason(s)
Manual gearbox	
Noisy operation	Oil level low
	Worn bearings or gears
Ineffective synchromesh	Worn synchro rings
Jumps out of gear	Worn synchro units
	Worn gears
	Worn selector forks
	Worn detent balls, springs or plungers
Difficulty in engaging gears	Clutch fault
	Worn selector components
	Seized input shaft spigot bearing

Automatic transmission
    Faults in these units are nearly always the result of low fluid level or incorrect adjustment of the selector linkage or kickdown cable. Internal faults should be diagnosed by a GM dealer who has the necessary equipment to carry out the work.

Chapter 7 Propeller shaft

Contents

Specifications

| Type .... | Two-piece tubular shaft with centre bearing, centre universal joint, and flexible disc joint connections to transmission and differential |

Torque wrench settings

Disc joint to propeller shaft transmission or differential:

	Nm	lbf ft
Hexagon bolt	100	74
Torx bolt:		
Stage 1	50	37
Stage 2	Tighten a further 45° to 60°	Tighten a further 45° to 60°
Centre bearing to bracket...	22	16
Bracket to underbody	20	15
Slider joint nut...	40	30

1 General description

A two-piece, tubular propeller shaft is fitted, incorporating a centre bearing supported in a rubber insulator. The rear section has a universal joint at its front end, and the front section has a slider joint at its rear end. The propeller shaft is attached to the transmission and differential by flexible disc joints. It is not possible to overhaul the universal joint.

2 Propeller shaft – removal and refitting

1   Chock the front wheels. Jack up the rear of the vehicle and support it on axle stands.
2   On models equipped with a catalytic converter, from underneath the vehicle, undo the retaining bolts and remove both the large and small catalytic converter heatshields from the vehicle underbody.
3   Apply the handbrake, then slacken the slider joint nut on the front propeller shaft section one turn (photo).
4   Using a conventional, or Torx, socket as applicable, unscrew the bolts securing the front flexible disc joint to the transmission output flange (photo).
5   At the rear of the propeller shaft, unscrew the bolts securing the rear disc joint to the differential flange (photo).
6   Support the centre of the propeller shaft on an axle stand, then unbolt the centre bearing support bracket from the underbody, noting the location of any allignment shims.

7   Push the front section rearwards along the slider joint splines until clear of the transmission output flange.
8   Withdraw the propeller shaft forwards, making sure that the front section remains on the slider joint splines.
9   Unbolt the centre support bracket from the centre bearing, noting the location of any alignment shims.
10   Unbolt the front and rear disc joints from the propeller shaft. Note that on some models a vibration damper is fitted at the front of the propeller shaft.
11   Refitting is a reversal of removal, but tighten all nuts and bolts to the specified torque. Tighten the slider joint nut last to avoid any strain on the disc joints (photo). If a new propeller shaft is being fitted, loosen the slider joint nut before commencing the refitting procedure.

3 Centre bearing – renewal

1   Remove the propeller shaft as described in Section 2.
2   Mount the rear propeller shaft section in a vice, using shaped blocks of wood to prevent damage.
3   Mark the front and rear sections in relation to each other, then pull the front section from the splines.
4   Using circlip pliers, extract the circlip from the groove in front of the centre bearing.
5   Support the centre bearing on a vice, and press or drive the rear propeller shaft section down through the bearing.

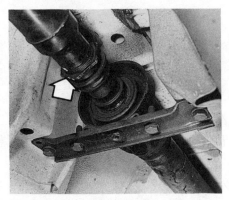

2.3 Propeller shaft slider joint nut (arrowed)

2.4 Propeller shaft front flexible disc joint connection

2.5 Propeller shaft rear flexible disc joint connection

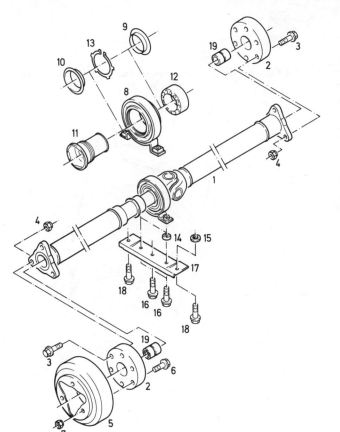

Fig. 7.1 Propeller shaft components (Sec 1)

1 Complete propeller shaft	10 Ring deflector
2 Flexible disc joint	11 Collar
3 Bolt	12 Centre ball bearing
4 Nut	13 Snap ring
5 Vibration damper	14 Spacer
6 Bolt	15 Washer
7 Nut	16 Bolt
8 Centre bearing housing and insulator	17 Centre bearing bracket
9 Ring	18 Bolt
	19 Bush

2.11 Tightening the slider joint nut

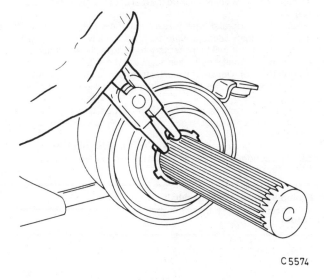

C 5574

Fig. 7.2 Extracting the centre bearing circlip (Sec 3)

6   Similarly press or drive the ball bearing from the centre bearing housing, and remove the dust cover.

7   Clean the removed components and the end of the propeller shaft.

Lightly grease the splines.

8   Press or drive the new ball bearing into the housing, and align the dust cover.

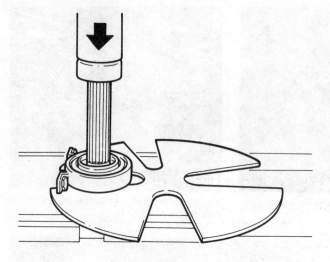

Fig. 7.3 Pressing the rear propeller shaft section through the centre bearing (Sec 3)

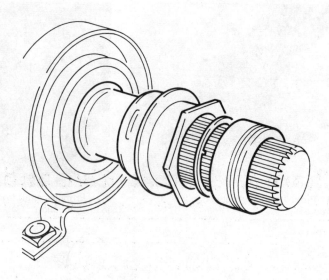

Fig. 7.4 Slider joint components on the propeller shaft rear section (Sec 3)

9   Support the rear section universal joint on a vice, and press or drive the centre bearing over the splines using a metal tube on the inner track. Make sure that the bearing makes contact with its seating shoulder.
10   Mount the rear section in a vice, and fit the front dust cover and the circlip, making sure that it is correctly located in the groove.
11   Locate the dust cover over the splines, followed by the slider nut, washer and plastic sleeve.
12   Fit the front section on the rear section splines, making sure that the previously-made marks are aligned. Note that a master spline is fitted to ensure correct assembly.
13   Start the slider joint nut on its thread, but do not tighten until after the propeller shaft has been refitted.

4   Disc joints – renewal

1   Chock the front wheels. Jack up the rear of the vehicle and support it on axle stands.
2   Apply the handbrake, then loosen only the slider joint nut on the front propeller shaft section. Note that, on models equipped with a catalytic converter, it will be necessary to remove the small heatshield from the vehicle underbody to gain access to the nut.
3   Unbolt the propeller shaft flange(s) from the flexible disc joint(s).
4   Unbolt the flexible disc joint from the transmission and/or differential drive flange(s).
5   Push the appropriate propeller shaft section towards the centre bearing and remove the disc joint(s). If necessary, use a lever to prise the propeller shaft clear of the drive flange(s).
6   Fit the new flexible disc joint(s) using a reversal of the removal procedure, but tighten all nuts and bolts to the specified torque. Tighten

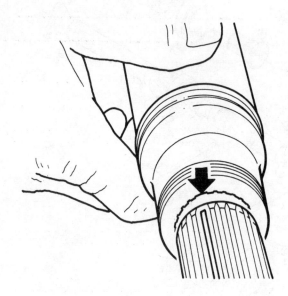

Fig. 7.5 Master spline on the slider joint (Sec 3)

the slider joint nut last to avoid any strain on the disc joints. Where Torx head bolts are fitted, observe the angle tightening procedure given in the Specifications.

5   Fault diagnosis - propeller shaft

Symptom	Reason(s)
Vibration	Worn universal joint
	Worn centre bearing
	Deteriorated rubber insulator on centre bearing
'Rumble' increasing with road speed	Worn centre bearing

Chapter 8 Final drive and driveshafts

For modifications, and information applicable to later models, see Supplement at end of manual

Contents

Specifications

Final drive

Type	Unsprung, attached to rear suspension crossmember and underbody
Ratio..	3.70:1
Number of teeth:	
Crown wheel...	37
Pinion	10

Driveshaft

Type	Maintenance-free double constant velocity joint

Lubrication

Final drive lubricant type/specification:	
Except limited-slip differential..	Hypoid gear oil, viscosity SAE 90 (Duckhams Hypoid 90S)
Limited-slip differential	GM special lubricant 19 42 382 (9 293 688) (Duckhams Hypoid 90DL)
Capacity:	
Saloon...	0.8 litre (1.4 pints)
Estate..	1.0 litre (1.8 pints)
Driveshaft CV joint grease type	GM special grease 19 41 522 (90 007 999)

Torque wrench settings

	Nm	lbf ft
Rear damping block to underbody:		
Stage 1..	30	22
Stage 2..	Tighten a further 30° to 45°	Tighten a further 30° to 45°
Rear damping block to final drive unit	110	81
Final drive unit rear cover	60	44
Final drive unit to crossmember:		
Stage 1..	110	81
Stage 2..	Tighten a further 30° to 45°	Tighten a further 30° to 45°
Driveshaft to hub:		
Stage 1..	50	37
Stage 2..	Tighten a further 45° to 60°	Tighten a further 45° to 60°
Final drive unit filler plug...	22	16
Propeller shaft slider joint nut...	40	30
Propeller shaft centre bearing bracket....................................	20	15
Propeller shaft to flexible joint (Hexagon bolt).......................	100	74
Propeller shaft to flexible joint (Torx bolt):		
Stage 1..	50	37
Stage 2..	Tighten a further 45° to 60°	Tighten a further 45° to 60°
Anti-roll bar clamps	22	16
Speed sensor bracket (with ABS)..	60	44
Speed sensor to bracket (with ABS)	7	5

1 General description

The final drive unit is mounted on the rear suspension crossmember and is of unsprung type. A rubber damping block attached to the rear of the final drive unit acts as a mounting for the rear suspension crossmember. Two driveshafts transmit drive from the final drive differential to the rear wheels which are attached to the fully independent rear suspension.

A limited-slip differential may be fitted as an option to new vehicles, or it may be service-installed at a later date, however special tools are required and the existing crownwheel must be heated to a pre-determined temperature before bolting the limited-slip differential to it. Because of this, the procedure is not included in this Chapter. General overhaul of the final drive differential is also not included.

2 Routine maintenance

1   Carry out the following procedures at the intervals given in *Routine Maintenance* at the front of this manual.

Check final drive unit oil level
2   Jack up the front and rear of the vehicle and support it on axle stands so that the vehicle is level.
3   Using a hexagon key, unscrew the filler plug from the right-hand side of the final drive unit.
4   Check that the oil level is up to the bottom of the filler plug aperture using a piece of bent wire or small screwdriver as a dipstick.
5   If necessary top-up with the correct type of oil as given in the Specifications.
6   Refit and tighten the filler plug to the specified torque, and wipe clean.
7   Check the pinion final drive unit oil seal and differential bearing oil seals for leaks. If evident, renew them.
8   Lower the car to the ground.

Check driveshaft rubber bellows
9   Chock the front wheels then jack up the rear of the vehicle and support it on axle stands.
10   With the handbrake released turn each wheel separately and check the driveshaft rubber bellows for splits and damage. Check also that the clips are secure.
11   Lower the vehicle to the ground.

3 Final drive unit – removal and refitting

1   Chock the front wheels. Jack up the rear of the vehicle and support it on axle stands. Remove both rear wheels.
2   Remove both driveshafts with reference to Section 8.
3   Loosen the centre slider joint nut on the propeller shaft approximately one complete turn.
4   Unhook the exhaust system mounting rubbers and lower the rear of the system approximately 300 mm (12.0 in). Support or tie the system in this position.
5   Unbolt the propeller shaft centre bearing bracket from the underbody noting the location of any alignment shims.
6   Unbolt the propeller shaft rear flange from the flexible drive joint and lever the propeller shaft from the joint. Support the propeller shaft on an axle stand.
7   Support the final drive unit on a trolley jack.
8   Loosen only the bolts securing the rear damping bracket to the final drive unit.
9   On models equipped with an anti-lock braking system (ABS), unbolt the speed sensor brackets from the rear of the final drive unit.
10   Unbolt the rear damping bracket from the underbody (photo).
11   Disconnect the rear brake hoses from the semi-trailing arms by pulling out the retaining clips.
12   Lower the final drive unit and rear suspension crossmember several inches, then unscrew the bolts securing the rear anti- roll bar clamps to the crossmember. Pivot the anti-roll bar upwards.

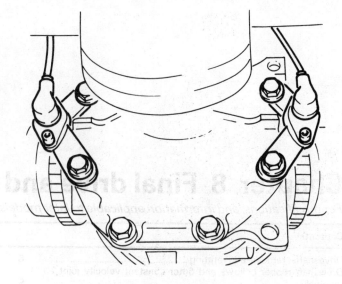

Fig. 8.1 ABS speed sensor brackets on the rear of the final drive unit (Sec 3)

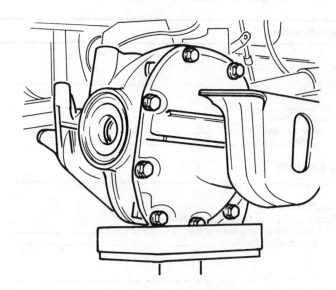

Fig. 8.2 Lowering the final drive unit (Sec 3)

13   Unscrew the final drive front and rear mounting bolts from the top of the rear suspension crossmember (photo).
14   Lower the final drive unit and withdraw it from under the vehicle. Unbolt and remove the rear damping bracket, and the rubber disc joint.
15   Refitting is a reversal of removal but tighten all nuts and bolt to the specified torque. Refit the driveshafts with reference to Section 8. Check the oil level in the final drive unit as described in Section 2.

4 Final drive unit damping bracket – renewal

1   Chock the front wheels. Jack up the rear of the vehicle and support it on axle stands.
2   Support the final drive unit on a trolley jack.
3   Loosen the bolts securing the rear damping bracket to the final drive unit.
4   Unbolt the rear damping bracket from the underbody.
5   Lower the final drive unit and rear suspension crossmember, then unscrew the bolts and remove the damping bracket.

3.10 Rear damping bracket mounting bolts (arrowed)

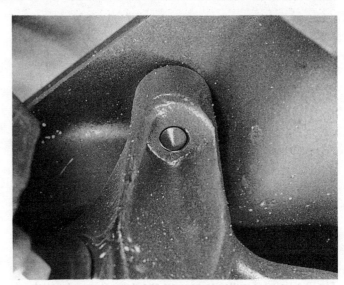

3.13 Lower view of a final drive unit front mounting bolt

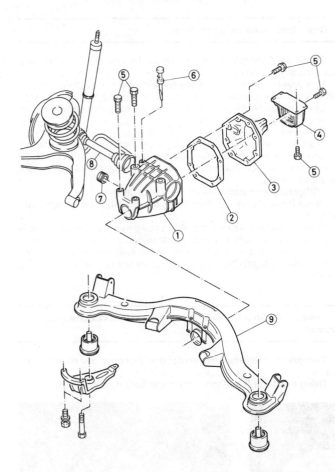

Fig. 8.3 Final drive unit components (Sec 3)

1 Final drive unit housing	6 Vent
2 Gasket	7 Filler plug
3 Rear cover	8 Driveshaft
4 Rear damping bracket	9 Rear suspension
5 Bolts	crossmember

6   Fit the new bracket using a reversal of the removal procedure, but tighten all nuts and bolts to the specified torque.

5 Final drive unit rear cover gasket – renewal

1   Remove the damping bracket as described in Section 4.
2   Position a suitable container under the final drive unit, then unbolt and remove the cover. Remove the gasket and allow the oil to drain.
3   Thoroughly clean the joint faces of the cover and final drive unit.
4   Locate the new gasket on the final drive unit using a little grease to hold it in place.
5   Refit the cover, then insert and tighten the bolts progressively to the specified torque. It is recommended that new bolts are used.
6   Refit the damping bracket with reference to Section 4.
7   With the vehicle on a level surface, unscrew the filler plug from the final drive unit and pour in the specified grade of oil until it reaches the lower edge of the hole. Refit and tighten the filler plug to the specified torque.
8   Lower the vehicle to the ground.

6 Final drive unit pinion oil seal – renewal

1   Remove the final drive unit as described in Section 3.
2   Mount the unit in a vice.
3   Mark the drive flange nut in relation to the drive flange and pinion.
4   Hold the drive flange stationary by bolting a length of metal bar to it, then unscrew the nut noting the exact number of turns necessary to remove it.
5   Using a suitable puller, draw the drive flange from the pinion.
6   Lever the oil seal from the final drive casing with a screwdriver. Wipe clean the oil seal seating.
7   Smear a little oil on the sealing lip of the new oil seal, then drive it squarely into the casing until flush with the outer face. Ideally use metal tubing to fit the oil seal, but alternatively a block of wood may be used on each side of the pinion.
8   Locate the drive flange on the pinion in its original position and refit the nut to its original position as well.
9   To check that the final drive bearings are pre-loaded correctly, check that the turning torque of the drive flange is between 90 and 120 Ncm (8.0 and 10.6 lbf in). To do this, either fit a socket on the pinion nut, and use a special torque meter, or a length of string and a spring balance.
10   Refit the final drive unit with reference to Section 3.

7 Final drive unit differential bearing oil seal – renewal

1   Chock the front wheels. Jack up the rear of the vehicle and support it

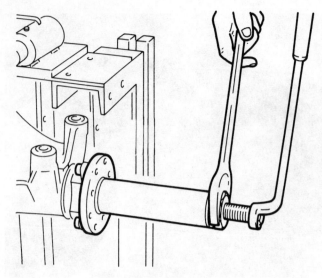

Fig. 8.4 Using a puller to remove the drive flange from the final drive unit (Sec 6)

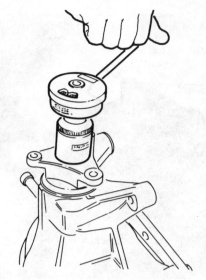

Fig. 8.5 Checking the turning torque of the final drive unit pinion (Sec 6)

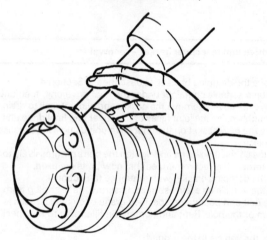

Fig. 8.6 Removing the outer joint cover (Sec 9)

on axle stands. Remove the appropriate rear wheel.
2   Remove the appropriate driveshaft with reference to Section 8.
3   Note the fitted depth of the oil seal in the final drive casing.
4   Using a screwdriver or hooked instrument, lever out the oil seal (photo). Wipe clean the oil seal seating.
5   Smear a little oil on the sealing lip of the new oil seal. Using suitable metal tubing drive the oil seal squarely into the casing to the previously noted position.
6   Refit the driveshaft with reference to Section 8.
7   Refit the wheel and lower the vehicle to the ground.

8   Driveshaft – removal and refitting

1   Chock the front wheels, then jack up the rear of the vehicle and support it on axle stands.
2   Unscrew the socket-head bolts securing the driveshaft to the rear hub while holding the rear wheel stationary. Recover the lockwashers.
3   Lever the driveshaft from the rear hub and support it above the disc brake assembly.
4   Remove the rear wheel.
5   Position a container under the final drive unit to catch any spilled oil.
6   Carefully lever the driveshaft from the final drive unit differential. On models with anti-lock braking take care not to damage the speed sensor and trigger wheel.
7   Withdraw the driveshaft from the side of the vehicle.
8   Check the circlip on the inner end of the driveshaft and if necessary renew it.
9   Refitting is a reversal of removal, but make sure that the driveshaft is fully entered in the differential side gear with the circlip engaged in its groove. Tighten the mounting bolts in the two stages given in the Specifications (photo).Check and if necessary top up the oil level in the final drive unit.

9   Driveshaft rubber bellows and outer constant velocity joint – renewal

1   Remove the driveshaft as described in Section 8, and mount it in a vice.
2   Using a small drift, top the metal cover from the outer joint.

7.4   Differential bearing oil seal

8.9A   Torque tightening the driveshaft bolts

8.9B   Angle tightening the driveshaft bolts

3   Loosen and remove both clips from the rubber bellows.
4   Using a sharp knife slice through the rubber bellows and remove them from the driveshaft.
5   Scoop out the grease from the joint and wipe the driveshaft clean.
6   Using circlip pliers, extract the circlip from the outer end of the driveshaft.
7   Support the outer joint on a vice, then tap the driveshaft down through it.
8   Fill the inner joint with the specified type of grease using a wooden spatula.
9   Fit the new inner bellows, check that it is not twisted then fit and tighten the clips.
10   Locate the outer bellows on the driveshaft.
11   Fit the outer joint using metal tubing with the driveshaft mounted in a vice. Make sure that the joint abuts the shoulder.
12   Fit the circlip making sure that it fully enters the groove.
13   Using the wooden spatula fill the outer joint with grease.
14   Locate the outer bellows on the plate, check that it is not twisted then fit and tighten the clips.
15   Locate the cover on the joint using two driveshaft bolts to ensure correct alignment. Tap the cover on the joint with a mallet.
16   Extract the retaining circlip from the inner end of the driveshaft and fit a new one.
17   Refit the driveshaft with reference to Section 8.

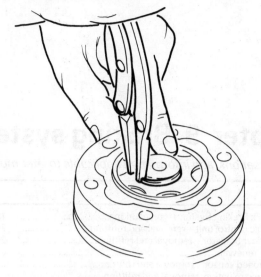

Fig. 8.7 Extracting the circlip from the driveshaft (Sec 9)

10   Fault diagnosis – final drive and driveshafts

Symptom	Reason(s)
Noise from final drive unit	Lack of lubricant
	Worn bearing, crownwheel and pinion
	Loose final drive unit mountings
	Worn rear damping bracket
Oil leakage from final drive unit	Pinion oil seal or differential bearing oil seals worn
Metallic grating noise from driveshafts	Worn driveshaft joints

Chapter 9 Braking system

For modifications, and information applicable to later models, see Supplement at end of manual

Contents

Specifications

System type .... Front and rear discs, floating front calliper, fixed rear calliper, tandem master cylinder with hydraulic system split front/rear, vacuum servo unit, and rear brake proportioning valve. Anti-lock braking system (ABS) on some models. Cable-operated handbrake to shoes inside rear discs.

Front brakes
Disc diameter	258 mm (10.2 in)
Minimum thickness:	
Non-ventilated	10.7 mm (0.422 in)
Ventilated	22.0 mm (0.866 in)
Thickness variation (maximum)	0.007 mm (0.0003 in)
Run-out (maximum)	0.1 mm (0.004 in)
Minimum brake pad thickness (including backplate)	7.0 mm (0.276 in)

Rear brakes
Disc diameter	270 mm (10.6 in)
Minimum thickness	8.0 mm (0.315 in)
Thickness variation (maximum)	0.007 mm (0.0003 in)
Run-out (maximum)	0.1 mm (0.004 in)
Minimum brake pad thickness (including backplate)	7.0 mm (0.276 in)
Handbrake shoes minimum thickness (lining only)	1.0 mm (0.04 in)

General
Brake fluid type/specification	Hydraulic fluid to FMVSS 571 or 116, DOT 3 or 4, or SAE J1703 (Duckhams Universal Brake and Clutch Fluid)
Rear wheel speed sensor-to-impulse wheel clearance	0.5 to 1.5 mm (0.02 to 0.06 in)

Torque wrench settings
	Nm	lbf ft
Calliper bleed screw	9	7
Master cylinder front mounting	20	15
Vacuum servo	20	15
Brake disc	4	3
Rear calliper	65	48
Front calliper mounting bolts (renew every time, and use thread-locking fluid)*:		
Stage 1	95	70
Stage 2	Angle-tighten a further 30 to 45°	Angle-tighten a further 30 to 45°

Refer to Chapter 13 for further information

Torque wrench settings (continued)

	Nm	lbf ft
Front calliper frame	95	70
Calliper hollow bolt	40	30
ABS modulator	8	6
ABS modulator front frame	10	7
Handbrake lever	20	15
Vacuum servo support	18	13
Master cylinder to vacuum servo	22	16
Brake line union nuts/bolts	11	8
Wheel bolts	90	60

1 General description

The braking system is of dual hydraulic circuit type with front and rear discs. The front and rear hydraulic circuits are operated independently, so that in the event of a failure in one circuit the remaining circuit still functions. The handbrake is cable-operated to brake shoes inside the rear brake discs, the inner part of the discs being drums. The disc brakes are self- adjusting in use, however the handbrake is adjusted manually.

Some Saloon models and all Estate models are fitted with a rear brake proportioning valve which is deceleration-dependent. The valve prevents the rear wheels being locked by decreasing the pressure to the rear brakes during deceleration.

GM's anti- lock braking system (ABS) is fitted as standard equipment to some models and as optional equipment to others. It effectively regulates the hydraulic pressure to each separate brake in order to prevent one wheel locking ahead of the others. The system incorporates an electronic control unit which is supplied with signals from the wheel speed sensors. The signals are compared with each other and, if one wheel is found to be decelerating ahead of the others the hydraulic pressure to that wheel is reduced until its speed matches the other wheels. For this purpose the two front brakes are modulated separately, but the two rear brakes are modulated together. The ABS unit is fitted in the hydraulic lines leading from the master cylinder to the brakes, the vacuum servo unit and master cylinder being of similar type for both non-ABS and ABS models.

Should the ABS develop a fault, it is recommended that a complete test be carried out by a GM garage who will have the necessary equipment to make an accurate diagnosis.

2 Routine maintenance

1 Carry out the following procedures at the intervals given in *Routine maintenance* at the front of this manual.
2 Check that the brake fluid is at or near the maximum mark on the translucent reservoir. Note that the level will drop slightly as the brake pad linings wear, and topping up to correct this is not necessary. If the level is near the minimum mark the hydraulic circuit should be thoroughly checked for leaks.
3 Where necessary top up the level to the maximum mark using fresh brake fluid (photo).
4 Check the brake pad linings for wear with reference to Sections 3 and 4.
5 Check the handbrake shoe linings for wear with reference to Section 8.
6 Thoroughly check all rigid brake lines and flexible hoses for damage, leakage and any signs of chafing, splits or deterioration. Where evident, renew the particular line or hose with reference to Section 14.
7 Check vacuum servo unit operation with reference to Section 15.
8 Renew the hydraulic brake fluid as follows. Remove the brake fluid reservoir filler cap and syphon or draw out all of the fluid.
9 Refer to Section 13 and bleed the remaining fluid from each brake calliper. On completion make sure that all the bleed screws are tight.
10 Fill the brake fluid reservoir with fluid and proceed to bleed the system as instructed in Section 13, but allowing several additional pedal strokes in order to clear any remaining old fluid.

3 Front brake pads – inspection and renewal

1 Apply the handbrake. Jack up the front of the vehicle and support it on axle stands. Remove the front wheels.
2 Turn the steering to full right-hand lock and check the wear of the linings on the right-hand brake pads. Check that the thickness of the

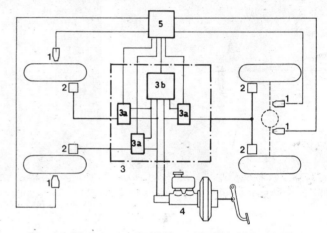

Fig. 9.1 Diagram of the GM anti-lock braking system (Sec 1)

1 Wheel speed sensors
2 Brake callipers
3 Hydraulic modulator
3a Solenoid valves
3b Return pump
4 Tandem brake master cylinder
5 Electronic control unit

2.3 Topping up the brake fluid level

3.6   Removing the front brake pad pins

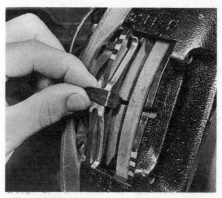

3.7A Disconnecting the pad wear warning lamp sensor and anti-rattle spring

3.7B Pad wear sensor location stub and slot (arrowed)

3.9   Removing the outer front brake pad

3.11 Piston cut-away recess position on the front brake pads (arrowed)

3.13 Inserting the front brake pad pins

lining including the backing plate is as shown in the Specifications using a steel rule or vernier callipers.

3   Turn the steering to full left-hand lock and check the left-hand brake pads in the same way.

4   If any brake pad is worn below the minimum thickness, renew all the front pads as a set together with new anti-rattle springs.

5   Extract the spring clips from the inner ends of the brake pad pins where fitted.

6   Note how the anti-rattle spring is located, then drive out the pins using a thin punch from the inside (photo).

7   Remove the anti-rattle spring. At the same time, where applicable, disconnect the pad wear warning lamp sensor from the inner pad, and disconnect the sensor cable from the wiring harness in the engine compartment (photos). Also release the cable from the clips and the anti-rattle spring. Note that the sensor and cable must always be renewed when fitting new brake pads as the sensor will be worn.

8   Push the brake pads apart slightly.

9   Pull the brake pads from the calliper (photo). If they are tight, use pliers or grips on the backplates. Also remove the intermediate plates where fitted.

10   Brush the dust and dirt from the calliper and intermediate plates, but take care not to inhale it. Clean any rust from the edge of the brake disc.

11   Press the piston fully into the calliper in order to accommodate the new brake pads. Where applicable, the cut-away recess in the piston should be positioned as shown (photo).

12   Insert the new brake pads and intermediate plates in the calliper, and check that they are free to move.

13   Locate the anti-rattle spring on the pads then insert the pins from the outside, with the springs located beneath the pins (photo).

14   Fit the spring clips to the inner ends of the brake pad pins where applicable.

15   Where applicable, fit the new pad wear warning lamp sensor to the slot on the inner pad then feed the cable into the engine compartment and connect it to the wiring harness. Attach the cable to its clips.

16   Renew the brake pads on the remaining front wheel using the procedure given in paragraphs 5 to 15.

17   Depress the footbrake pedal several times in order to reset the brake pads to their normal position.

18   Refit the front wheels and lower the vehicle to the ground.

4   Rear brake pads – inspection and renewal

1   Chock the front wheels then jack up the rear of the vehicle and support it on axle stands. Release the handbrake. Remove the rear wheels.

2   Inspect the brake pad linings for wear. Using a steel rule or vernier callipers, check that the thickness of the lining including the backing plate is as shown in the Specifications.

3   If any brake pad is worn below the minimum thickness, renew all the rear pads as a set together with new anti-rattle springs.

4   Note how the anti-rattle spring is located, then drive out the pins using a thin punch from the outside (photo).

5   Remove the anti-rattle spring.

6   Push the brake pads apart slightly to give a small clearance then pull them from the calliper together with the intermediate plates (photo). If they are tight, use pliers or grips to remove them.

7   Brush the dust and dirt from the calliper and intermediate plates, but take care not inhale it. Clean any rust from the edge of the brake disc.

8   Press both pistons fully into their cylinders using a length of wood or a hammer handle.

9   Check that the cut-away recesses on the pistons are positioned downwards at approximately 23° to the horizontal. A template made of

4.4   Removing the rear brake pad pins

4.6   Removing the inner rear brake pad

4.9   Checking the rear calliper piston recess angle with a card template

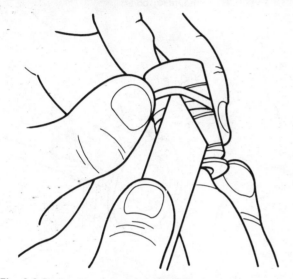

Fig. 9.2 Removing the piston seal from the front brake calliper (Sec 5)

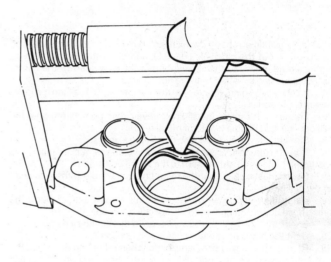

Fig. 9.3 Removing the seal from the sliding sleeve (Sec 5)

card may be used to check the setting (photo). If necessary, turn the pistons to their correct positions.

10   Apply a little brake grease to the top and bottom edges of the backplates on the new brake pads.

11   Insert the new brake pads and intermediate plates in the calliper, and check that they are free to move.

12   Locate the anti-rattle spring on the pads, then insert the pins from the inside while depressing the spring. Tap the pins firmly into the calliper.

13   Renew the brake pads on the remaining rear wheel using the procedure given in paragraphs 4 to 12.

14   Depress the footbrake pedal several times in order to reset the brake pads to their normal position.

15   Refit the rear wheels and lower the vehicle to the ground.

5   Front brake calliper – removal, overhaul and refitting

1   Apply the handbrake then jack up the front of the vehicle and support it on axle stands. Remove the wheel.

2   Fit a brake hose clamp to the flexible hose leading to the brake calliper. Alternatively remove the cap from the hydraulic fluid reservoir and refit it with a piece of polythene sheeting covering the opening to help prevent loss of brake fluid when the calliper hose is disconnected.

3   Remove the brake pads as described in Section 3.

4   Unscrew the hollow bolt securing the brake hose to the calliper and remove the two copper washers (photo).

5   Lever the caps from the calliper mounting bolts with a screwdriver (photo).

6   Using an Allen key, unscrew the mounting bolts and withdraw the calliper from the steering knuckle.

7   Clean the outer surfaces of the calliper.

8   Prise the outer plastic caps from the sliding sleeves.

9   Prise the dust cover from the calliper and piston.

10   Press the sliding sleeves slightly inwards, and remove the inner caps from their grooves.

11   Remove the sliding sleeves but identify them for location.

12   Position a block of wood inside the calliper in place of the disc pads, then using air pressure from an air line or foot pump through the fluid inlet, carefully force the piston from the cylinder. Remove the piston.

13   Mount the calliper in a vice and unbolt the frame.

14   Prise the piston seal from the cylinder taking care not to scratch the bore surface.

15   Clean the piston and cylinder with methylated spirit and allow to dry. Examine the surfaces of the piston and cylinder bore for wear, damage and corrosion. If evident, renew the calliper complete, however if the surfaces are good obtain a repair kit which includes a piston seal and dust cover. Also obtain a tube of brake cylinder paste.

16   Apply a little brake cylinder paste to the piston, cylinder bore and piston seal.

17   Locate the piston seal in the cylinder groove, then insert the piston carefully until it enters the seal. It may be necessary to rotate the piston to prevent it jamming in the seal.

18   Ease the dust cover into the piston groove then press it into the calliper using a suitable length of metal tubing.

19   Refit the frame and tighten the bolts to the specified torque.

20   Check the sliding sleeves for wear and for condition of the seals. If

5.4 Front brake hose securing bolt on the calliper (arrowed)

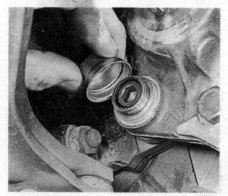

5.5 Removing the front brake calliper mounting bolt caps

6.5 Removing the rear brake calliper mounting bolts

necessary obtain a repair kit which includes four caps, four seals and grease. Pick out the old seals (Fig. 9.3), and clean the sliding sleeves. Apply a little grease to the sleeves and fit the new seals to the centre grooves, making sure that they are not twisted.

21 Insert the sliding sleeves in the calliper with the cap grooves towards the frame.

22 Fit the inner caps to the sliding sleeves, then press them onto the calliper using a suitable length of metal tubing.

23 Similarly fit the outer caps to the sliding sleeves.

24 To refit the calliper locate it on the steering knuckle, insert the mounting bolts and tighten them to the specified torque.

25 Fit the plastic caps over the mounting bolts and top them fully up to the calliper.

26 Using new copper washers, insert the hollow bolt through the brake hose union and tighten to the specified torque.

27 Check that the calliper moves freely on the sliding sleeves.

28 Refit the brake pads with reference to Section 3.

29 Remove the brake hose clamp or polythene sheeting and bleed the hydraulic system as described in Section 13. Provided that there has been no loss of brake fluid, it should only be necessary to bleed the calliper which was removed, however if brake fluid has been lost bleed the complete system.

30 Refit the wheel and lower the vehicle to the ground.

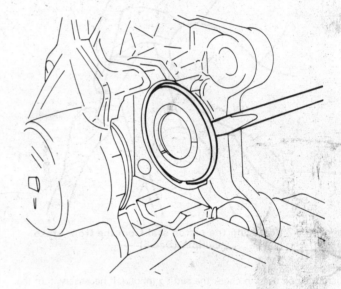

Fig. 9.4 Removal of rear brake calliper dust cover ring (Sec 6)

6 Rear brake calliper – removal, overhaul and refitting

1 Chock the front wheels then jack up the rear of the vehicle and support it on axle stands. Remove the wheel.

2 Fit a brake hose clamp to the flexible hose leading to the brake calliper. Alternatively remove the cap from the hydraulic fluid reservoir and refit it with a piece of polythene sheeting covering the opening to help prevent loss of brake fluid when the calliper hose is disconnected.

3 Remove the brake pads as described in Section 4.

4 Unscrew the union nut securing the rigid brake line to the calliper, and remove the brake line.

5 Unscrew the hexagon mounting bolts and withdraw the calliper from the semi-trailing arm (photo).

6 Clean the outer surfaces of the calliper.

7 Note that no attempt must be made to separate the two halves of the calliper.

8 Prise the rings and dust covers from each side of the calliper and pull the covers from the piston grooves.

9 Position a thin piece of wood between the pistons, then using air pressure from an air line or foot pump through the fluid inlet, carefully force the pistons from the cylinders. Remove the pistons.

10 Prise the piston seals from the cylinders, taking care not to scratch the bore surfaces.

11 Clean the pistons and cylinders with methylated spirit and allow to dry. Examine the surfaces of the pistons and cylinder bores for wear, damage and corrosion. If evident, renew the calliper complete, however if the surfaces are good obtain a repair kit which includes piston seals and dust covers. Also obtain a tube of brake cylinder paste.

12 Apply a little brake cylinder paste to the pistons, cylinder bores and piston seals.

13 Locate the piston seals in the cylinder grooves, then insert the pistons carefully until they enter the seals. It may be necessary to rotate the pistons to prevent them jamming in the seals.

14 Ease the dust covers into the piston grooves then locate them on the calliper housing. Press the retaining rings over the dust covers.

15 Press the pistons into their cylinders, then turn them so that the cut-away recesses are positioned downwards at an angle of approximately 23°. Make up a card template to check the setting.

16 To refit the calliper locate it on the semi-trailing arm, insert the mounting bolts and tighten them to the specified torque.

17 Locate the rigid brake line on the calliper and tighten the union nut to the specified torque.

18 Refit the brake pads with reference to Section 4.

19 Remove the brake hose clamp or polythene sheeting and bleed the hydraulic system as described in Section 13. Provided that there has been no loss of brake fluid, it should only be necessary to bleed the calliper which was removed, however if brake fluid has been lost bleed the complete system.

20 Refit the wheel and lower the vehicle to the ground.

7.7 Front brake disc securing screw

7.8A Removing the rear brake disc securing screw

7.8B Removing the rear brake disc

8.6 Handbrake shoe anti-rattle spring

8.8A Handbrake shoe adjuster and spring

8.8B Handbrake shoe lower lever assembly

8.22 Showing method of adjusting handbrake shoes (rear brake disc removed for clarity)

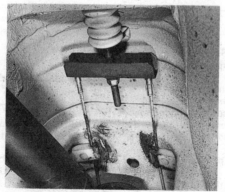

9.2 Front end of handbrake inner cables, and compensator bar

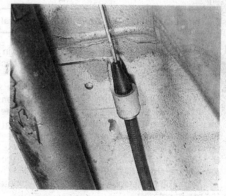

9.6 Front end of handbrake outer cable in the guide

7 Brake disc – examination, removal and refitting

1   Jack up the front or rear of the vehicle as applicable and support it on axle stands. Release the handbrake and chock the front wheels if checking a rear disc. Remove the appropriate wheel.
2   Check that the brake disc securing screw in tight, then refit and tighten a wheel bolt opposite the screw using a spacer washer approximately 10.0 mm (0.4 in) thick.
3   Rotate the brake disc and examine it for deep scoring or grooving. Light scoring is normal, but if excessive, the disc should be removed and either renewed or machined within limits by a suitable engineering works. It is worth mentioning that some garages may be able to regrind

the discs in position using a specially adapted electric grinder.
4   Using a dial gauge, or metal block and feeler gauges, check that the disc run-out does not exceed the amount given in Specifications, measured 10.0 mm (0.4 in) from the outer edge of the disc. Check the run-out at several positions around the disc.
5   If the run-out is excessive, remove the disc and check that the disc-to-hub surfaces are perfectly clean. Refit the disc and check the run-out again.
6   To remove the brake disc, first remove the brake pads as described in Section 3 or 4.
7   To remove a front disc, remove the securing screw (photo), then withdraw the disc from the hub, tilting it as necessary to clear the brake calliper. On some models it may be necessary to unbolt the frame from

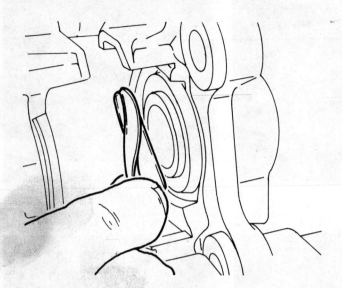

Fig. 9.5 Removal of the dust cover (Sec 6)

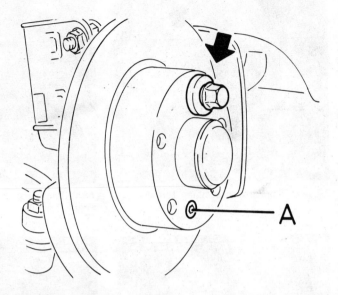

Fig. 9.6 Refit a wheel bolt (arrowed) and tighten the screw (A) before checking a brake disc for run-out (Sec 7)

the calliper.

8   To remove a rear disc, unbolt the brake calliper from the semi-trailing arm, and support it away from the disc taking care not to damage the rigid brake line. Remove the securing screw and withdraw the disc from the hub (photos).

9   Refitting is a reversal of removal, but make sure that the mating faces of the disc and hub are perfectly clean, and before inserting the securing screw apply a little locking fluid to its threads. Refit the brake pads with reference to Section 3 or 4.

8   Handbrake shoes – inspection and renewal

1   Remove the rear brake discs as described in Section 7.

2   Brush the dust and dirt from the shoes, backplate and from inside the disc drum.

3   Check the thickness of the linings on the shoes and if less than shown in the Specifications, renew the shoes on both sides as a set.

4   Also check the surface inside the drums. These should not normally be worn unless the handbrake has been sticking on.

5   Unhook the return spring from the lever on the backplate then unhook the handbrake cable.

6   Using a screwdriver through a hole in the hub flange twist and remove the anti-rattle springs (photo).

7   Mark the brake shoes for location. Also note the fitted positions of the return springs.

8   Prise the brake shoes from the adjuster and lever, and disconnect the return springs (photos).

9   Remove the adjuster and lever.

10   Clean the backplate, springs, adjuster and lever.

11   Apply a little brake grease to the threads of the adjuster then screw it together to its minimum length.

12   Fit one brake shoe and secure to the backplate with the anti-rattle spring.

13   Fit the lever in position.

14   Fit the remaining brake shoe and secure with the anti-rattle spring.

15   Hook the lower return spring onto the brake shoes.

16   Fit the adjuster between the upper ends of the shoes, then hook the upper return spring to the shoes.

17   Refit the handbrake cable and return spring to the rear of the backplate.

18   Refit the rear brake disc with reference to Section 7 but do not refit the wheel at this stage.

19   Repeat the procedure given in paragraphs 5 to 18 on the opposite side.

20   In order to hold the discs centrally while adjusting the shoes, fit and tighten a wheel bolt opposite the securing screws using a spacer washer approximately 10.0 mm (0.4 in) thick.

21   At the front end of the handbrake cable, loosen the cable adjustment nut to the end of the threaded handbrake lever rod.

22   Working on each rear disc in turn, insert a screwdriver through the unthreaded hole in the disc and hub then turn the adjuster upwards until the disc/drum is locked. Back off the adjuster until the disc/drum just turns freely (photo).

23   Refit the rear wheels.

24   Pull up the handbrake lever to the sixth notch, then working under the vehicle tighten the cable adjustment nut until both rear wheels are locked. The adjustment nut is of the self-locking type. Check the adjustment by releasing and applying the handbrake lever two or three times.

25   Lower the vehicle to the ground.

9   Handbrake cable – removal and refitting

1   Chock the front wheel, then jack up the rear of the vehicle and support it on axle stands. Remove the rear wheels and release the handbrake.

2   At the front of the handbrake cable unscrew the adjustment nut from the threaded handbrake lever rod and slide off the compensator bar (photo).

3   Working on each side in turn, unhook the return spring from the lever on the backplate then unhook the cable.

4   Pull the rear of the outer cable from the guide on the semi-trailing arm on both sides.

5   Bend back the intermediate clips and release the cables.

6   Pull the front ends of the outer cables from the guides (photo), and unhook the inner cables. Withdraw the cable assembly from under the vehicle.

7   Refitting is a reversal of removal but note that the shorter, black sheathed cable is fitted on the right-hand side. Apply some molybdenum disulphide paste to the plastic guides at the front of the inner cables. Finally adjust the handbrake shoes and the cable as described in Section 8, paragraphs 20 to 25.

10   Handbrake lever – removal and refitting

1   Chock the front wheels then jack up the rear of the vehicle and support it on axle stands.

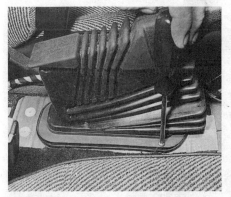

10.11 Removing the handbrake lever gaiter frame

10.13A Handbrake lever mounting bolts (arrowed)

10.13B Warning switch wiring location (arrowed)

11.5 Brake master cylinder and brake line locations

12.3 Rear brake proportioning valve

13.3 Bleeding the brake hydraulic system

14.5A Front brake flexible hose attachment to the suspension strut

14.5B Front brake flexible hose attachment to the inner wing panel

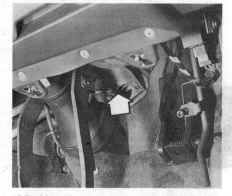

17.7 Vacuum servo unit to brake pedal pushrod (arrowed)

2   At the front of the handbrake cable unscrew the adjustment nut from the threaded handbrake lever rod, and slide off the compensator bar.

3   Prise the rubber gaiter from the underbody and remove it from the handbrake lever rod.

4   On manual gearbox models unclip the gear lever gaiter from the centre console inside the vehicle, and pull upwards over the gear lever so that it is turned inside out. Untie the cord and remove the gaiter. Remove the screws and withdraw the gear lever surround.

5   On automatic transmission models unclip the selector lever position panel and flexible slot cover. Remove the screw, lift the selector lever cover and disconnect the illumination lamp.

6   On models with on board computer remove the cover and position in the centre console.

7   On models with rear seat heating, prise out the control switch panel and position in the centre console.

8   Prise the cover from the centre console tray and remove the two exposed screws.

9   Remove the four front mounting screws and withdraw the centre console.

10   On models with electric windows, disconnect the two multiplugs.

11   Remove the four screws and lift the handbrake lever gaiter frame over the lever (photo).

12   Pull off the handbrake lever gaiter.

13   Unscrew the handbrake lever mountings bolts, then disconnect the wiring from the warning switch (photos).

14   Remove the handbrake lever from the vehicle.

15   Refitting is a reversal of removal, but on completion adjust the handbrake cable as described in Section 8.

11   Master cylinder – removal, overhaul and refitting

Note: *Do not dismantle the master cylinder from an anti-lock braking system*

1   Depress the footbrake pedal several times to dissipate the vacuum in the servo unit.

2   Disconnect the wiring for the brake fluid level warning lamp from

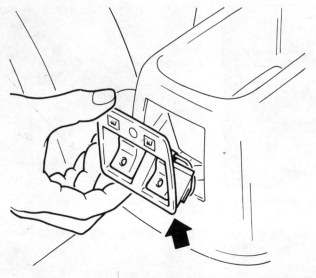

Fig. 9.7 Rear seat heating switch removal for access to
handbrake lever (Sec 10)

18.1   Brake stop-lamp switch

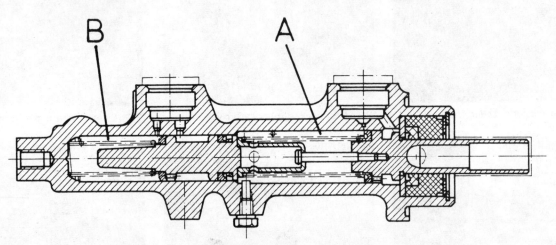

Fig. 9.8 Cross-section of the tandem brake master cylinder
(Sec 11)

A   *Primary chamber (front brakes)*
B   *Secondary chamber (rear brakes)*

the reservoir filler cap.

3   If available use a pipette or syphon to remove the brake fluid from
the reservoir. This will reduce loss of fluid later.

4   Locate a container beneath the master cylinder to catch spilled fluid.

5   Identify the brake lines for position, then unscrew the union nuts
and pull the lines from the master cylinder (photo).

6   Unbolt the front bracket.

7   Unscrew the mounting nuts and withdraw the master cylinder from
the studs on the vacuum servo unit. Take care not to drop any brake
fluid on the body paintwork. If accidentally spilt, swill off immediately
with copious amounts of cold water.

8   Clean the exterior surfaces of the unit then prise out the fluid
reservoir and rubber seals.

9   Depress the primary piston slightly with a screwdriver, then extract
the circlip from the mouth of the master cylinder.

10   Withdraw the primary piston assembly.

11   Depress the secondary piston and unscrew the stop pin from the
cylinder body.

12   Withdraw the secondary piston assembly by tapping the unit on
the bench.

13   Clean all the components in methylated spirit and examine them
for wear and damage. In particular check the surfaces of the pistons and
cylinder bore for scoring and corrosion. If the bore is worn renew the

complete master cylinder, otherwise obtain a repair kit which will
include pistons and seals. If the pistons are in good condition it may be
possible to obtain just the rubber seals.

14   Check that the inlet and outlet ports are clear. If applicable, fit the
new seals to the pistons using the fingers only to manipulate them into
position. The open ends of the seals must face the appropriate ends of
the pistons.

15   Dip the secondary piston assembly in clean brake fluid and insert
in the cylinder. Depress the secondary piston and tighten the stop pin in
the body.

16   Dip the primary piston assembly in clean brake fluid and insert in
the cylinder. Depress the piston and refit the circlip.

17   Press in the rubber seals and refit the fluid reservoir.

18   If necessary renew the O-ring seal on the master cylinder flange.

19   Refitting is a reversal of removal but tighten the mounting nuts and
union nuts to the specified torque, and finally bleed the hydraulic
system as described is Section 13.

---

12   Rear brake proportioning valve – removal and refitting

1   Chock the front wheels. Jack up the rear of the vehicle and support it

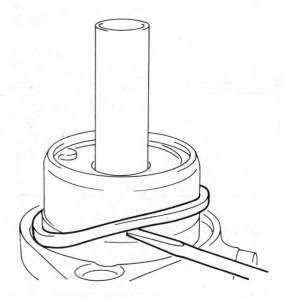

Fig. 9.9 Removing the O-ring seal from the master cylinder flange (Sec 11)

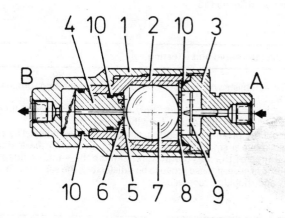

Fig. 9.10 Cross-section of the rear brake proportioning valve (Sec 12)

1 Housing (valve)	7 Ball
2 Housing (ball)	8 Orifice plate
3 Cap	9 Tappet plate and tappet
4 Piston	10 O-ring
5 Clamping ring	A Inlet
6 Piston seal	B Outlet

on axle stands.

2 Remove the cap from the brake fluid reservoir and refit it with a piece of polythene sheeting covering the opening to help prevent loss of brake fluid when the valve is removed.

3 Unscrew the union nuts and disconnect the two brake lines from the valve (photo).Plug the ends of the brake lines.

4 Pull out the locking plate and remove the valve from the bracket.

5 Refitting is a reversal of removal but bleed the rear hydraulic system as described in Section 13.

13 Hydraulic system – bleeding

1 If any of the hydraulic components in the braking system have been removed or disconnected, or if the fluid level in the reservoir has been allowed to fall appreciably, air will have been introduced into the system. The following paragraphs describe the procedure for removing the air.

2 The front and rear hydraulic circuits are entirely separate, therefore unless the master cylinder has been removed or the brake fluid is being changed, it will only be necessary to bleed the circuit which has been disturbed.

3 There are a variety of do-it-yourself brake bleeding kits available from motor accessory shops, and it is recommended that one of these kits is used wherever possible as they greatly simplify the bleeding operation. Follow the kit manufacturer's instructions in conjunction with the following procedure (photo).

4 During the bleeding operation do not allow the brake fluid level in the reservoir to drop below the minimum mark, and only use new fluid for topping-up. Never re-use fluid bled from the system.

5 Before starting, check that all rigid pipes and flexible hoses are in good condition and that all hydraulic unions are tight. Take great care not to allow hydraulic fluid to come into contact with the vehicle paintwork, otherwise the finish will be seriously damaged. Wash off any spilt fluid immediately with cold water.

6 If a brake bleeding kit is not being used, gather together a clean jar, a suitable length of plastic or rubber tubing which is a tight fit over the bleed screws and a new tin of brake fluid.

7 Clean the area around the bleed screw on one of the front brake callipers and remove the dust cap. Connect one end of the tubing to the bleed screw and immerse the other end in the jar containing sufficient brake fluid to keep the end of the rubber submerged.

8 Open the bleed screw half a turn and have an assistant depress the brake pedal to the floor and then slowly release it. Tighten the bleed

screw at the end of each downstroke to prevent the expelled air and fluid from being drawn back into the system. Continue this procedure until clean brake fluid, free from air bubbles, can be seen flowing into the jar, and then finally tighten the bleed screw.

9 Remove the tube, refit the dust cap and repeat this procedure on the remaining front brake calliper.

10 Repeat the procedure on the rear brake callipers, noting that on models fitted with ABS, at least fifteen pedal depressions are required to bleed the rear brake circuit.

11 When bleeding is complete, top-up the fluid level in the reservoir and refit the cap.

14 Hydraulic brake lines and hoses – removal and refitting

1 Remove the cap from the brake fluid reservoir and refit it with a piece of polythene sheeting covering the opening to help prevent subsequent loss of brake fluid.

2 Jack up the vehicle and support it on axle stands.

Front flexible hose

3 Remove the front wheel.

4 Turn the steering on full lock. Unscrew the bolt securing the hose to the calliper and recover the copper washers.

5 Pull the locking plates from the mountings (photos).On models with ABS disconnect the hose from the clips.

6 Unscrew the rigid brake line union, and remove the hose.

7 Refitting is a reversal of removal, but make sure that the hose is not twisted. Bleed the hydraulic system as described in Section 13.

Rear flexible hose

8 Pull the locking plates from the mountings.

9 Unscrew the rigid brake line unions, and remove the hose.

10 Refitting is a reversal of removal, but make sure that the hose is not twisted, Bleed the hydraulic system as described in Section 13.

Brake lines

11 Some commonly-used brake lines can be obtained from GM parts stores already formed complete with unions, however other brake lines must be prepared out of 4.75 mm (0.19 in) diameter brake pipe. Kits for making the brake lines can be obtained from motor accessory shops.

12 To remove a brake line, unscrew the unions at each end and release it from the clips.

13   Refitting is a reversal of removal. Bleed the hydraulic system as described in Section 13.

15   Vacuum servo unit – testing

1   To establish whether or not the servo is operating, proceed as follows.
2   With the engine stopped, apply the brake pedal several times in order to dissipate the vacuum from the servo unit.
3   Hold the brake pedal depressed, then start the engine. The pedal should move a small distance towards the floor with the additional assistance of the servo unit. If not, check the vacuum hose and non-return valve. If these prove to be satisfactory, the servo unit itself is faulty and should be renewed.

16   Vacuum servo unit – hose and non-return valve renewal

1   When new, the vacuum hose is shrunk onto the non-return valve using a heat process, therefore when the valve is first renewed it is necessary to fit a conventional vacuum hose, using clips to secure it. Thereafter the hose and valve may be renewed separately.
2   Unscrew the hose union nut at the inlet manifold.
3   Pull or prise the elbow connector out of the servo.
4   Release the hose from the plastic straps.
5   Cut the hose off the non-return valve, the elbow and the inlet manifold union.
6   Cut the new hoses to length (it is sold in 5.0 metre lengths) and secure to the non-return valve, elbow and union using clips. Make sure that the arrows on the valve point towards the inlet manifold end.
7   Press the elbow into the servo rubber grommet and tighten the union nut on the inlet manifold. Fit new plastic straps.

17   Vacuum servo unit – removal and refitting

1   Depress the footbrake pedal several times to dissipate the vacuum in the servo unit.
2   Disconnect the wiring for the brake fluid level warning lamp from the reservoir filler cap.
3   Unbolt the master cylinder front bracket.
4   Unscrew the master cylinder mounting nuts and pull the unit from the studs on the vacuum servo unit sufficiently to allow room for removal of the servo unit. Leave the brake lines connected to the master cylinder.
5   Pull or prise out the vacuum hose elbow connector. Move the bulkhead wiring harness to one side.
6   Working inside the vehicle unhook the return spring from the brake pedal.
7   Extract the spring clip and pull out the clevis pin securing the servo pushrod to the brake pedal (photo).
8   Unscrew the mounting nuts, then tilt the servo unit and remove it from the bulkhead into the engine compartment. Recover the gasket.
9   Loosen the locknut and unscrew the clevis fork from the pushrod. Unscrew the locknut.
10   Unscrew the nuts and remove the support bracket and gasket from the servo unit.
11   Commence refitting by screwing the locknut and clevis fork onto the pushrod. With the pushrod in its rest position adjust the fork so that the distance between the servo mounting face and the clevis pin centre line is 211.0 + 1.0 mm (8.31 + 0.04 in). Tighten the locknut.
12   Locate the support bracket on the servo unit together with a new gasket. Fit and tighten the nuts.
13   Refit the servo unit to the bulkhead using a new gasket. Fit and tighten the mounting nuts.
14   Connect the pushrod to the brake pedal with the clevis pin and spring clip.
15   Reconnect the brake pedal return springs.
16   Press the vacuum hose elbow connector in the servo rubber grommet.

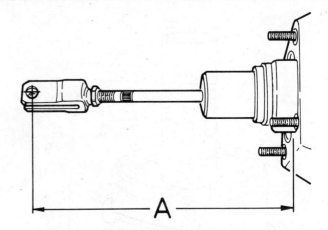

Fig. 9.11 Vacuum servo unit pushrod setting dimension (Sec 17)

$$A = 211.0 + 1.0 \text{ mm } (8.31 + 0.04 \text{ in})$$

17   If necessary, renew the O-ring seal on the master cylinder flange then locate the unit on the servo studs. Fit and tighten the mounting nuts.
18   Refit and tighten the bolts for the master cylinder front bracket to the specified torque.
19   Reconnect the wiring to the brake fluid reservoir filler cap.

18   Brake pedal – removal and refitting

1   Working inside the vehicle disconnect the wiring from the brake stop-lamp switch, then unscrew the switch from the pedal bracket noting its fitted position (photo).
2   Unhook both the brake and clutch pedal return springs.
3   Extract the spring clip and pull out the clevis pin securing the servo pushrod to the brake pedal.
4   Disconnect the cable from the clutch pedal with reference to Chapter 5, Section 3.
5   Unscrew the nut from the end of the pedal shaft, and remove the washer.
6   Unscrew the nuts holding the pedal bracket to the bulkhead and turn the bracket around the steering column to allow removal of the pedal shaft. Note that, on later models, it may be necessary to remove the steering column to allow the pedal bracket to be slid off its retaining studs. The column can be removed as described in Chapter 10, Section 22, noting that it is not necessary to remove the steering wheel or the lock cylinder; the column can be removed with these items still in position.
7   Remove the pedal location clips and withdraw the shaft until the brake pedal can be removed. Recover the thrustwashers.
8   Refitting is a reversal of removal, but lubricate the shaft with grease. Adjust the clutch cable as described in Chapter 5, Section 3, then check the clutch pedal adjustment as described in Chapter 5, Section 2.

19   Anti-lock braking system (ABS) – precautions

1   If the ABS develops a fault, it is recommended that the complete system is tested by a GM dealer, who will have the special equipment necessary to make a quick and accurate diagnosis of the problem. Because of the electronic nature of the system, it is not practical for the DIY mechanic to carry out the test procedure.
2   To prevent possible damage to the integrated circuits, always disconnect the multi-plug from the electronic control unit before carrying out electrical welding work. It is recommended that the control unit is removed if the vehicle is being subjected to high temperatures as may be encountered, for instance, during certain paint drying processes.
3   Do not disconnect the control unit multi-plug with the ignition switched on.
4   Do not use a battery booster to start the engine.

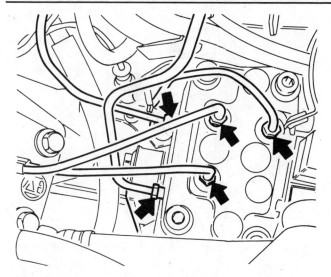

Fig. 9.12 Brake line connections to the ABS hydraulic modulator (Sec 20)

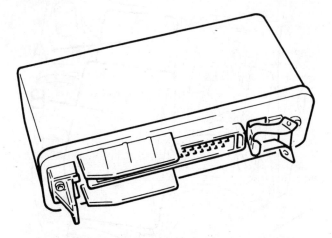

Fig. 9.13 ABS electronic control unit (Sec 21)

20 ABS hydraulic modulator – removal and refitting

1   Disconnect the battery negative lead.
2   Remove the cap from the brake fluid reservoir and refit it with a piece of polythene sheeting covering the opening to help prevent subsequent loss of brake fluid.
3   Unscrew the bolt from the power steering reservoir clamp and tie the reservoir to one side.
4   Remove the screw and withdraw the cover from the hydraulic modulator.
5   Remove the screws and lift away the wiring harness securing clamp.
6   Pull off the multi-plug, if necessary using a screwdriver to lever it from the terminals.
7   Identify all the brake lines on the modulator for location, then unscrew the union nuts and pull the brake lines just clear of the modulator. If possible, plug the ends of the brake lines, or at least cover them to prevent the ingress of dust and dirt. Also cover the modulator ports.
8   Unscrew the modulator mounting nuts and remove the cover.
9   Slightly tilt the modulator and pull it forward from the bracket, then unscrew the nut and disconnect the earth cable.
10   Remove the modulator from the engine compartment taking care not to spill brake fluid on the vehicle bodywork.
11   If a new modulator is being fitted, unscrew the two relays and transfer them to the new unit. No attempt must be made to dismantle the modulator.
12   Check that the modulator mounting bracket bolts are tight, and that the rubber mountings on the modulator are in good condition.
13   Refitting is a reversal of removal but tighten all nuts and bolts to the specified torque, and finally bleed the hydraulic system as described in Section 13. Check that the ABS warning light goes out after starting the engine. On completion take the vehicle to a GM dealer and have the complete system tested with the ABS test equipment.

21 ABS electric control unit – removal and refitting

1   With the ignition switched off, disconnect the battery negative lead.
2   Inside the vehicle remove the trim panel from the left-hand side of the passenger footwell.
3   Pull the bonnet release lever then unclip the electronic control unit from its mounting.
4   Disconnect the wiring multi-plug and withdraw the unit.
5   Refitting is a reversal of renewal. Check that the ABS warning light goes out after starting the engine. On completion take the vehicle to a GM dealer and have the complete system tested with the ABS test equipment.

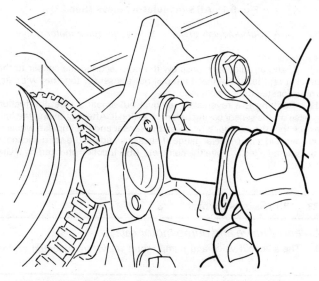

Fig. 9.14 Removing an ABS rear wheel speed sensor (Sec 22)

22 ABS wheel speed sensor – removal and refitting

1   Disconnect the battery negative lead.
2   Jack up the front or rear of the vehicle as applicable and support it on axle stands.

Front sensor

3   Remove the front wheels.
4   Inside the engine compartment unclip the sensor wiring harness plug from the bracket, then separate the plug halves using a screwdriver.
5   Under the wheel arch, release the sensor wiring from the hose clips.
6   Pull the wiring grommets from the hose brackets.
7   Using an Allen key, unscrew the bolt securing the sensor to the steering knuckle, then lever out the sensor with a screwdriver.
8   Prise the wiring grommet from the inner panel and remove the wheel speed sensor.
9   Refitting is a reversal of removal but smear a little anti-friction grease on the sensor casing before inserting it. Have the complete ABS function checked by a GM dealer.

Rear sensor

10   Working beneath the vehicle unclip the sensor wiring harness plug from the bracket on the underbody, then separate the plug halves using

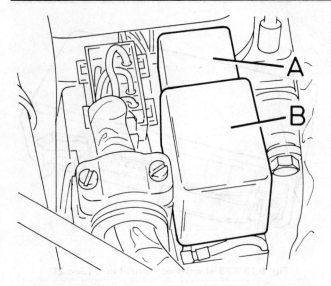

Fig. 9.15 ABS modulator relays (Sec 23)

A Solenoid valve relay   B Return pump motor relay

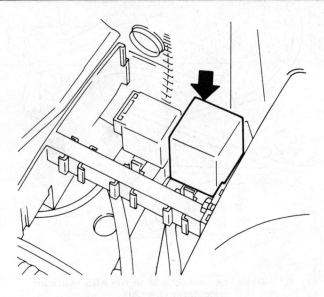

Fig. 9.16 ABS surge arrester relay (Sec 23)

a screwdriver.

11   Using an Allen key, unscrew the bolt securing the sensor to the bracket on the differential, then pull out the sensor together with any shims located under the flange.

12   Refitting is a reversal of removal but smear a little anti-friction grease on the sensor casing before inserting it. After tightening the bolt check that the clearance between the sensor and the impulse wheel is as specified using a feeler gauge. If necessary adjust the shim thickness as required. Finally, have the complete ABS function checked by a GM dealer.

23   ABS relays — renewal

Solenoid valve and pump motor relays

1   The solenoid valve and pump motor relays are mounted on the

hydraulic modulator. First disconnect the battery negative lead.

2   Unscrew the bolt from the power steering reservoir clamp and tie the reservoir to one side.

3   Remove the screw and withdraw the cover from the hydraulic modulator.

4   Pull out the appropriate relay. The small relay is for the solenoid valve, and the large one is for the return pump motor.

5   Fit the new relay using a reversal of the removal procedure.

Surge arrester relay

6   The surge arrester relay is located on the left-hand side of the engine compartment, behind the left-hand front suspension mounting. First disconnect the battery negative lead.

7   Remove the relay cover, and pull out the relay.

8   Fit the new relay and cover, and re-connect the battery negative lead.

24   Fault diagnosis — braking system

Symptom	Reason(s)
Excessive pedal travel	Air in hydraulic system Faulty master cylinder
Brake pedal feels spongy	Air in hydraulic system Faulty master cylinder
Judder felt through brake pedal or steering wheel when braking	Excessive run-out or distortion of brake discs Excessively worn brake pads
Excessive pedal pressure required to stop	Servo unit faulty Pads contaminated or worn excessively Seized calliper piston Failure of front or rear hydraulic circuit ABS hydraulic pump not working
Brakes pull to one side	Seized calliper piston Brakes pads contaminated or worn excessively

Chapter 10 Suspension and steering

For information applicable to later models, see Supplement at end of manual

Contents

Specifications

Front suspension

Type .... Independent MacPherson struts, coil springs and anti-roll bar, double-acting telescopic shock absorbers

Rear suspension

Type .... Independent, semi-trailing arms and coil springs, anti-roll bar, double-acting telescopic shock absorbers, air pressure type levelling system on some models

Rear shock absorber air pressure (when fitted):
  Unladen .... 0.8 bar (11.5 lbf/in²)
  Laden .... 3.0 bar (43.5 lbf/in²)

Steering

Type .... Recirculating ball, worm shaft and nut with sector shaft and drop arm, power-assisted
Ratio .... 14.5 : 1
Lubricant type .... Dexron II type ATF (Duckhams Uni-Matic or D-Matic)
Lubricant quantity .... 1.0 litre (1.8 pints)
Camber .... –1°45' to –0°15'
Maximum deviation left to right wheel .... 1°
Castor:
  Saloon .... +4°30' to +6°30'
  Estate .... +4° to +6°
Maximum deviation left to right wheel .... 1°
Toe-setting (total) .... 0°05' to 0°25' (1.0 to 3.0 mm) toe-in

Rear wheel alignment (laden*)

Camber:
  Saloon .... –2°20' to –1°
  Estate .... –2°5' to –0°45'
Maximum deviation left to right wheel .... 0°25'

Toe-setting:

Saloon	0°5' toe-out to 0°45' toe-in (0.5 to 5.0 mm)
Estate	0° to 0°50' toe-in (0 to 6.0 mm)
Maximum deviation left to right wheel	0°25'

Note: *Laden indicates a vehicle containing two front seat occupants and a half-filled fuel tank.*

Wheels

Type	Pressed steel or alloy
Size	5½J x 14

Tyres

Saloon	185/70 R 14 - 88H
Estate:	
Manual	185/70 R 14 - 88H
Automatic	175 R 14 - 88T or 185/70 R 14 - 88T

Tyre pressures (cold) – lbf/in² (bar)	Front	Rear
Up to three passengers:		
Saloon	32 (2.2)	32 (2.2)
Estate	29 (2.0)	32 (2.2)
Full load:		
Saloon	36 (2.5)	42 (2.9)
Estate	38 (2.6)	46 (3.2)

Torque wrench settings
Front suspension

	Nm	lbf ft
Lower suspension arm pivot bolt*:		
Front:		
Stage 1	120	89
Stage 2	tighten a further 30° to 45°	tighten a further 30° to 45°
Rear:		
Stage 1	70	52
Stage 2	tighten a further 45° to 60°	tighten a further 45° to 60°
Anti-roll bar front mounting	40	30
Strut to steering knuckle*:		
Stage 1	50	37
Stage 2	100	74
Stage 3	tighten a further 30° to 45°	tighten a further 30° to 45°
Hub nut	320	236
Strut top mounting	70	52
Anti-roll bar link	65	48
Front crossmember	170	126
Lower balljoint to knuckle	100	74
Lower balljoint to arm	35	26

Note *Values indicating angle-tightening apply to special bolts that must be renewed after removal.*

Rear suspension

	Nm	lbf ft
Crossmember	125	92
Driveshaft to rear hub:		
Stage 1	50	37
Stage 2	tighten a further 45° to 60°	tighten a further 45° to 60°
Semi-trailing arm pivot bolt	100	74
Anti-roll bar	22	16
Shock absorber lower mounting	110	81
Shock absorber upper mounting	20	15
Rear hub nut	300	221

Steering

	Nm	lbf ft
Steering column	22	16
Steering wheel	25	19
Flexible coupling	22	16
Steering gear adjustment locknut	30	22
Steering gear mounting	40	30
Steering gear cover	30	22
Bearing cap locknut	150	111
Drop arm	160	118
Power steering union	42	31
Power steering pump	25	19
Tie-rod balljoint nut	60	44
Outer tie-rod clamp bolt	10	7
Idler mounting	55	41
Idler arm	45	33

Wheels

	Nm	lbf ft
Wheel bolts	90	66

1 General description

The front suspension is of independent MacPherson strut type incorporating coil springs and double-acting telescopic shock absorbers. An anti-roll bar is mounted forward of the suspension arms.

The rear suspension is of independent type with semi-trailing arms, coil springs and double-acting telescopic shock absorbers. The anti-roll bar is mounted on the crossmember. A rear suspension levelling system is fitted to some models, which enables the rear ride height to be adjusted by means of air pressure from an air line.

Power-assisted steering is fitted to all models. It is of worm and sector shaft type with a recirculating ball type nut. On fuel injection models, the hydraulic system includes a pressure switch (photo). This operates an auxiliary air valve in order to increase the engine idling speed and compensate for the additional load imposed by the power steering pump.

2 Routine maintenance

1 Carry out the following procedures at the intervals given in *Routine maintenance* at the front of this manual.

2 With the engine stopped, remove the cap from the power steering fluid reservoir and check the level. There are two marks: with the engine hot the level should be at the upper mark, and with it cold the level should be at the lower mark.

3 Top up if necessary with the specified fluid, but if a leak is suspected, thoroughly check the hoses and connections.

4 Support the front of the vehicle on axle stands, then check for excessive play in the steering tie-rod balljoints and lower suspension balljoints. Also check for splits in the balljoint rubber dust covers. Check that the steering tie-rods move freely on the ball-pins.

5 Renew the balljoints if necessary referring to Section 6.

6 Examine the full length of the power steering pump drivebelt for wear, damage and deterioration.

7 Check the drivebelt tension with reference to Section 29.

1.1 Power steering pressure switch

8 Examine the tyre walls and tread for wear and damage, in particular splits and bulges which if evident will require renewal of the tyre. If abnormal tyre wear is evident, a thorough check of the steering and suspension should be made. Check and adjust the tyre pressures at the same time.

3 Front suspension strut – removal and refitting

1 Apply the handbrake, then jack up the front of the vehicle and support it on axle stands. Remove the front wheel.

2 Prise off the metal caps, and unscrew the brake calliper mounting bolts using an Allen key.

3 Remove the brake calliper and support it so that the hydraulic hose is not strained.

4 Pull out the clip and disconnect the hydraulic hose from the bracket on the strut.

5 On models fitted with an anti-lock braking system (ABS), remove the wheel speed sensor and cable with reference to Chapter 9.

6 Unscrew the nut and separate the bottom of the link from the anti-roll bar. To prevent the ball-pin from turning, hold it stationary with a spanner on the two flats provided.

7 Unscrew the nut from the steering tie-rod balljoint, and use a proprietary balljoint separator to release the ball-pin from the steering knuckle.

8 Unscrew and discard the pinch-bolt, and pull down the lower suspension arm to release the balljoint from the steering knuckle.

9 Support the suspension strut then unscrew the nut from the upper mounting. Withdraw the strut from under the vehicle (photos).

10 Commence refitting by inserting the strut up into the upper mounting. Refit the nut and tighten it to the specified torque while holding the piston rod stationary with an Allen key.

11 Insert the balljoint in the steering knuckle, then fit a new pinch-bolt with its head facing the rear. Tighten to the specified torque. **Note:** *On no account should the old pinch-bolt be used again.*

12 Reconnect the steering tie-rod balljoint and tighten the nut to the specified torque.

13 Reconnect the link to the anti-roll bar and tighten the nut to the specified torque.

14 On models with ABS refit the wheel speed sensor and cable.

15 Clip the hydraulic hose to the bracket on the strut.

16 Refit the brake caliper with reference to Chapter 9.

17 Refit the front wheel and lower the vehicle to the ground.

18 Finally have the front wheel alignment checked and if necessary adjusted. If the strut has been dismantled the camber setting will also have to be checked by a GM dealer using specialised equipment.

4 Front suspension strut – overhaul

Note: *A purpose-made spring compressor is essential for this work. Use of makeshift or unsuitable tools may result in injury.*

1 Remove the strut as described in Section 3 and mount it in a vice.

2 Fit the spring compressor and tighten it to unload the pressure on the upper seat and mounting.

3 Hold the piston rod stationary with an Allen key, then unscrew the nut and withdraw the upper seat and mounting. Separate the bearing from the mounting and recover the piston rod stop washers.

4 Remove the coil spring and upper seat, and remove the rubber boot, damping rings, and rubber buffer.

5 Unbolt the anti-roll bar link from the strut.

6 Mark the top of the steering knuckle in relation to the strut in order to

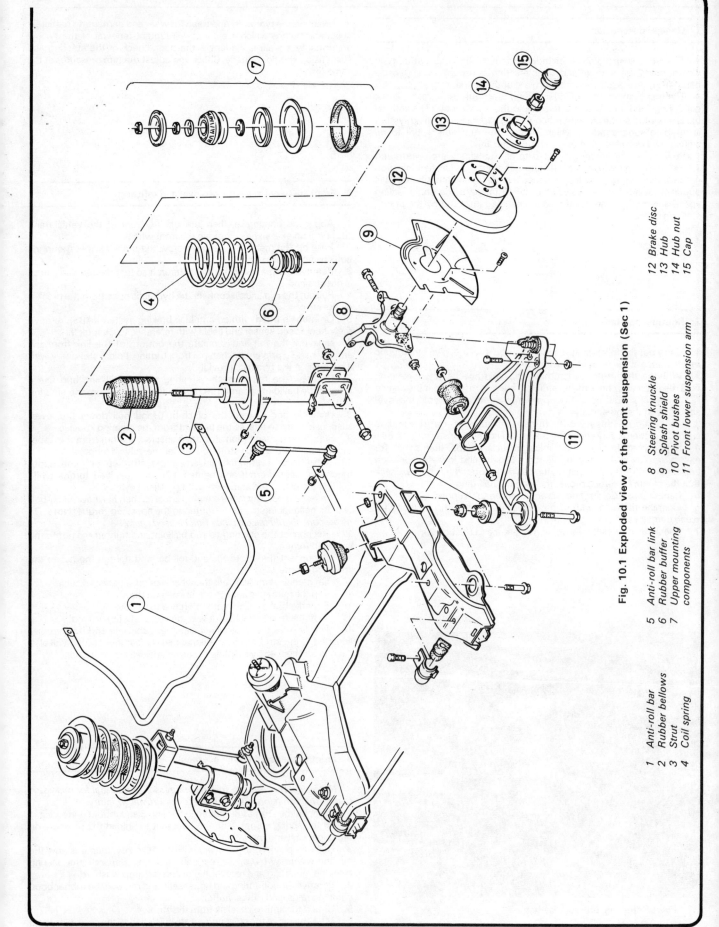

Fig. 10.1 Exploded view of the front suspension (Sec 1)

1 Anti-roll bar
2 Rubber bellows
3 Strut
4 Coil spring
5 Anti-roll bar link
6 Rubber buffer
7 Upper mounting components
8 Steering knuckle
9 Splash shield
10 Pivot bushes
11 Front lower suspension arm
12 Brake disc
13 Hub
14 Hub nut
15 Cap

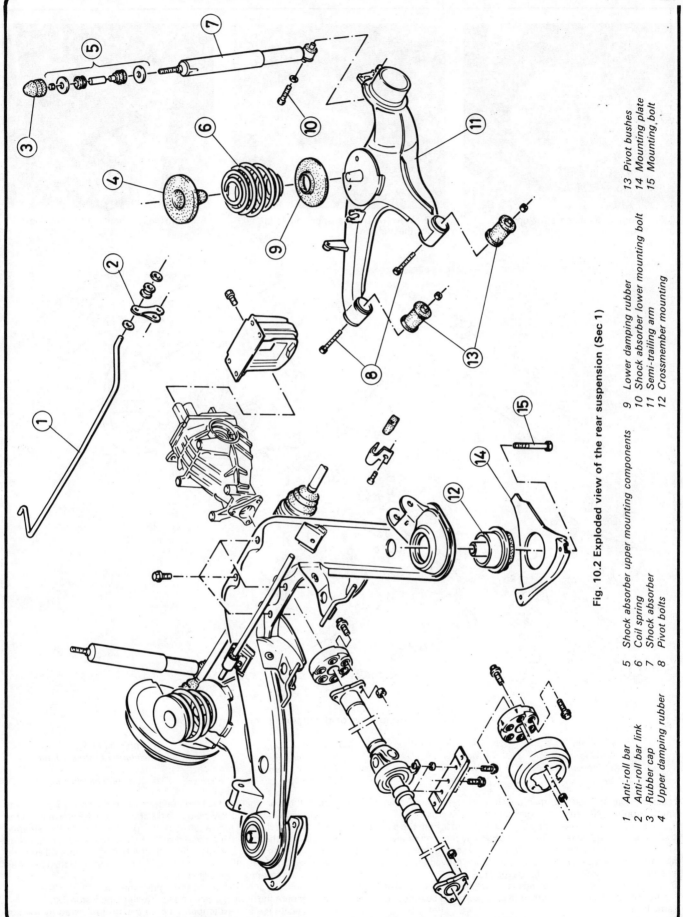

Fig. 10.2 Exploded view of the rear suspension (Sec 1)

1 Anti-roll bar
2 Anti-roll bar link
3 Rubber cap
4 Upper damping rubber
5 Shock absorber upper mounting components
6 Coil spring
7 Shock absorber
8 Pivot bolts
9 Lower damping rubber
10 Shock absorber lower mounting bolt
11 Semi-trailing arm
12 Crossmember mounting
13 Pivot bushes
14 Mounting plate
15 Mounting bolt

3.9A   Front suspension strut upper mounting

3.9B   View of front suspension strut under the vehicle

4.6   Front suspension strut-to-knuckle bolts

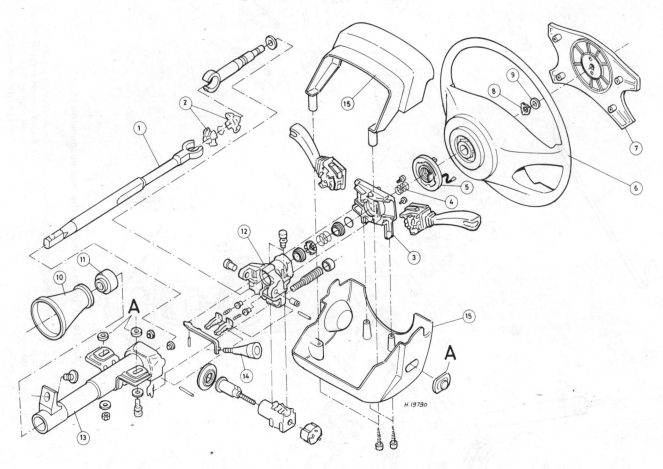

Fig. 10.3 Exploded view of the steering column (Sec 1)

1	Inner column	5	Horn contact ring	9	Retaining nut	13	Outer column
2	Universal joint	6	Steering wheel	10	Rubber gaiter	14	Height adjustment hand
3	Switch housing	7	Horn pad	11	Lower column bush		lever
4	Spring	8	Locktab	12	Height adjustment mechanism	15	Steering column shrouds

retain the camber setting, then unscrew the bolts, and remove the knuckle (photo). Note that the bolt heads face forwards.

7   It is not possible to separate the shock absorber from the strut, so if the shock absorber is faulty the strut assembly must be renewed. The shock absorber may be tested by mounting the strut upright in a vice and moving the piston rod up and down. If the movement of the rod is uneven, weak or loose, a new unit is required.

8   Clean all the components and examine them for wear and damage. If renewing the coil spring, both front springs should be renewed at the same time.

9   Commence reassembly by locating the steering knuckle on the strut. If the original strut is being refitted, insert the new bolts from the front, align the previously-made marks and tighten the new nuts to the specified torque. If a new strut is being fitted, secure the steering knuckle to the strut using the old bolts, tighten to the specified torque and have the camber angle adjusted by a GM dealer immediately on completion of the refitting operation. The new bolts can then be fitted during the camber angle adjustment.

10   Refit the anti-roll bar link and tighten the nut.

11   Mount the strut in a vice and fully extend the piston rod.

12   Locate the lower damping ring on the strut followed by the coil spring.

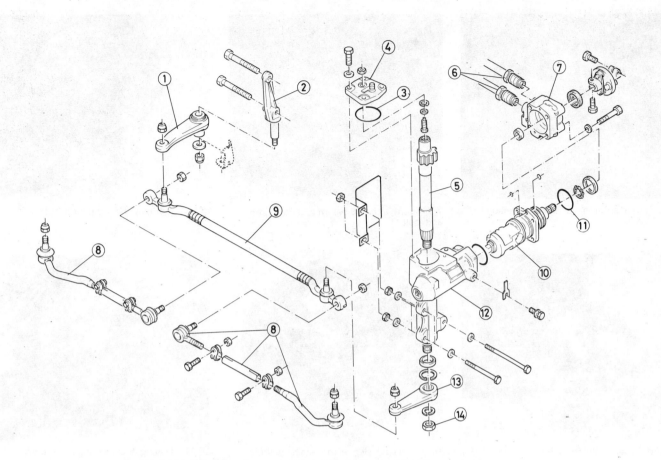

Fig. 10.4 Exploded view of the power steering gear (Sec 1) (LHD shown RHD similar)

1	Idler arm	5	Sector shaft	9	Centre tie-rod
2	Idler	6	Fluid pipe union nuts	10	Control valve
3	O-ring seal	7	Control valve end housing	11	O-ring seal
4	Cover	8	Side tie-rods	12	Housing

13 Drop arm
14 Nut

13 Fit the spring compressor to the coil spring.

14 Refit the rubber buffer.

15 Fit the rubber boot and upper damping ring on the coil spring upper seat.

16 Position a stop washer on the piston rod with its concave side facing downwards, then locate the upper seat on the coil spring. The small hole in the upper seat must be positioned on the opposite side of the steering knuckle (Fig. 10.5).

17 Locate the bearing in the upper mounting with the yellow coloured inner race facing out, then fit the mounting onto the piston rod.

18 Position a stop washer on the piston rod with its concave side uppermost. Refit and tighten the nut.

19 Release the spring compressor and make sure that the coil spring locates correctly on the damping rings.

20 The front suspension strut may now be refitted with reference to Section 3.

5 Front lower suspension arm – removal and refitting

1 Apply the handbrake, then jack up the front of the vehicle and support it on axle stands. Remove the front wheel.

2 Unscrew and remove the pinch-bolt, and pull down the lower suspension arm to release the balljoint from the steering knuckle.

3 Unscrew the nuts and separate the bottom of the links from the anti-roll bar. Support the anti-roll bar as far upwards as possible.

4 Unscrew the vertical front mounting bolt and the horizontal rear mounting bolt, discard them, and withdraw the lower suspension arm

from under the vehicle. Note the horizontal bolt head faces forwards.

5 Refer to Section 6 if renewing the suspension balljoint. Examine the rubber bushes in the arm and if necessary renew them by pressing out the old ones and pressing in the new bushes. Use a long bolt, nut, metal tubing and packing washers, and dip the new bushes in soapy water before fitting them. The vertical bush should be removed upwards from the arm, and the new bush pressed downwards. The horizontal bush should be removed from front to rear, and the new bush fitted from rear to front. The narrow lead on the horizontal bush must face forward.

6 Commence refitting by locating the arm on the underbody and inserting the new mounting bolts. **Note:** *On no account must the old bolts be used again.*

7 Hold the arm horizontally and tighten the nuts and bolts to the specified torque.

8 Insert the balljoint in the steering knuckle and refit the pinch-bolt with its head facing the rear. Tighten to the specified torque.

9 Reconnect the links to the anti-roll bar and tighten the nuts.

10 Refit the front wheel and lower the vehicle to the ground.

11 Finally check and if necessary adjust the front wheel alignment (Section 30).

6 Front suspension lower balljoint – renewal

1 Remove the front lower suspension arm as described in Section 5.

2 The balljoint is rivetted to the suspension arm when new, with subsequent balljoints bolted on. Where necessary drill out the rivets

7.2   Front anti-roll bar link connection

7.3   Front anti-roll bar mounting clamp and bolt

10.9A   Remove the front hub nut ...

10.9B   ... and the front hub

10.10   Plastic sleeve for retaining the bearing inner tracks during fitting (arrowed)

10.11   Driving the bearing inner tracks onto the stub axle

using a 12.0 mm (0.47 in) drill. One side of each rivet has a centre punch to facilitate accurate drilling in order to prevent enlarging the holes in the arm (Fig. 10.6).
3   Using only the special bolts supplied, fit the new balljoint and tighten the nuts to the specified torque. The nuts must face downwards.
4   Refit the front lower suspension arm with reference to Section 5.

7   Front anti-roll bar – removal and refitting

1   Apply the handbrake, then jack up the front of the vehicle and support it on axle stands. Remove the front wheels.
2   Unscrew the nuts and separate the bottoms of the links from the anti-roll bar (photo). Prevent the link ball-pins from turning by holding them with a spanner on the two flats provided.
3   From inside the engine compartment unscrew the anti-roll bar mounting clamp bolts, and unclip the clamps (photo).
4   Withdraw the anti-roll bar from under the vehicle.
5   Examine the mounting rubbers for wear and deterioration and, if necessary, prise them from the bar. Dip the new rubbers in silicone oil and fit them on the bar with their slits facing forwards.
6   Insert the anti-roll bar from under the front of the vehicle, and refit the clamps. Insert the bolts loosely.
7   Reconnect the links and tighten the nuts to the specified torque.
8   Tighten the mounting clamp bolts to the specified torque.
9   Refit the front wheels and lower the vehicle to the ground.

8   Front anti-roll bar link – removal and refitting

1   Apply the handbrake, then jack up the front of the vehicle and

support it on axle stands. Remove the appropriate front wheel.
2   Note which way round the link is fitted, then unscrew the nuts while holding the ball-pins with a spanner on the two flats provided.
3   Remove the link from the strut and anti-roll bar.
4   Refitting is a reversal of removal but tighten the nuts to the specified torque.

9   Steering knuckle – removal and refitting

1   Remove the front hub as described in Section 10.
2   Unbolt the disc shield from the steering knuckle.
3   Unscrew the nut from the steering tie-rod balljoint, and use a proprietary balljoint separator to release the ball-pin.
4   On models with an anti-lock braking system remove the wheel speed sensor and cable with reference to Chapter 9.
5   Unscrew and remove the pinch-bolt, and pull down the lower suspension arm to release the balljoint from the steering knuckle.
6   Mark the top of the steering knuckle in relation to the strut in order to retain the camber setting, then unscrew and discard the bolts and remove the knuckle. Note that the bolt heads face forwards.
7   Refitting is a reversal of removal, but be sure to use new bolts and nuts. On no account should the old bolts be used. Tighten to the specified torque wrench settings and if necessary have the camber and wheel alignment checked by a GM dealer.

10   Front hub and bearings – removal and refitting

Note *A torque wrench capable of measuring the high torque of the front hub nut should be obtained before commencing work. If such a torque wrench is not available, it is recommended that the work is entrusted to a GM dealer.*

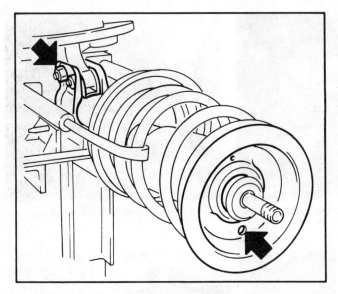

Fig. 10.5 Correct position of the front coil spring upper seat (Sec 4)

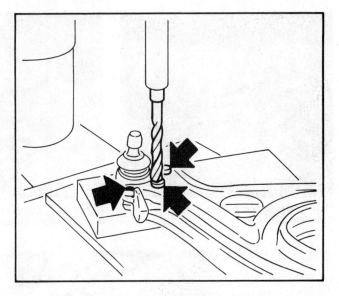

Fig. 10.6 Drilling the front suspension lower balljoint rivets (Sec 6)

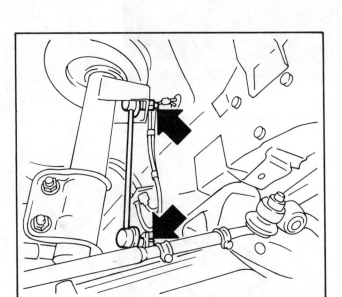

Fig. 10.7 Front anti-roll bar link mounting nuts (Sec 8)

1   Apply the handbrake, then jack up the front of the vehicle and support it on axle stands. Remove the appropriate front wheel. On vehicles fitted with alloy wheels remove the disc in the centre of the wheel.

2   Lever the metal cap from the hub, refit the wheel and lower the vehicle to the ground. (Leave the wheel cover off if fitted).

3   Place blocks of wood, or similar, behind every wheel to ensure that the vehicle cannot move in either direction.

4   Using a socket, sturdy T-bar and a long extension bar for leverage, slacken the hub nut half a turn. Note that the nut is tightened to a very high torque setting, and considerable effort will be required to slacken it.

5   Jack up the front of the vehicle and support it on axle stands. Remove the appropriate wheel.

6   Prise off the metal caps and unscrew the brake calliper mounting bolts using an Allen key.

7   Remove the brake calliper and support it so that the hydraulic hose is not strained.

8   Unscrew the retaining screw and remove the brake disc.

9   Remove the hub nut, and pull the hub from the stub axle. If the inner bearing track remains on the stub axle, remove it with a puller and recover the oil seal which will have been pulled out of the hub (photos).

10   The bearings cannot be renewed separately to the hub, so if the bearings are worn or the oil seal leaking the complete hub must be renewed. The new hub includes a plastic sleeve which holds the bearing inner tracks together while fitting the hub (photo).

11   Locate the hub and plastic sleeve on the stub axle, then carefully drive the inner tracks onto the stub axle using a suitable size socket or metal tube (photo). Remove the plastic sleeve.

12   Refit the components in the reverse order to removal but note the following points:

(a)   Tighten all nuts and bolts to the specified torque
(b)   Apply locking fluid to the threads of the brake disc retaining screw and tighten it to 4 Nm (3 lbf ft)
(c)   Refit the brake calliper as described in Chapter 9

---

11   Front suspension crossmember – removal and refitting

1   Apply the handbrake, then jack up the front of the vehicle and support it on axle stands positioned under the underbody channel sections.

2   Remove both front lower suspension arms as described in Section 5.

3   From inside the engine compartment, unscrew the anti-roll bar front mounting clamp bolts and unclip the clamps.

4   Unscrew the nuts securing both engine mountings to the crossmember and engine brackets. Recover the washers.

5   Support the weight of the engine using a hoist or engine support bar (Fig. 10.8). If using a hoist, remove the bonnet first (Chapter 11).

6   Support the crossmember on a trolley jack and stout length of wood.

7   Unscrew the four mounting bolts and lower the crossmember to the ground. Recover the engine mountings.

8   Refitting is a reversal of removal, but tighten all nuts and bolts to the specified torque settings.

---

12   Rear shock absorber – removal and refitting

1   Position the vehicle over an inspection pit or on car ramps. The rear of the vehicle may be jacked up and supported by axle stands under the

12.2A Rear shock absorber upper mounting (Saloon)

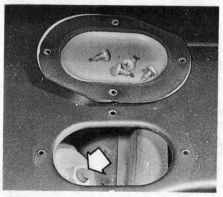

12.2B Rear shock absorber upper mounting (Estate) (arrowed)

13.18   Rear semi-trailing arm pivot bolt

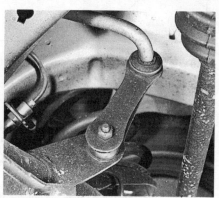

15.3   Rear anti-roll bar link

16.15   Rear crossmember front mounting

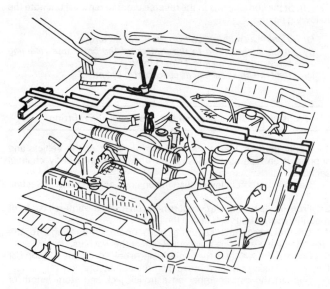

Fig. 10.8 Using an engine support bar to support the weight of the engine (Sec 11)

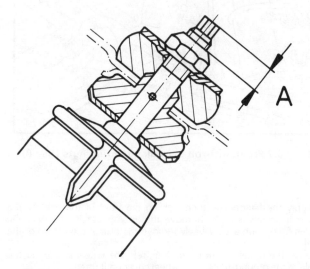

Fig. 10.9 Rear shock absorber upper mounting fitting dimension (Sec 12)

A = 13.0 mm (0.5 in)

semi-trailing arms, however the arms slope down from the centre of the vehicle making it difficult to position the axle stands safely. Alternatively jack up the semi-trailing arm with a trolley jack and suitable wooden saddle.

2   On Saloon models open the boot lid and remove the rubber cap from the top of the shock absorber (photo). On Estate models remove the screws and lift the cover over the shock absorber (photo).

3   Unscrew the upper mounting nuts and remove the washer and rubber buffer.

4   On models fitted with rear suspension levelling, release the air pressure from the schrader valve then unclip the pressure line from the shock absorber.

5   Unscrew the bottom mounting bolt and remove the shock absorber.

6   Commence refitting by locating the shock absorber on the semi-trailing arm and inserting the bottom mounting bolt loosely.

7 On models fitted with rear suspension levelling, refit the pressure line and carefully inflate the shock absorber until it protrudes through the top mounting.

8 Refit the upper mounting rubber buffer and washer, and tighten the nut and locknut to the specified torque. The distance between the locknut and the top of the shock absorber stub must be 13.0 mm (0.5 in).

9 Tighten the bottom mounting bolt to the specified torque.

10 Refit the cover (Estate models) or rubber cap (Saloon models).

11 Lower the vehicle to the ground.

12 On models fitted with rear suspension levelling, inflate the system to the specified amount.

13 Rear semi-trailing arm – removal and refitting

1 Chock the front wheels, then jack up the rear of the vehicle and support on axle stands positioned under the crossmember mountings.

2 Using an Allen key unscrew the socket-head bolts securing the driveshaft to the rear hub while holding the rear wheel stationary. Recover the lock washers.

3 Lever the driveshaft from the rear hub and support it to one side.

4 Disconnect the hydraulic brake hose from the bracket on the semi-trailing arm.

5 Remove the rear wheel, then unbolt and remove the brake calliper and support it to one side without straining the hydraulic brake hose.

6 Unscrew the retaining screw and remove the brake disc.

7 Unhook the return spring and disconnect the handbrake cable from the lever on the semi-trailing arm. Disconnect the cable from the bracket.

8 Using a socket through the unthreaded holes in the hub unscrew the brake anchor plate bolts and remove the locking plate.

9 Remove the rear hub with reference to Section 19, then withdraw the brake anchor plate and brake shoes as an assembly.

10 If removing the left-hand semi-trailing arm disconnect the exhaust rear mounting rubbers and lower the exhaust approximately 30 cm (12 in). Support the exhaust in this position with wire or string.

11 Unbolt the rear anti-roll bar link from the semi-trailing arm and turn the link upwards. Remove the rubber mounting from the semi-trailing arm.

12 Using a trolley jack slightly raise the semi-trailing arm.

13 On models fitted with rear suspension levelling, release the air pressure from the schrader valve then unclip the pressure line from the shock absorber.

14 Unscrew the shock absorber bottom mounting bolt.

15 Lower the jack until the rear spring and damping rubbers can be removed.

16 Completely lower the jack.

17 Support the final drive unit on the trolley jack and unbolt the rear damping bracket from the underbody.

18 Slightly lower the final drive unit then unscrew and remove the pivot bolts and withdraw the semi-trailing arm from the crossmember (photo).

19 If the pivot bushes are worn, they may be renewed. Cut the rubber shoulders from the old bushes and press out the bushes using a long bolt, nut, washers and suitable metal tube. Fit the new bushes in a similar way, but dip them in soapy water first to assist fitting.

20 Refitting is a reversal of removal, but adjust the handbrake with reference to Chapter 9 and on models fitted with rear suspension levelling inflate the system to the specified amount. Tighten all nuts and bolts to the specified torque. Note that the semi-trailing arm pivot bolt heads must face each other.

14 Rear coil spring – removal and refitting

1 Chock the front wheels, then jack up the rear of the vehicle and support on axle stands positioned under the crossmember mountings. Remove the rear wheel.

2 Disconnect the hydraulic brake hose from the bracket on the semi-trailing arm by pulling out the locking plate.

3 Using a trolley jack, slightly raise the semi-trailing arm.

4 On models fitted with rear suspension levelling, release the air pressure from the schrader valve, then unclip the pressure line from the shock absorber.

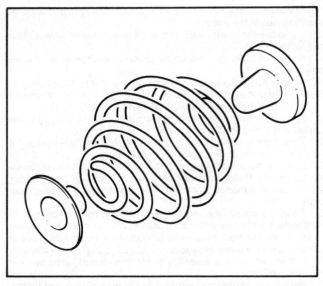

Fig. 10.10 Rear coil spring and damping rubbers (Sec 14)

5 Unscrew the shock absorber bottom mounting belt.

6 If removing the left-hand coil spring disconnect the exhaust rear mounting rubbers and lower the exhaust approximately 30 cm (12 in). Support the exhaust in this position with wire or string.

7 On models fitted with ABS, unclip the wheel speed sensor cables from the underbody.

8 Using a further trolley jack or bottle jack support the final drive unit then unbolt the rear damping bracket from the underbody.

9 Lower the final drive unit and semi-trailing arm until the rear coil spring and damping rubbers can be removed. Note that the upper damping rubber incorporates a buffer.

10 Refitting is a reversal of removal, but tighten all nuts and bolts to the specified torques.

15 Rear anti-roll bar – removal and refitting

1 Chock the front wheels, then jack up the rear of the vehicle and support on axle stands.

2 Support the final drive unit on a trolley jack. Unbolt the rear damping bracket from the underbody, then lower the final drive unit slightly.

3 Unbolt the two links from the semi-trailing arms, and remove the rubber mountings (photo).

4 Unscrew the clamp bolts from the top of the crossmember, release the clamps, and withdraw the anti-roll bar from under the vehicle.

5 Remove the links and mounting rubbers from the anti-roll bar. If necessary the rubbers may be pressed from the links and renewed, using metal tubing, washers and long bolt and nut. Dip the new rubbers in soapy water to assist fitting them.

6 Refitting is a reversal of removal, but tighten all nuts and bolts to the specified torques.

16 Rear axle (complete) – removal and refitting

1 Chock the front wheels, then jack up the rear of the vehicle and support it on axle stands positioned under the rear underbody channel sections. Remove both rear wheels.

2 Remove the intermediate and rear sections of the exhaust system with reference to Chapter 3.

3 Note the position of the adjustment nut on the handbrake rod, then unscrew it and slide off the compensator bar.

4 Working on one side disconnect the return spring and unhook the handbrake cable from the shoe operating lever. Disconnect the cable from the bracket on the semi-trailing arm.

5 Disconnect the hydraulic brake hose from the bracket on the semi-trailing arm by pulling out the locking plate.

6 Unbolt the rear brake calliper from the semi-trailing arm and support it away from the disc, taking care not to damage the rigid brake line.

7   Repeat the procedure described in paragraphs 4, 5, and 6 on the remaining side of the vehicle.

8   On models fitted with ABS, unbolt the wheel speed sensors from the final drive unit.

9   Loosen the slider joint nut on the propeller shaft front section one complete turn.

10   At the rear of the propeller shaft unscrew the bolts securing the rear disc joint to the differential flange. Push the propeller shaft forwards and disconnect it from the flange. Support it on an axle stand.

11   Position a length of wood beneath the semi-trailing arms and support in the middle with a trolley jack.

12   Unbolt the final drive unit rear damping bracket from the underbody and lower the unit onto the length of wood.

13   Unscrew the shock absorber bottom mounting bolts on each side.

14   Lower the trolley jack until both rear coil springs and damping rubbers can be removed. Note that the upper damping rubbers incorporate buffers.

15   Raise the trolley jack until the rear damping bracket touches the underbody, then unscrew the three bracket bolts and centre bolt from the crossmember front mountings (photo). As a precaution, have an assistant steady the assembly to prevent it falling from the trolley jack.

16   Lower the rear axle assembly to the ground and withdraw from under the vehicle.

17   Refitting is a reversal of removal, but tighten all nuts and bolts to the specified torques.

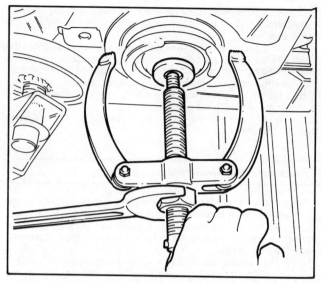

Fig. 10.11 Withdrawing the crossmember mountings (Sec 18)

17 Rear suspension crossmember – removal and refitting

1   Remove the rear axle assembly as described in Section 16.

2   Unscrew the anti-roll bar clamp bolts from the top of the crossmember and release the clamps.

3   Unscrew the final drive unit mounting bolts and lower the unit from the crossmember.

4   Unscrew and remove the semi-trailing arm pivot bolts, noting that the bolt heads are facing each other on each arm. Remove the crossmember.

5   If necessary renew the mountings with reference to Section 18.

6   Refitting is a reversal of removal, but tighten all nuts and bolts to the specified torques. The semi-trailing arms should be positioned horizontally before tightening the pivot bolts.

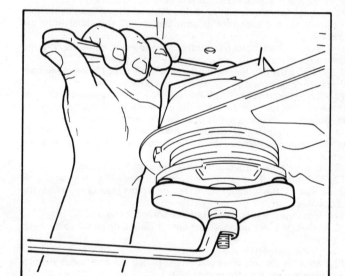

Fig. 10.12 Pressing in the crossmember mountings (Sec 18)

18 Rear suspension crossmember mountings – renewal

1   Chock the front wheels, then jack up the rear of the vehicle and support on axle stands positioned under the rear underbody channel sections. Remove both rear wheels.

2   Disconnect the exhaust rear mounting rubbers and lower the exhaust approximately 30 cm (12 in). Support the exhaust in this position with wire or string.

3   Disconnect the hydraulic brake hoses from the brackets on the semi-trailing arms by pulling out the locking plates.

4   Support the final drive unit on a trolley jack.

5   Unscrew the three bracket bolts and one centre bolt from the crossmember mountings on each side and remove the brackets.

6   The mountings must now be pulled from the crossmember. The GM tool for this task is shown in Fig. 10.11. The crossmember is lowered slightly and the mounting bolt inserted from the top, then the puller is assembled as shown and the nut tightened to withdraw the mounting. If a similar arrangement using a conventional puller is not possible, use metal tubing, a long bolt, and large washers or a metal plate to remove the mounting.

7   The GM tool for inserting the mountings is shown in Fig. 10.12, and here again a similar tool may be fabricated from metal plate and a long bolt.

8   Refitting is a reversal of removal.

19 Rear hub and bearing – removal and refitting

Note: *A torque wrench capable of measuring the high torque of the rear hub nut should be obtained before commencing work. If such a torque wrench is not available, it is recommended that the work is entrusted to a GM dealer.*

1   Chock the front wheels, then jack up the rear of the vehicle and support it on axle stands.

2   Unscrew the socket-head bolts securing the driveshaft to the rear hub while holding the rear wheel stationary. Recover the lockwashers.

3   Lever the driveshaft from the rear hub and support it to one side.

4   Remove the rear wheel.

5   Disconnect the hydraulic brake hose from the bracket on the semi-trailing arm by pulling out the locking plate.

6   Unbolt and remove the brake calliper and support it to one side without straining the hydraulic brake hose.

7   Unscrew the retaining screw and remove the brake disc.

8   Using an Allen key through an unthreaded hole in the hub drive flange, unscrew the brake backplate mounting bolts. Note that the upper bolts are shorter and are fitted with a locking plate.

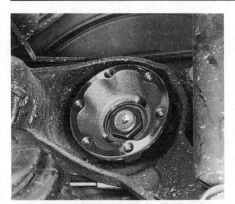

19.9 Driveshaft flange and rear hub nut

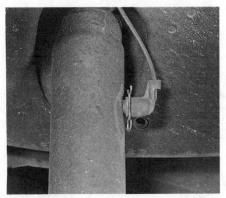

20.8 Pressure line connection to the rear shock absorber

20.10 Inflating the rear suspension levelling system

21.3 Disconnecting the horn pad wiring

21.5A Unscrew the retaining nut ...

21.5B ... and remove the locktab

21.6 Removing the steering wheel

21.8 Spring on the top of the inner column

22.5A Remove the screws ...

9   Insert the wheel bolts and use a long bar to hold the hub stationary, then unscrew the central nut from the inner side of the hub (photo).
10   Pull off the driveshaft flange using a suitable puller.
11   Press the rear hub outwards from the bearing using a suitable puller bolted to the semi-trailing arm.
12   Extract the circlip from the semi-trailing arm then press out the bearing, again using a puller bolted to the arm.
13   If the inner bearing track has remained on the hub remove it with a puller.
14   Clean all the components and examine them for wear and damage. Obtain a new bearing.
15   Press the new bearing into the semi-trailing arm using pressure on the outer track. If necessary, a long bolt and washers may be used to do this.
16   Fit the bearing retaining circlip.
17   Support the wheel bearing inner track on the inside with a metal tube, then carefully drive in the rear hub from the outside.

18   Fit the driveshaft flange on the inside of the hub. If necessary, support the outside of the hub and drive the flange fully on from the inside.
19   Refit the hub nut and tighten to the specified torque while holding the hub stationary. Drive in the special collar to lock the nut.
20   Refitting is a reversal of removal but note the following points:

(a)   Tighten all nuts and bolts to the specified torque wrench settings
(b)   Adjust the handbrake with reference to Chapter 9.

20 Rear suspension levelling system components – removal and refitting

1   Open the boot lid or tailgate, lift the carpet by the spare wheel and unscrew the cap from the levelling system schrader valve.

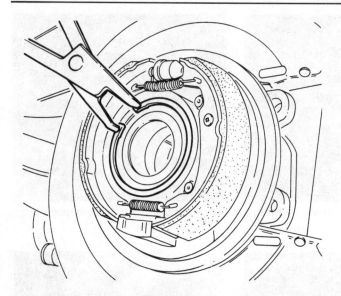

Fig. 10.13 Extracting the rear hub bearing circlip (Sec 19)

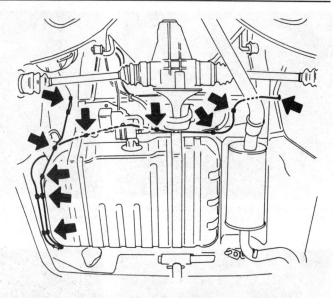

Fig. 10.14 Rear suspension levelling system pressure line retaining clip positions (Sec 20)

2   Using a screwdriver depress the valve centre core and depressurise the system.

Filler valve

3   Unscrew the ring from the valve.
4   Compress the lugs with pliers and press the valve down through the floor.
5   Chock the front wheels, then jack up the rear of the vehicle and support it on axle stands.
6   Squeeze the clip ends together and remove both pressure lines from the valve. Withdraw the valve.

Pressure line

7   Chock the front wheels, then jack up the rear of the vehicle and support on axle stands.
8   Squeeze the clip ends together and remove the pressure line from the shock absorber and filler valve (photo).
9   Release the pressure line from the clips on the underbody.

Refitting

10   Refitting is a reversal of removal, but on completion inflate the system to 8.0 bar (116 lbf/in²) and check for leaks, then reduce the pressure to 0.8 bar (11.6 lbf/in²) (photo).

---

21   Steering wheel – removal and refitting

1   Disconnect the battery negative lead.

2   Set the front wheels in the straight-ahead position.
3   Prise the horn pad from the centre of the steering wheel and disconnect the two wires (photo).
4   With the ignition key inserted check that the steering lock is disengaged.
5   Bend back the locktab and unscrew the retaining nut. Remove the locktab (photos).
6   Mark the inner column and steering wheel in relation to each other then remove the steering wheel by carefully rocking it from side to side (photo). Do not use a hammer or mallet to remove it.
7   If necessary, unclip the horn contact ring from the steering wheel, noting that the direction indicator return segment points to the left.
8   Check that the spring is located on the inner column (photo), and lightly lubricate the horn contact finger with a copper-based grease.
9   Refitting is a reversal of removal, but tighten the nut to the specified torque and bend up the locktab to lock it.

---

22   Steering column – removal and refitting

1   Disconnect the battery negative lead.
2   Working inside the vehicle, mark the inner column in relation to the flexible coupling, then unscrew and remove the clamp bolt.
3   Remove the steering wheel as described in Section 21.

22.5B   ... and withdraw the lower shroud ...

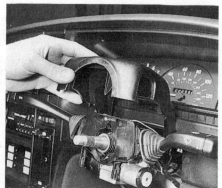

22.5C   ... and upper shroud

22.7   Removing the windscreen wiper switch

22.12 Locating the switch rubber grommets in the upper shroud

23.8 Disconnecting the ignition switch wiring plug

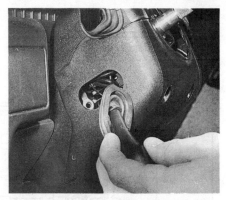

24.2 Removing the height adjustment lever

24.5 Removing the ignition switch grub screws

25.6 Steering gear drop arm

25.7 View of the power-assisted steering gear (engine removed for clarity)

27.2 Side tie-rod outer balljoint

27.5 Centre tie-rod-to-drop arm nut (arrowed)

28.2 Steering idler

4   Where applicable unscrew the height adjustment lever.
5   Remove the screws and withdraw the shroud sections from the steering column (photos).
6   With the ignition key inserted at position II, depress the small detent spring and pull out the lock cylinder. Also disconnect the wiring plug.
7   Depress the plastic clips and remove the direction indicator switch and the windscreen wiper switch (photo).
8   Disconnect the wire from the horn contact finger.
9   Unscrew the lower mounting bolt.
10   The upper column mounting consists of a nut and a shear bolt. Ideally a bolt extractor should be used to remove the shear bolt by first drilling a 3.2 mm (⅛ in) hole then using the extractor to unscrew the bolt. Alternatively, drill off the head and use grips to unscrew the remainder of the bolt later.
11   Unscrew the upper mounting nut and withdraw the steering column rearwards from the flexible coupling. The column should be handled carefully to avoid damage to the latticed safety outer column and special inner column.

12   Refitting is a reversal of removal but tighten all nuts and bolts to the specified torque. Before tightening the shear bolt, check that the column is correctly aligned then tighten the bolt until the head shears off. Check that, with the front wheels in the straight-ahead position, the clamp bolt on the flexible coupling is horizontally at the top, and that the steering wheel spokes are centred and pointing downwards. Before tightening the clamp bolt, pull the inner column upwards until it touches the stop on the ball bearing, then hold it in this position while tightening the bolt. Make sure that the switch rubber grommets are correctly located in the upper shroud (photo).

23   Steering column (without height adjustment) – overhaul

Note: *Renewal of the upper bearing may be carried out without removing the complete column, however it must be removed to renew the lower bush*

1   Remove the steering wheel as described in Section 21.
2   Remove the screws and withdraw the shroud sections from the

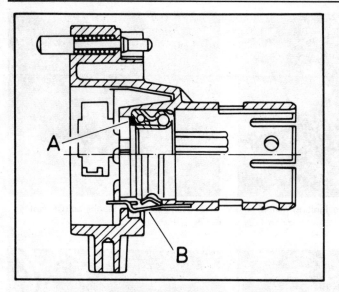

Fig. 10.15 Correct position of thrustwasher (A) and contact spring (B) in the switch housing (Sec 23)

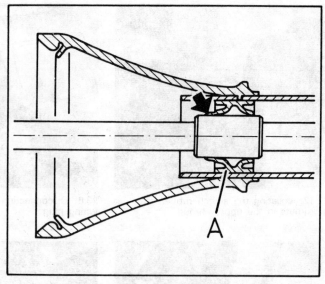

Fig. 10.16 Cross section of the lower column bush (A) showing long sealing lip (arrowed) (Sec 23)

steering column.

3   With the ignition key inserted and at position II, depress the small detent spring and pull out the lock cylinder.

4   Depress the plastic clips and remove both the direction indicator switch and windscreen wiper switch. There is no need to disconnect the switch wiring.

5   Remove the spring and washer from the inner column.

6   Using a screwdriver prise the top and bottom safety plugs from the outer column.

7   Turn the switch housing anti-clockwise and remove it from the outer column.

8   Disconnect the ignition switch wiring plug (photo), then unscrew the two grub screws and remove the ignition switch.

9   Mount the switch housing in a vice and press out the bearing while lifting the locking lugs and contact springs.

10   Press in the new bearing making sure that the locking lugs and contact springs are correctly seated, and the thrust washer is located at the upper end of the housing.

11   If it is required to renew the lower column bush remove the complete column with reference to Section 22, and withdraw the rubber gaiter and inner column. Depress the two plastic tabs and remove the bush and foam seal.

12   Fit the new bush and foam seal to the outer column with the long sealing lip pointing downwards. Fill the internal cavity with multi-purpose grease.

13   Reassembly is a reversal of dismantling but observe the instructions given in Section 22, paragraph 12.

24 Steering column (with height adjustment) – overhaul

Note: *Renewal of the upper bearing may be carried out without removing the complete column, however it must be removed to renew the lower bush.*

1   Remove the steering wheel as described in Section 21.

2   Unscrew the hand adjustment lever for the steering wheel height adjustment (photo).

3   Remove the screws and withdraw the shroud sections from the steering column.

4   With the ignition key inserted and at position II, depress the small detent spring and pull out the lock cylinder.

5   Disconnect the ignition switch wiring plug, then unscrew the two grub screws and remove the ignition switch (photo).

6   Using a Torx key, unscrew the switch housing mounting bolts.

7   Depress the plastic clips and remove both the direction indicator switch and windscreen wiper switch. There is no need to disconnect the switch wiring.

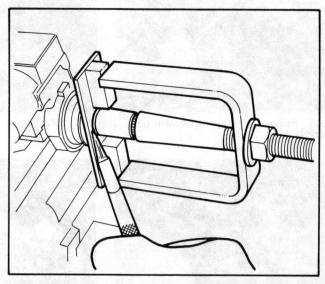

Fig. 10.17 Removing the height adjuster circlip (Sec 24)

8   For further dismantling remove the complete column with reference to Section 22, and withdraw the rubber gaiter.

9   To renew the lower bush, depress the two plastic tabs and slide the bush off the lower end of the inner column. Fill the inner cavity of the new bush with multi-purpose grease and fit it to the outer column with the long sealing lip pointing downwards.

10   To remove the height adjuster mechanism the upper spring must be compressed in order to extract the circlip. The GM tool for doing this is shown in Fig. 10.17 and a similar tool may be made using a metal plate and the existing steering wheel retaining nut.

11   With the circlip removed, withdraw the depressor ring, spring, pressure ring, and bearing ring.

12   Compress the height adjustment spring and remove it. The spring is very strong and care must be taken to prevent it flying out.

13   Pull out the pivot pins and remove the bearing housing.

14   If necessary the steering lock housing may be removed by drilling out the shear-bolts. Coat the threads of the new bolts with locking fluid, fit the new housing and tighten the bolts until the heads shear off. Note that the ball bearings cannot be renewed separately from the housing.

15   Remove the adjustment lever and detent levers from the bearing housing.

16   If necessary separate the universal joint halves. The inner bearing may be driven off the upper column stub and renewed.

17   Reassembly is a reversal of dismantling but note the following:

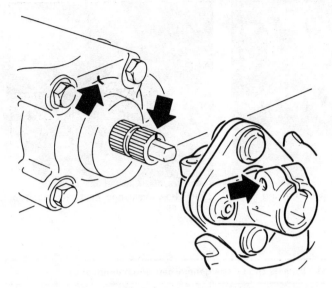

Fig. 10.18 Centre alignment marks on the worm shaft and housing (Sec 25)

(a) *After fitting the pivot pins stake them at three points to secure.*
(b) *After renewing the steering lock housing check that the gap between the two stop buffers and housing is equal using a feeler gauge. If not, compensate by fitting a stop buffer of different thickness.*
(c) *If the complete steering column has been removed observe the instructions given in Section 22, paragraph 12 when refitting.*

25   Steering gear – removal and refitting

1   Working inside the vehicle by the foot pedals lift the cover, then unscrew and remove the clamp bolt from the steering column flexible coupling.
2   Position a container beneath the steering gear to catch any spilt fluid.
3   Identify the pressure and return lines for location then unscrew the union nuts and pull the lines from the steering gear. Plug the line ends and steering gear ports.
4   Apply the handbrake then jack up the front of the vehicle and support it on axle stands.
5   On models fitted with ABS remove the front exhaust downpipe with reference to Chapter 3.
6   Unscrew the nut securing the steering drop arm to the bottom of the steering gear, then use a suitable puller to pull the arm from the splines on the sector shaft (photo).
7   Unscrew the mounting bolts and nut and withdraw the steering gear downwards from under the vehicle (photo). Recover any shims fitted to the upper stud. On some models it may be necessary to remove an exhaust heat shield first.
8   Unscrew the clamp bolt and remove the flexible coupling from the steering gear.
9   Commence refitting by locating the flexible coupling on the worm shaft splines, so that the clamp bolt hole on the **column side** of the coupling is horizontally on top with the worm shaft in its central position. The shaft and housing are marked as shown in Fig. 10.18. Insert and tighten the clamp bolt, but check that the rubber cap on the steering gear is not pressed against the housing.
10   With the steering wheel centralised lift the steering gear into its position and engage the flexible coupling with the inner column.
11   Insert the mounting bolts and hand-tighten.
12   Refit the removed shims and hand-tighten the upper mounting nut.
13   Tighten the flexible coupling upper clamp bolt followed by the

steering gear mounting bolts and nut to the specified torque.
14   Refit the exhaust heat shield where applicable.
15   Refit the steering drop arm to the sector shaft and tighten the nut to the specified torque.
16   Refit the front exhaust downpipe on models fitted with ABS.
17   Lower the vehicle to the ground.
18   Remove the plugs, refit the pressure and return lines, and tighten the union nuts to the specified torque.
19   Refit the cover to the bulkhead.
20   Check and if necessary top up the fluid level in the power steering fluid reservoir. Refit the cap.
21   With the engine idling, turn the steering from lock to lock several times in order to bleed trapped air from the system, then recheck and top-up the fluid level.

26   Steering gear – adjustment in situ

1   The steering gear may be adjusted whilst in the vehicle. First jack up the front of the car and support it on axle stands.
2   Unscrew the nut securing the steering drop arm to the bottom of the steering gear, then use a suitable puller to pull the arm from the splines on the sector shaft.
3   Prise the horn pad from the centre of the steering wheel.
4   Centralise the steering wheel by turning it from lock to lock then halving the number of turns. Turn the steering wheel approximately one turn anti-clockwise from centre.
5   Using a torque meter on the steering wheel nut, measure and record the turning torque. Now measure the torque while passing through the centre position. The second torque should be between 50 and 80 Ncm (4.4 and 7.1 lbf in) greater than the first, and the torque recorded should be between 110 and 150 Ncm (9.7 and 13.3 lbf in).
6   If necessary, adjust the sector shaft adjustment screw on the steering gear as required, then tighten the locknut and recheck the setting.
7   Refit the drop arm and tighten the nut to the specified torque, then lower the vehicle to the ground.

27   Steering tie-rods – removal and refitting

1   Apply the handbrake, jack up the front of the vehicle and support it on axle stands. Remove the front wheels.
2   To remove a side tie-rod unscrew the nuts and use a proprietary balljoint removal tool to press out the ball-pins (photo). If it is required to renew just one tie-rod end, disconnect the appropriate end only.
3   Loosen the clamp bolts and unscrew the tie-rod ends, counting the exact number of turns required to remove them.
4   To remove the centre tie-rod, the side tie-rods must first be disconnected at their inner ends as described in paragraph 2.
5   Unscrew the nuts and disconnect the tie-rod from the drop arm and idler arm using the balljoint removal tool (photo).
6   Refitting is a reversal of removal, but use new self-locking nuts and tighten all nuts and bolts to the specified torques. On completion check and if necessary adjust the front wheel toe-in setting as described in Section 30.

28   Steering idler – removal and refitting

1   Apply the handbrake, jack up the front of the vehicle and support on axle stands. Remove the left-hand wheel.
2   Disconnect the centre tie-rod by unscrewing the nut and using a balljoint removal tool to press out the ball-pin (photo).
3   Unscrew the nut from the bottom of the idler bracket, and remove the heat shield followed by the idler arm. It is not possible to renew the bush separately from the arm.
4   If necessary, unbolt the idler bracket from the underbody.
5   Refitting is a reversal of removal, but use new self-locking nuts, and tighten nuts and bolts to the specified torques. When fitting the idler bracket bolts apply a little locking compound to their threads.

29.3A Loosening the adjustment rod outer nut

29.3B Removing the power steering pump drivebelt

29.10 Power steering fluid reservoir cap and dipstick

29 Power steering pump – removal and refitting

1   Loosen the two pivot bolts on top of the pump.
2   Loosen the tensioner nut and bolt under the pump, and the inner adjustment rod nut.
3   Unscrew the outer nut on the adjustment rod until the drivebelt can be released from the two pulleys (photos).
4   Position a container beneath the pump, then unscrew the union nut and disconnect the pressure pipe. Loosen the clip and disconnect the supply hose. Drain the fluid into the container.
5   Support the pump and remove the three mounting bolts. Withdraw the pump from the engine compartment.
6   Refit the pump using a reversal of the removal procedure, however leave the mounting bolts loose until completing the following tensioning procedure.
7   With the drivebelt on the two pulleys, unscrew the inner adjustment locknut then tighten the outer adjustment locknut until there is approximately 13.0 mm (0.5 in) movement under firm thumb pressure mid-way between the pulleys. Ideally a tension gauge should be used to set the drivebelt to the correct tension, but the above method should be satisfactory. Tighten the inner locknut on completion.
8   Tighten all nuts and bolts to the specified torques.
9   Pour fresh fluid into the reservoir to the maximum level. Start the engine briefly, then switch off and top-up the fluid level. Do this several times until the level remains constant. With the engine idling, slowly turn the steering several times from lock to lock in order to purge air from the system.
10   With the engine stopped top up the fluid to the hot or cold level on the dipstick depending on the temperature of the engine (photo).Refit the cap on completion.

30 Wheel alignment – checking and adjustment

1   Accurate wheel alignment is essential for good steering and to prevent excessive tyre wear. Before checking it, make sure that the car is only loaded to kerbside weight and that the tyre pressures are correct.
2   Camber and castor angles are best checked by a garage using specialised equipment. The castor angle is not adjustable but the camber angle is.
3   The toe-in setting may be checked as follows. Place the car on level ground with the wheels in the straight-ahead position, then roll the car backwards 4 metres (13 feet) and forwards again.
4   Using an accurate wheel alignment gauge, check that the front wheels are aligned as given in the Specifications.
5   If adjustment is necessary loosen the clamp bolts on the side tie-rods and turn the adjustment tubes by equal amounts. Both tie-rods must be equal in length.
6   After making an adjustment, centralise the balljoints and tighten the clamp bolts.

31 Wheels and tyres – general care and maintenance

Wheels and tyres should give no real problems in use provided that a close eye is kept on them with regard to excessive wear or damage. To this end, the following points should be noted.

Ensure that tyre pressures are checked regularly and maintained correctly. Checking should be carried out with the tyres cold and not immediately after the vehicle has been in use. If the pressures are checked with the tyres hot, an apparently high reading will be obtained owing to heat expansion. Under no circumstances should an attempt be made to reduce the pressures to the quoted cold reading in this instance, or effective underinflation will result.

Underinflation will cause overheating of the tyre owing to excessive flexing of the casing, and the tread will not sit correctly on the road surface. This will cause a consequent loss of adhesion and excessive wear, not to mention the danger of sudden tyre failure due to heat build-up.

Overinflation will cause rapid wear of the centre part of the tyre tread coupled with reduced adhesion, harsher ride, and the danger of shock damage occurring in the tyre casing.

Regularly check the tyres for damage in the form of cuts or bulges, especially in the sidewalls. Remove any nails or stones embedded in the tread before they penetrate the tyre to cause deflation. If removal of a nail *does* reveal that the tyre has been punctured, refit the nail so that its point of penetration is marked. Then immediately change the wheel and have the tyre repaired by a tyre dealer. Do *not* drive on a tyre in such a condition. In many cases a puncture can be simply repaired by the use of an inner tube of the correct size and type. If in any doubt as to the possible consequences of any damage found, consult your local tyre dealer for advice.

Periodically remove the wheels and clean any dirt or mud from the inside and outside surfaces. Examine the wheel rims for signs of rusting, corrosion or other damage. Light alloy wheels are easily damaged by 'kerbing' whilst parking, and similarly steel wheels may become dented or buckled. Renewal of the wheel is very often the only course of remedial action possible.

The balance of each wheel and tyre assembly should be maintained to avoid excessive wear, not only to the tyres but also to the steering and suspension components. Wheel imbalance is normally signified by vibration through the vehicle's bodyshell, although in many cases it is particularly noticeable through the steering wheel. Conversely, it should be noted that wear or damage in suspension or steering components may cause excessive tyre wear. Out-of-round or out-of-true tyres, damaged wheels and wheel bearing wear/maladjustment also fall into this category. Balancing will not usually cure vibration caused by such wear.

Wheel balancing may be carried out with the wheel either on or off the vehicle. If balanced on the vehicle, ensure that the wheel-to-hub relationship is marked in some way prior to subsequent wheel removal so that it may be refitted in its original position.

General tyre wear is influenced to a large degree by driving style – harsh braking and acceleration or fast cornering will all produce more rapid tyre wear. Interchanging of tyres may result in more even wear, but this should only be carried out where there is no mix of tyre types on the vehicle. However, it is worth bearing in mind that if this is completely effective, the added expense of replacing a complete set of tyres simultaneously is incurred, which may prove financially restrictive for many owners.

Front tyres may wear unevenly as a result of wheel misalignment. The front wheels should always be correctly aligned according to the settings specified by the vehicle manufacturer.

Legal restrictions apply to the mixing of tyre types on a vehicle. Basically this means that a vehicle must not have tyres of differing construction on the same axle. Although it is not recommended to mix tyre types between front axle and rear axle, the only legally permissible combination is crossply at the front and radial at the rear. When mixing radial ply tyres, textile braced radials must always go on the front axle, with steel braced radials at the rear. An obvious disadvantage of such mixing is the necessity to carry two spare tyres to avoid contravening the law in the event of a puncture.

In the UK, the Motor Vehicles Construction and Use Regulations apply to many aspects of tyre fitting and usage. It is suggested that a copy of these regulations is obtained from your local police if in doubt as to the current legal requirements with regard to tyre condition, minimum tread depth, etc.

32   Fault diagnosis – suspension and steering

Symptom	Reason(s)
Excessive play in steering	Worn or maladjusted steering gear
	Worn tie-rod balljoints
	Worn lower suspension arm balljoints
	Worn flexible coupling
Wanders or pulls to one side	Incorrect wheel alignment
	Worn tie-rod balljoints
	Worn lower suspension arm balljoints
	Uneven tyre pressures
	Faulty shock absorber
Heavy or stiff steering	Seized tie-rod or suspension balljoint
	Incorrect wheel alignment
	Low tyre pressures
	Lack of lubricant in steering gear
	Faulty power steering system
Wheel wobble and vibration	Roadwheels out of balance or damaged
	Faulty shock absorbers
	Worn wheel bearings
	Worn tie-rod or suspension balljoint
Excessive tyre wear	Incorrect wheel alignment
	Faulty shock absorbers
	Incorrect tyre pressures
	Roadwheels out of balance

Chapter 11 Bodywork and fittings

For modifications, and information applicable to later models, see Supplement at end of manual

Contents

Specifications

Torque wrench settings

	Nm	lbf ft
Air conditioning compressor to bracket:		
Front	35	26
Rear	25	19
Air conditioning compressor bracket to engine	40	30
Hose plate to air conditioning compressor	25	19
Bonnet hinge:		
To bonnet	20	15
To bulkhead	25	19
Seat belts	35	26
Bumpers	12	9

---

1 General description

The bodyshell is of all-steel welded construction, treated extensively for corrosion protection. One unusual feature is that the bulkhead assembly is glued to the bodyshell using the same glue as for bending the windscreen in position. The manufacturing process includes the use of robots and electronic measurement equipment.

2 Routine maintenance

1 Carry out the following procedures at the intervals given in *Routine maintenance* at the front of this manual.
2 Lubricate the door hinges, bonnet hinges, and boot lid or tailgate hinges with a little oil.
3 Apply a little grease to the contact surfaces of all locks, strikers and door check arms (photo).
4 Examine the air conditioning hoses and pipes for damage and deterioration.
5 Remove the radiator grille (Section 11), and use a soft brush to clean any leaves or debris from the condenser. On completion refit the grille.
6 Raise the front and rear of the vehicle and check the underbody for damage and corrosion. Check the condition of the underseal.

such dulling is usually caused because regular washing has been neglected. Care needs to be taken with metallic paintwork, as special non-abrasive cleaner/polisher is required to avoid damage to the finish. Always check that the door and ventilator opening drain holes and pipes are completely clear so that water can be drained out. Bright work should be treated in the same way as paint work. Windscreens and windows can be kept clear of the smeary film which often appears by the use of a proprietary glass cleaner like Holts Mixra. Never use any form of wax or other body or chromium polish on glass.

2.3 Lubricating the bonnet lock

4 Maintenance – upholstery and carpets

Mats and carpets should be brushed or vacuum cleaned regularly to keep them free of grit. If they are badly stained remove them from the vehicle for scrubbing or sponging and make quite sure they are dry before refitting. Seats and interior trim panels can be kept clean by wiping with a damp cloth and Turtle Wax Carisma. If they do become stained (which can be more apparent on light coloured upholstery) use a little liquid detergent and a soft nail brush to scour the grime out of the grain of the material. Do not forget to keep the headlining clean in the same way as the upholstery. When using liquid cleaners inside the vehicle do not over-wet the surfaces being cleaned. Excessive damp could get into the seams and padded interior causing stains, offensive odours or even rot. If the inside of the vehicle gets wet accidentally it is worthwhile taking some trouble to dry it out properly, particularly where carpets are involved. *Do not leave oil or electric heaters inside the vehicle for this purpose.*

3 Maintenance – bodywork and underframe

The general condition of a vehicle's bodywork is the one thing that significantly affects its value. Maintenance is easy but needs to be regular. Neglect, particularly after minor damage, can lead quickly to further deterioration and costly repair bills. It is important also to keep watch on those parts of the vehicle not immediately visible, for instance the underside, inside all the wheel arches and the lower part of the engine compartment.

The basic maintenance routine for the bodywork is washing – preferably with a lot of water, from a hose. This will remove all the loose solids which may have stuck to the vehicle. It is important to flush these off in such a way as to prevent grit from scratching the finish. The wheel arches and underframe need washing in the same way to remove any accumulated mud which will retain moisture and tend to encourage rust. Paradoxically enough, the best time to clean the underframe and wheel arches is in wet weather when the mud is thoroughly wet and soft. In very wet weather the underframe is usually cleaned of large accumulations automatically and this is a good time for inspection.

Periodically, except on vehicles with a wax-based underbody protective coating, it is a good idea to have the whole of the underframe of the vehicle steam cleaned, engine compartment included, so that a thorough inspection can be carried out to see what minor repairs and renovations are necessary. Steam cleaning is available at many garages and is necessary for removal of the accumulation of oily grime which sometimes is allowed to become thick in certain areas. If steam cleaning facilities are not available, there are one or two excellent grease solvents available, such as Holts Engine Cleaner or Holts Foambrite, which can be brush applied. The dirt can then be simply hosed off. Note that these methods should not be used on vehicles with wax-based underbody protective coating or the coating will be removed. Such vehicles should be inspected annually, preferably just prior to winter, when the underbody should be washed down and any damage to the wax coating repaired using Holts Undershield. Ideally, a completely fresh coat should be applied. It would also be worth considering the use of such wax-based protection for injection into door panels, sills, box sections, etc, as an additional safeguard against rust damage where such protection is not provided by the vehicle manufacturer.

After washing paintwork, wipe off with a chamois leather to give an unspotted clear finish. A coat of clear protective wax polish, like the many excellent Turtle Wax polishes, will give added protection against chemical pollutants in the air. If the paintwork sheen has dulled or oxidised, use a cleaner/polisher combination such as Turtle Extra to restore the brilliance of the shine. This requires a little effort, but

5 Minor body damage – repair

The colour bodywork repair sequences between pages 32 and 33 illustrate the operations detailed in the following sub-sections.
Note: *For more detailed information about bodywork repair, the Haynes Publishing Group publish a book by Lindsay Porter called The Car Bodywork Repair Manual. This incorporates information on such aspects as rust treatment, painting and glass fibre repairs, as well as details on more ambitious repairs involving welding and panel beating.*

Repair of minor scratches in bodywork

If the scratch is very superficial, and does not penetrate to the metal of the bodywork, repair is very simple. Lightly rub the area of the scratch with a paintwork renovator like Turtle Wax New Color Back, or a very fine cutting paste like Holts Body + Plus Rubbing Compound to remove loose paint from the scratch and to clear the surrounding bodywork of wax polish. Rinse the area with clean water.

Apply touch-up paint, such as Holts Dupli-Color Color Touch or a paint film like Holts Autofilm, to the scratch using a fine paint brush; continue to apply fine layers of paint until the surface of the paint in the scratch is level with the surrounding paintwork. Allow the new paint at least two weeks to harden: then blend it into the surrounding paintwork by rubbing the scratch area with a paintwork renovator or a very fine cutting paste, such as Holts Body + Plus Rubbing Compound or Turtle Wax New Color Back. Finally, apply wax polish from one of the Turtle Wax range of wax polishes.

Where the scratch has penetrated right through to the metal of the bodywork, causing the metal to rust, a different repair technique is required. Remove any loose rust from the bottom of the scratch with a penknife, then apply rust inhibiting paint, such as Turtle Wax Rust Master, to prevent the formation of rust in the future. Using a rubber or nylon applicator fill the scratch with bodystopper paste like Holts Body + Plus Knifing Putty. If required, this paste can be mixed with cellulose thinners, such as Holts Body + Plus Cellulose Thinners, to provide a very thin paste which is ideal for filling narrow scratches. Before the stopper-paste in the scratch hardens, wrap a piece of smooth cotton rag around the top of a finger. Dip the finger in cellulose thinners, such as Holts Body + Plus Cellulose Thinners, and then quickly sweep it across the surface of the stopper-paste in the scratch; this will ensure that the surface of the stopper-paste is slightly hollowed. The scratch can now be painted over as described earlier in this Section.

Repair of dents in bodywork

When deep denting of the vehicle's bodywork has taken place, the first task is to pull the dent out, until the affected bodywork almost attains its original shape. There is little point in trying to restore the original shape completely, as the metal in the damaged area will have stretched on impact and cannot be reshaped fully to its original contour. It is better to bring the level of the dent up to a point which is about ⅛ in (3 mm) below the level of the surrounding bodywork. In cases where the dent is very shallow anyway, it is not worth trying to pull it out at all. If the underside of the dent is accessible, it can be hammered out gently from behind, using a mallet with a wooden or plastic head. Whilst doing this, hold a suitable block of wood firmly against the outside of the panel to absorb the impact from the hammer blows and thus prevent a large area of the bodywork from being 'belled-out'.

Should the dent be in a section of the bodywork which has a double skin or some other factor making it inaccessible from behind, a different technique is called for. Drill several small holes through the metal inside the area – particulary in the deeper section. Then screw long self-tapping screws into the holes just sufficiently for them to gain a good purchase in the metal. Now the dent can be pulled out by pulling on the protruding heads of the screws with a pair of pliers.

The next stage of the repair is the removal of the paint from the damaged area, and from an inch or so of the surrounding 'sound' bodywork. This is accomplished most easily by using a wire brush or abrasive pad on a power drill, although it can be done just as effectively by hand using sheets of abrasive paper. To complete the preparation for filling, score the surface of the bare metal with a screwdriver or the tang of a file, or alternatively, drill small holes in the affected area. This will provide a really good 'key' for the filler paste.

To complete the repair see the Section on filling and re-spraying.

Repair of rust holes or gashes in bodywork

Remove all paint from the affected area and from an inch or so of the surrounding 'sound' bodywork, using an abrasive pad or a wire brush on a power drill. If these are not available a few sheets of abrasive paper will do the job just as effectively. With the paint removed you will be able to gauge the severity of the corrosion and therefore decide whether to renew the whole panel (if this is possible) or to repair the affected area. New body panels are not as expensive as most people think and it is often quicker and more satisfactory to fit a new panel than to attempt to repair large areas of corrosion.

Remove all fittings from the affected area except those which will act as a guide to the original shape of the damaged bodywork (eg headlamp shells etc). Then, using tin snips or a hacksaw blade, remove all loose metal and any other metal badly affected by corrosion. Hammer the edges of the hole inwards in order to create a slight depression for the filler paste.

Wire brush the affected area to remove the powdery rust from the surface of the remaining metal. Paint the affected area with rust inhibiting paint like Turtle Rust Master; if the back of the rusted area is accessible treat this also.

Before filling can take place it will be necessary to block the hole in some way. This can be achieved by the use of aluminium or plastic mesh, or aluminium tape.

Aluminium or plastic mesh or glass fibre matting, such as the Holts Body + Plus Glass Fibre Matting, is probably the best material to use for a large hole. Cut a piece to the approximate size and shape of the hole to be filled, then position it in the hole so that its edges are below the level of the surrounding bodywork. It can be retained in position by several blobs of filler paste around its periphery.

Aluminium tape should be used for small or very narrow holes. Pull a piece off the roll and trim it to the approximate size and shape required, then pull off the backing paper (if used) and stick the tape over the hole; it can be overlapped if the thickness of one piece is insufficient. Burnish down the edges of the tape with the handle of a screwdriver or similar, to ensure that the tape is securely attached to the metal underneath.

Bodywork repairs – filling and re-spraying

Before using this Section, see the Sections on dent, deep scratch, rust holes and gash repairs.

Many types of bodyfiller are available, but generally speaking those proprietary kits which contain a tin of filler paste and a tube of resin hardener are best for this type of repair, like Holts Body + Plus or Holts No Mix which can be used directly from the tube. A wide, flexible plastic or nylon applicator will be found invaluable for imparting a smooth and well contoured finish to the surface of the filler.

Mix up a little filler on a clean piece of card or board – measure the hardener carefully (follow the maker's instructions on the pack) otherwise the filler will set too rapidly or too slowly. Alternatively, Holts No Mix can be used straight from the tube without mixing, but daylight is required to cure it. Using the applicator apply the filler paste to the prepared area; draw the applicator across the surface of the filler to achieve the correct contour and to level the filler surface. As soon as a contour that approximates to the correct one is achieved, stop working the paste – if you carry on too long the paste will become sticky and begin to 'pick up' on the applicator. Continue to add thin layers of filler paste at twenty-minute intervals until the level of the filler is just proud of the surrounding bodywork.

Once the filler has hardened, excess can be removed using a metal plane or file. From then on, progressively finer grades of abrasive paper should be used, starting with a 40 grade production paper and finishing with 400 grade wet-and-dry paper. Always wrap the abrasive paper around a flat rubber, cork, or wooden block – otherwise the surface of the filler will not be completely flat. During the smoothing of the filler surface the wet-and-dry paper should be periodically rinsed in water. This will ensure that a very smooth finish is imparted to the filler at the final stage.

At this stage the 'dent' should be surrounded by a ring of bare metal, which in turn should be encircled by the finely 'feathered' edge of the good paintwork. Rinse the repair area with clean water, until all of the dust produced by the rubbing-down operation has gone.

Spray the whole repair area with a light coat of primer, either Holts Body + Plus Grey or Red Oxide Primer – this will show up any imperfections in the surface of the filler. Repair these imperfections with fresh filler paste or bodystopper, and once more smooth the surface with abrasive paper. If bodystopper is used, it can be mixed with cellulose thinners to form a really thin paste which is ideal for filling small holes. Repeat this spray and repair procedure until you are satisfied that the surface of the filler, and the feathered edge of the paintwork are perfect. Clean the repair area with clean water and allow to dry fully.

The repair area is now ready for final spraying. Paint spraying must be carried out in a warm, dry, windless and dust free atmosphere. This condition can be created artificially if you have access to a large indoor working area, but if you are forced to work in the open, you will have to pick your day very carefully. If you are working indoors, dousing the floor in the work area with water will help to settle the dust which would otherwise be in the atmosphere. If the repair area is confined to one body panel, mask off the surrounding panels; this will help to minimise the effects of a slight mis-match in paint colours. Bodywork fittings (eg chrome strips, door handles etc) will also need to be masked off. Use genuine masking tape and several thicknesses of newspaper for the masking operations.

Before commencing to spray, agitate the aerosol can thoroughly, then spray a test area (an old tin, or similar) until the technique is mastered. Cover the repair area with a thick coat of primer; the thickness should be built up using several thin layers of paint rather than one thick one. Using 400 grade wet-and-dry paper, rub down the surface of the primer until it is really smooth. While doing this, the work area should be thoroughly doused with water, and the wet-and-dry paper periodically rinsed in water. Allow to dry before spraying on more paint.

Spray on the top coat using Holts Dupli-Color Autospray, again building up the thickness by using several thin layers of paint. Start spraying in the centre of the repair area and then, with a single side-to-side motion, work outwards until the whole repair area and about 2 inches of the surrounding original paintwork is covered. Remove all masking material 10 to 15 minutes after spraying on the final coat of paint.

Allow the new paint at least two weeks to harden, then, using a paintwork renovator or a very fine cutting paste such as Turtle Wax New Color Back or Holts Body + Plus Rubbing Compound, blend the edges of the paint into the existing paintwork. Finally, apply wax polish.

Plastic components

With the use of more and more plastic body components by the vehicle manufacturers (eg bumpers, spoilers, and in some cases major

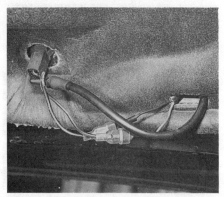

7.2 Heated windscreen washer jet wiring and tubing

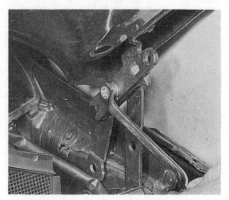

7.3A Unscrew the central bolts ...

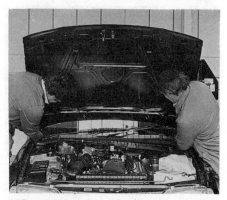

7.3B ... and remove the bonnet

7.5 Bonnet safety catch and striker pin

8.1 Boot lid hinge

8.5A Lock control rod (arrowed) and central locking operating rod

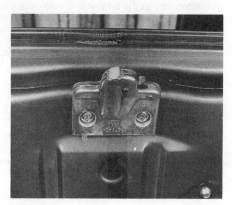

8.5B Boot lid lock

8.6 Boot lid striker

body panels), rectification of more serious damage to such items has become a matter of either entrusting repair work to a specialist in this field, or renewing complete components. Repair of such damage by the DIY owner is not really feasible owing to the cost of the equipment and materials required for effecting such repairs. The basic technique involves making a groove along the line of the crack in the plastic using a rotary burr in a power drill. The damaged part is then welded back together by using a hot air gun to heat up and fuse a plastic filler rod into the groove. Any excess plastic is then removed and the area rubbed down to a smooth finish. It is important that a filler rod of the correct plastic is used, as body components can be made of a variety of different types (eg polycarbonate, ABS, polypropylene).

Damage of a less serious nature (abrasions, minor cracks etc) can be repaired by the DIY owner using a two-part epoxy filler repair material like Holts Body + Plus or Holts No Mix which can be used directly from the tube. Once mixed in equal proportions (or applied

direct from the tube in the case of Holts No Mix), this is used in similar fashion to the bodywork filler used on metal panels. The filler is usually cured in twenty to thirty minutes, ready for sanding and painting.

If the owner is renewing a complete component himself, or if he has repaired it with epoxy filler, he will be left with the problem of finding a suitable paint for finishing which is compatible with the type of plastic used. At one time the use of a universal paint was not possible owing to the complex range of plastics encountered in body component applications. Standard paints, generally speaking, will not bond to plastic or rubber satisfactorily, but Holts Professional Spraymatch paints to match any plastic or rubber finish can be obtained from dealers. However, it is now possible to obtain a plastic body parts finishing kit which consists of a pre-primer treatment, a primer and coloured top coat. Full instructions are normally supplied with a kit, but basically the method of use is to first apply the pre-primer to the

9.2 Disconnecting the tailgate struts

9.5 Tailgate hinge

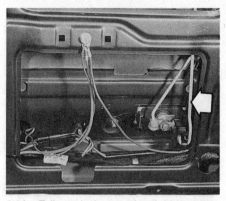

9.6A Tailgate lock control rod (arrowed) and central locking operating rod

9.6B Tailgate lock

9.7A Removing the plastic protector ...

9.7B ... for access to the tailgate striker

component concerned and allow it to dry for up to 30 minutes. Then the primer is applied and left to dry for about an hour before finally applying the special coloured top coat. The result is a correctly coloured component where the paint will flex with the plastic or rubber, a property that standard paint does not normally possess.

6 Major body damage – repair

Where serious damage has occurred or large areas need renewal due to neglect, it means that completely new sections or panels will need welding in, and this is best left to professionals. If the damage is due to impact, it will also be necessary to completely check the alignment of the bodyshell structure. Due to the principle of construction, the strength and shape of the whole car can be affected by damage to one part. In such instances the services of a GM dealer with specialist checking jigs are essential. If a body is left misaligned, it is first of all dangerous as the car will not handle properly, and secondly uneven stresses will be imposed on the steering, engine and transmission, causing abnormal wear or complete failure. Tyre wear may also be excessive.

7 Bonnet – removal and refitting

1   Support the bonnet in its open position and place some cardboard or rags beneath the corners.
2   As applicable, disconnect the wiring and tubing from the engine compartment light and washer jets and feed through the bonnet frame (photo).
3   With the help of an assistant, support the bonnet then unscrew the single central bolts on both hinges and lift the bonnet from the car (photos).
4   If the hinges remain undisturbed on the bonnet and body, no adjustment will be necessary when refitting the bonnet, however if the

hinge sections require renewal, unbolt them.
5   Refitting is a reversal of removal. If necessary, adjust the hinge positions so that the bonnet is central within its aperture, and aligned with the surrounding bodywork. The height of the front edge of the bonnet can be adjusted by the two screw- in rubber grommets. Check that the dimension between the striker pin nut and washer is 45.0 mm (1.77 in), and if necessary adjust it by loosening the nut and turning the pin (photo).

8 Boot lid – removal and refitting

1   Open the boot lid and mark the position of the bolts on the hinges with a pencil (photo).
2   On models fitted with a rear spoiler, disconnect the pneumatic strut.
3   With the help of an assistant unscrew the hinge bolts and withdraw the boot lid.
4   The torsion springs may be removed if necessary, however it is recommended that the special GM tools KM-125 and KM-614 are used as the use of inappropriate tools may result in personal injury. The tools enable the torsion springs to be unhooked from their locations.
5   If necessary the lock may be removed by disconnecting the control rod and unscrewing the mounting screws (photos).
6   Refitting is a reversal of removal. Check that the boot lid is central in its aperture and aligned with the surrounding bodywork. Check that the striker enters the lock centrally, and if necessary adjust its position (photo).

9 Tailgate – removal and refitting

1   Support the tailgate in its open position.
2   Disconnect the struts by prising out the spring clips (photo).
3   Remove the trim panel (Section 10).
4   Disconnect the wiring, and washer tubing.

10.1A Removing the tailgate speakers

10.1B Tailgate speaker wires

10.2 Removing the tailgate trim panel screws

10.3 Tailgate speaker mounting frame

11.2 Removing the radiator grille upper mounting screws

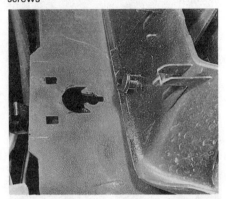

11.3 Releasing the radiator grille from the front bumper

12.2 Method of releasing the window regulator handle spring clip

12.3 Removing the window regulator handle collar

12.5 Locking knob surround removal

5 With the help of an assistant remove the hinge clips, drive out the pins and withdraw the tailgate from the car (photo).
6 The lock may be removed by disconnecting the control rod and removing the four retaining screws (photos).
7 Access to the striker is gained by removing the screws and rear plastic protector. The striker may then be unbolted (photos).
8 Refitting is a reversal of removal, but adjust the striker so that it enters the lock centrally.

10 Tailgate trim panel – removal and refitting

1 Open the tailgate and remove the speakers by extracting the screws with an Allen key and disconnecting the speaker wires (photos).
2 Remove the screws and withdraw the trim panel (photo).
3 If necessary unbolt the speaker mounting frames (photo).
4 Refitting is a reversal of removal.

11 Radiator grille – removal and refitting

1 Open the bonnet.
2 Remove the upper mounting screws (photos).
3 Push the bottom of the grille inwards to release it from the front bumper, then lift it away (photo).
4 Refitting is a reversal of removal.

12 Door trim panel – removal and refitting

1 Where manually operated windows are fitted fully close the window and note the position of the regulator handle.
2 Draw a piece of cloth behind the handle to release the spring clip, then remove the handle (photo).
3 Remove the collar (photo).

12.6A Prise out the inner door handle fingerplate ...

12.6B ... for access to the screw (arrowed)

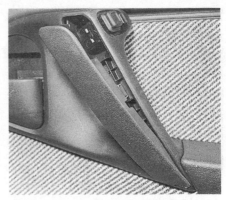

12.7A Prise out the plastic insert ...

12.7B ... and remove the screws (arrowed)

12.8 Removing the exterior mirror control switch

12.9 Disconnecting an electric window switch on a rear door

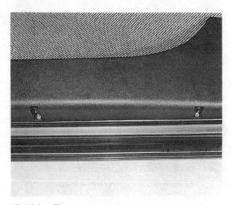

12.10A Door pocket lower screws ...

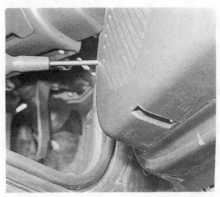

12.10B ... and front screw removal

12.11 Using the special tool to prise off the door trim panel

4 Disconnect the locking knob from the control rod. To do this it should be possible to prise out the red plastic insert, then to remove the knob from the rod. In most instances however, it will be found that this action breaks the insert, necessitating its renewal.

5 With the knob removed unscrew the screw and remove the surround (photos).

6 Prise out the inner door handle finger plate and remove the screw (photos).

7 Prise the plastic insert from the grip and remove the exposed screws (photos).

8 Where applicable extract the exterior mirror control switch and disconnect the wires (photo).

9 Where applicable prise out the electric window switch and disconnect the wiring (photo).

10 Where applicable remove the door pocket screws (photos). Also release the rear clip inside the pocket.

11 Using a wide blade screwdriver or a purpose-made tool (photo) prise the trim panel from the door. To avoid breakage of the plastic clips, insert the tool as near to them as possible.

12 Remove the trim panel while slightly opening the inner door handle. As applicable, disconnect the switch wiring plugs (photos).

13 Refitting is a reversal of removal. When refitting the locking knob, pull up the control rod to its unlocked position, locate the knob on the rod so that the red insert slot is just showing, then press in the insert.

12.12A Slightly open the inner door handle when removing the door trim panel

12.12B Door trim panel switch wiring plug

12.13A Door locking knob and red plastic insert

12.13B Pull up the control rod (arrowed) ...

12.13C ... then refit the locking knob and press in the insert

12.13D Refitting the window regulator handle (with spring clip fitted)

13.2 Using an Allen key to unscrew the door speaker screws

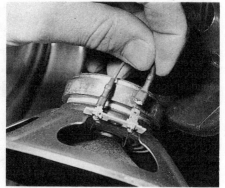

13.3 Disconnecting the door speaker wires

13.4A Remove the screws ...

When refitting the window regulator handle, fit the spring clip and press the handle directly onto the splined shaft (photos).

13 Door speaker – removal and refitting

1 Remove the door trim panel as described in Section 12.
2 Using an Allen key unscrew the mounting screws (photo).
3 Withdraw the speaker and disconnect the wiring noting which way round the wires are connected (photo).
4 Remove the screws and withdraw the enclosure (photos).
5 Refitting is a reversal of removal.

14 Inner door handle – removal and refitting

1 Remove the door trim panel as described in Section 12.
2 Push the handle forwards and release it from the aperture in the door, then twist it to release it from the control rod (photos).
3 Refitting is a reversal of removal.

15 Exterior door handle – removal and refitting

1 Remove the door trim panel as described in Section 12.
2 Disconnect the control rods.

13.4B ... and remove the speaker enclosure

14.2A Push the inner door handle forwards ...

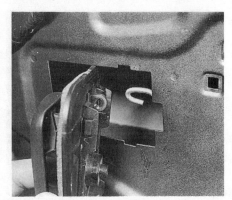

14.2B ... and disconnect it from the control rod

15.3 Exterior door handle retaining clip (arrowed)

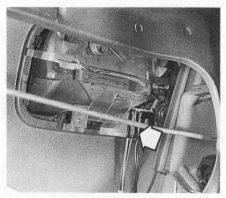

16.2 Central locking solenoid unit on the door handle fingerplate (arrowed)

17.3A Front door lock mounting Torx screws

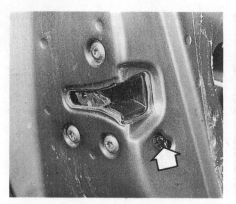

17.3B Rear door lock mounting screws, and child safety latch (arrowed)

17.4 Door lock striker

18.3 Extract the pin (arrowed) to release the door check arm

3   Slide out the retaining clip and remove the handle from the outside (photo).
4   Refitting is a reversal of removal.

16 Front door lock cylinder – removal and refitting

1   Remove the door trim panel (Section 12) and the exterior door handle (Section 15). Peel back the plastic membrane as far as required.
2   Remove the door handle fingerplate. Disconnect the central locking

solenoid wires where applicable (photo).
3   Extract the circlips and remove the lock cylinder from the fingerplate.
4   Refitting is a reversal of removal.

17 Door lock – removal and refitting

1   Remove the door trim panel (Section 12). Peel back the plastic membrane as far as required.

18.5 Door hinge

20.2A Window regulator adjustment bolts

20.2B Electrically operated window regulator

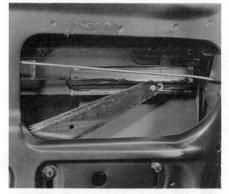

20.2C Window regulator arm connection to glass channel

20.5 Front door window guide rail and bolt (arrowed)

21.4 Rear door window guide rail

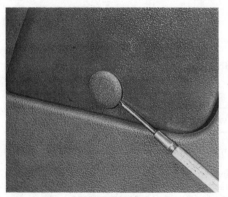

22.1 Prise out the cap ...

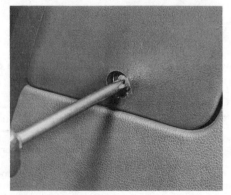

22.2 ... and remove the cover screw

22.3 Exterior mirror retaining screws (arrowed)

2 Disconnect the control rods from the lock, and on 1988-on models, disconnect the wiring connector from the central locking servo motor.

3 Using a Torx bit, undo the screws and withdraw the lock assembly from inside the door (photo).

4 Refitting is a reversal of the removal procedure, noting that on 1988-on models equipped with central locking, prior to refitting the lock assembly, the servo motor should be adjusted as described in Chapter 13. On all models, on completion check that the striker enters the lock centrally, and adjust if necessary.

18 Door – removal and refitting

1 Remove the door trim panel (Section 12). Peel back the plastic membrane as far as required.

2 Disconnect the wiring for the electric mirror, electric window, door-mounted speakers, and central locking as applicable.

3 Disconnect the check arm from the door pillar by extracting the pin (photo).

4 Support the door on blocks of wood.

5 Remove the lower caps and use a suitable drift to drive out the hinge pins in an upwards direction (photo). Withdraw the door from the car.

6 Refitting is a reversal of removal. Check that the striker enters the lock centrally, and if necessary, adjust its position.

19 Windscreen and tailgate/rear window – removal and refitting

The windscreen and tailgate/rear windows are bonded to the body

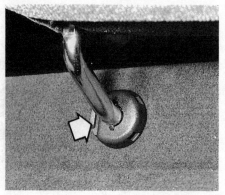

25.1 Headrest arm and side plunger (arrowed)

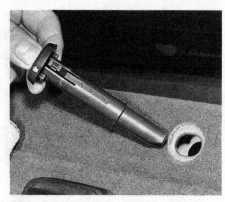

25.2 Removing the headrest guide

26.19A Removing the luggage cover

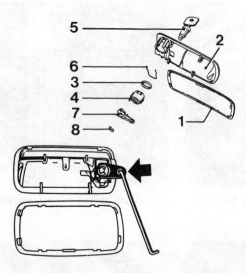

Fig. 11.1 Front door lock cylinder components (Sec 16)

1	Seal	5	Lock cylinder
2	Fingerplate	6	Circlip
3	Ring	7	Carrier
4	Housing	8	Circlip

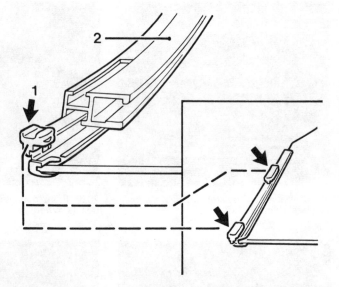

Fig. 11.2 Front door window guide stops (1) and guide rail (2) (Sec 20)

using special adhesive. Purpose-made tools are required to remove the old glass and to fit the new glass, therefore this work is best entrusted to a specialist.

20 Front door window – removal and refitting

1   Remove the door trim panel (Section 12) and peel back the plastic membrane.
2   Remove the window regulator by unscrewing the bolts, drilling out the rivets, and disconnecting the arms from the bottom glass channels. On electrically operated windows, disconnect the wiring (photos).
3   Remove the exterior mirror (Section 22).
4   Carefully remove the weatherseal strip and moulding from the door.
5   Unbolt and remove the front guide rail (photo).
6   Lift the window from the door.
7   Refitting is a reversal of the removal. Check that the rail and stops are correctly fitted to the front edge of the window. Adjust the position of the regulator so that the upper edge of the window is parallel to the upper door frame. Check that the window operates smoothly.

21 Rear door window – removal and refitting

1   Remove the door trim panel (Section 12) and peel back the plastic membrane.
2   Remove the window regulator by unscrewing the bolts, drilling out the rivets, and disconnecting the arms from the bottom glass channels. On electrically operated windows, disconnect the wiring.
3   Carefully remove the weatherseal strips and moulding from the door.
4   Lower the window then unbolt and remove the centre guide rail (photo).
5   Lift the window from the door.
6   Refitting is a reversal of removal. Make sure that the window stops are not pushed off of the centre guide rail. Check that the window operates smoothly.

22 Door exterior mirror – removal and refitting

1   Prise out the screw cap (photo).
2   Remove the screw and unclip the plastic cover (photo).
3   Support the exterior mirror, then unscrew the three cross-head screws and remove the mirror (photo). Note that, on electrically-operated mirrors, it will be necessary to disconnect the wiring connector as the mirror is removed.
4   Refitting is a reversal of removal.

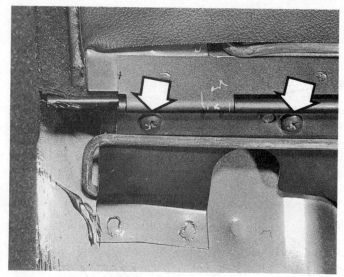

26.19B Roller channel screws (arrowed)

26.19C Luggage cover lock

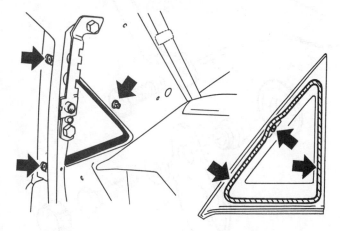

Fig. 11.3 Rear side windows cap nut locations (Sec 23)

23 Rear side window – removal and refitting

1 Remove the trim strip from the bottom of the side window.
2 Working inside the car remove the inner trim panels and the rear seat belt guide. Where necessary, also remove the outer seat upholstery.
3 Unscrew the cap nuts and withdraw the window outwards.
4 Refitting is a reversal of removal.

24 Rear door fixed window – removal and refitting

1 Remove the door trim panel (Section 12) and peel back the plastic membrane as far as necessary.
2 With the window lowered, unscrew the middle and upper screws holding the rear window guide channel. Push the channel forwards.
3 Prise out the upper and lower weatherseal strips, and withdraw the window forwards.
4 Refitting is a reversal of removal, but apply soapy water to the window channels when inserting the window.

25 Rear headrest guides – removal and refitting

1 Depress the side plungers, and withdraw the headrest from the

28.1 Front seat mounting bolt removal

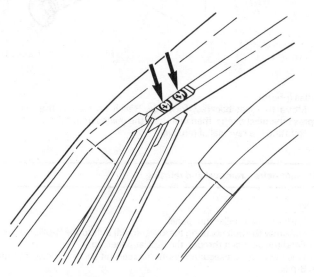

Fig. 11.4 Rear window guide channel upper screws (Sec 24)

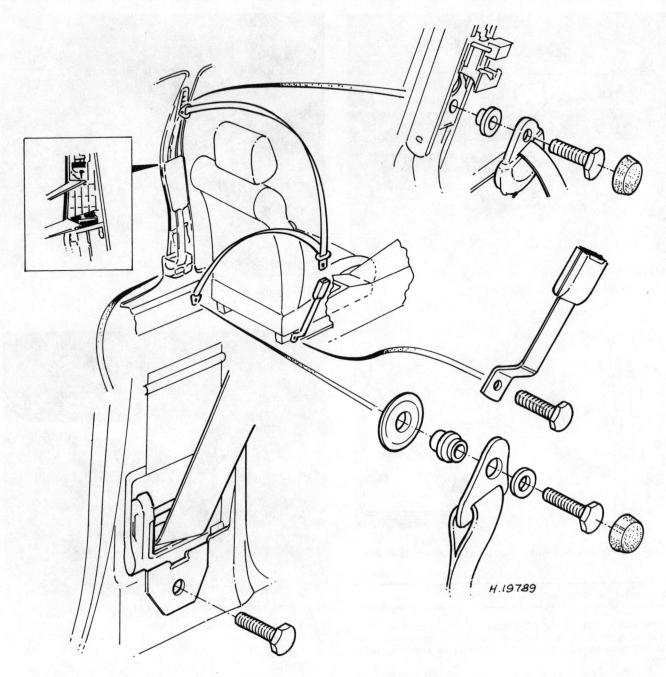

H.19789

Fig. 11.5 Front seat belt components (Sec 26)

guides (photo).
2   Move the seat backrest forwards. Reach up behind the guides, depress the plastic tabs, then withdraw the guides (photo).
3   Refitting is a reversal of removal.

26   Seat belts – removal and refitting

Front

1   Remove the B-pillar trim panel.
2   Unscrew the bolt securing the lower (rigid) belt to the B-pillar.
3   Feed the seat belt through the B-pillar panelling.
4   Unscrew the bolt securing the inertia reel unit and withdraw it from the B-pillar.
5   Unscrew the belt from the height adjuster.

6   To remove the seat belt stalk, first remove the seat as described in Section 28.
7   Refitting is a reversal of removal.

Rear (Saloon)

8   Remove the rear seat cushion and backrest (Section 28). Also remove the side upholstery.
9   Unscrew the bolt securing the lower (rigid) belt to the floor.
10   Unscrew the belt from the height adjuster.
11   Unscrew the bolt securing the inertia reel unit.
12   Pull the belt sideways from the rear quarter trim panel.
13   Unbolt and remove the stalk.
14   Refitting is a reversal of removal.

Rear (Estate)

15   Remove the rear seat cushion (Section 28).

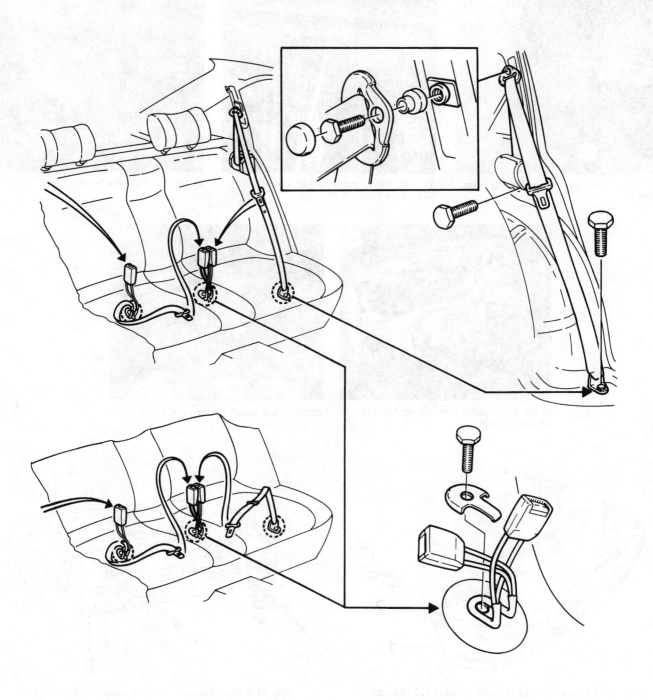

Fig. 11.6 Rear seat belt components (Sec 26)

16 Unscrew the bolt securing the lower (rigid) belt to the floor.
17 Unscrew the belt from the height adjuster.
18 Remove the trim panels from the under rear quarter window and wheel housing.
19 Where fitted remove the luggage cover and the panel covering the roller channel (photos).
20 Unscrew the bolt securing the inertia reel unit and remove the belt.
21 Unbolt and remove the stalks.
22 Refitting is a reversal of removal.

27 Bumpers – removal and refitting

Front

1 Jack up the front of the vehicle and support it on axle stands.
2 Where necessary, disconnect the wiring connectors from the front foglamps and outside air temperature sensor (as applicable), and free the wiring from any relevant retaining clips and ties.
3 Unscrew and remove the bolts securing the brackets to the under-body channel sections.
4 Release the plastic clips from the channel sections, and remove the

30.2   Glove compartment mounting bolts (arrowed)

30.13A   Removing a centre surround panel screw ...

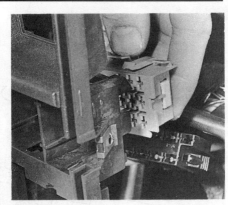

30.13B   ... and plug block

30.20   Facia panel with wiring harness before removal

30.21   Facia panel bottom mounting bolt

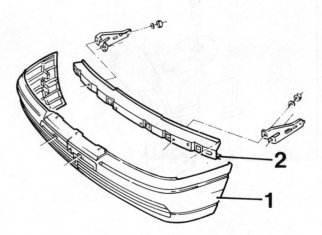

Fig. 11.7 Front bumper (1) and support (2) (Sec 27)

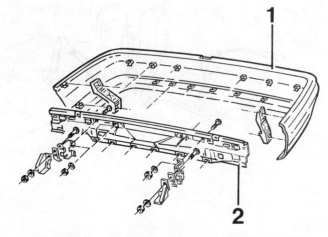

Fig. 11.8 Rear bumper (1) and support (2) (Sec 27)

brackets.
5   Disconnect the side sections and withdraw the bumper forwards.
6   Refitting is a reversal of removal.

Rear
7   Remove the rear lamp clusters as described in Chapter 13.
8   Disconnect the wiring for the number plate lights.
9   Remove the spare wheel on Estate models.
10   Remove the rear protector and trim panel.
11   Unbolt and remove the rear bumper.
12   Refitting is a reversal of removal.

28   Seats – removal and refitting

Front
1   Adjust the seat fully rearwards and unscrew the front rail mounting bolts (photo).
2   Adjust the seat fully forwards and unscrew the rear rail mounting bolts.
3   If applicable disconnect the seat heating wiring.
4   Remove the seat from the car.
5   Refitting is a reversal of removal.

Rear
6   Release the rear seat cushion from the lower brackets by pulling the

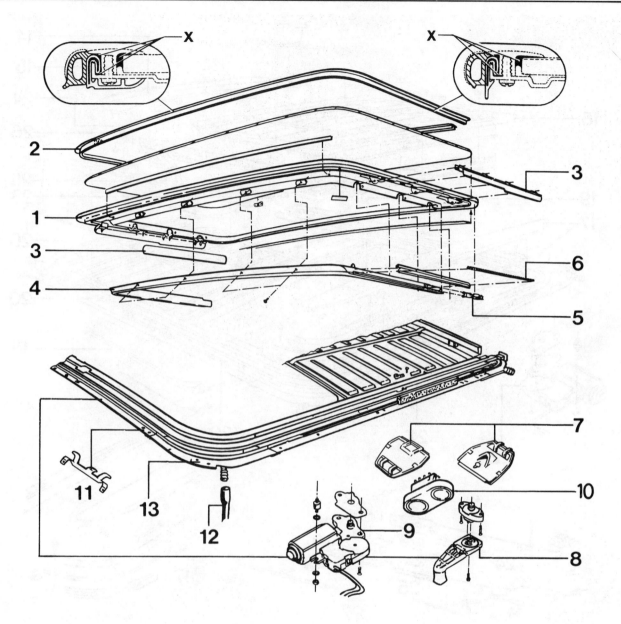

Fig. 11.9 Sun roof main components (Sec 29)

1	Safety glass	4	Cover (screwed to
2	Seal		bodyshell)
3	Cover (bodyshell side)	5	Spring clip
		6	Brush

7	Headlining cover	10	Rocker switch
8	Crank handle	11	Front support
9	Electric motor and gear	12	Water drain hose
	assembly	13	Operating unit assembly

special handles. If applicable disconnect the seat heating wiring.

7   Unbolt the backrest brackets and remove the backrest(s).

8   Refitting is a reversal of removal.

29   Sun roof – general

1   The component parts of the sun roof are shown in Figs. 11.9 and 11.10.

2   Should a fault develop in the sun roof it is recommended that a specialist be consulted, since incorrect assembly may result in water leaks.

30   Facia panel – removal and refitting

1   Remove the centre console (Section 31).

2   Unbolt and remove the glove compartment from the passenger side of the facia panel. Also disconnect the illumination light wiring (photo).

3   As applicable unbolt the ashtray, or remove the cassette storage case.

4   Remove the radio and, where necessary, the CD player or graphic equaliser, as described in Chapters 12 or 13 (as applicable).

5   Remove the heater control panel (Section 32).

6   Remove the facia panel switches (Chapter 12).

7   Remove the centre fresh air vents (Section 36) and disconnect the control rod.

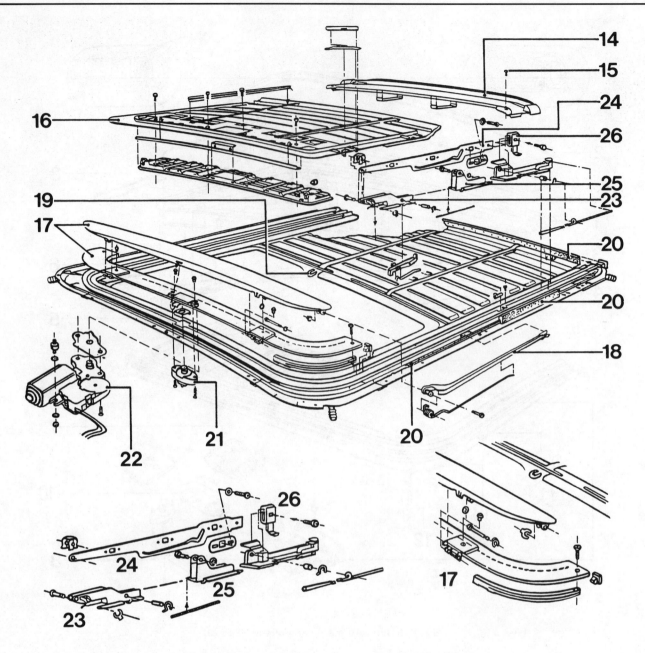

Fig. 11.10 Sun roof individual components (Sec 29)

14 Gutter
15 Allen bolt
16 Sun screen
17 Wind deflector with cable channel cover plate
18 Lifter arm
19 Seal (bodyshell)
20 Seals (frame)
21 Crank handle
22 Electric motor and gear assembly
23 Front guide
24 Side block guide
25 Rear guide
26 Hold-down clamp

8   Remove the steering wheel (Chapter 10).
9   Remove the combination switches (Chapter 12).
10   Disconnect the ignition switch wiring connector.
11   Remove the instrument panel (Chapter 12).
12   Remove the clock as described in Chapter 12, or the trip computer as described in Chapter 13 (as applicable).
13   Remove the screws securing the centre surround panel, and disconnect the plug block (photos). Disconnect the wiring from the cigarette lighter and illumination bulb, and withdraw the surround panel.
14   Remove the heater matrix (Chapter 33).

15   Remove the side fresh air vents (Section 37).
16   Remove the fusebox (Chapter 12).
17   Pull the weatherstrips from the A-pillars and remove the covering from the front loudspeakers. Remove the loudspeakers.
18   Disconnect all the air distribution ducts.
19   Using a cranked screwdriver remove the front screws and lift off the facia panel cover, by first raising its centre.
20   Note the location of the wiring harness then, starting from the left, disconnect it and withdraw it into the driver's footwell (photo).
21   Unscrew the facia panel mounting bolts. There are two at each side, three at the top front, and one at the bottom (photo).

31.3 Removing the rear console compartment cover

31.6 Removing the middle console cover

31.7A Centre console rear screws (arrowed) ...

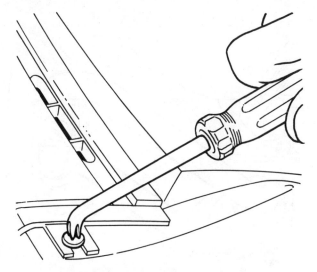

Fig. 11.11 Using a cranked screwdriver to remove the front screws retaining the facia panel cover (Sec 30)

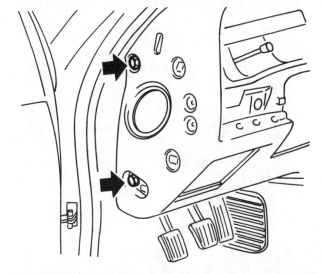

Fig. 11.12 Facia panel side mounting bolt location (Sec 30) (LHD shown, RHD similar)

31 Centre console – removal and refitting

1 Disconnect the battery negative lead.
2 On models with a centre console rear armrest, open up the storage compartment lid, then carefully prise the cassette storage box out of the console, or remove the retaining screw and lift the oddments box out of the console (as applicable).
3 On earlier models without a console armrest, using a screwdriver, carefully prise out the plastic cover from the base of the rear console compartment (photo).
4 On manual gearbox models, prise out the gear lever gaiter frame, then extract the two retaining screws and remove the gear lever surround panel.
5 On automatic transmission models, using a small flat-bladed screwdriver, carefully prise out the gear indicator panel and slot cover from the surround panel, and remove them from the selector lever. Undo the single retaining screw, then release the surround panel from the centre console. Pull the bulbholder out of the panel, and lift the panel off the selector lever.
6 Prise the middle cover out and remove it from the console (where necessary), disconnecting the switch wiring connector(s) as they becme accessible (photo).
7 Prise out the trim caps, then slacken and remove the six console retaining screws (two at the front, two at the rear and one either side) (photos).
8 Release the handbrake lever gaiter from the centre console, then lift the console over the gear/selector lever and handbrake lever whilst feeding the handbrake lever gaiter through the console aperture. Where necessary, disconnect the electric window switch wiring connectors, and remove the console from the vehicle (photo).
9 Refitting is a reversal of the removal procedure.

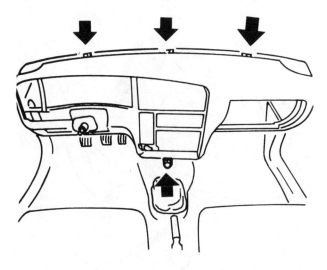

Fig. 11.13 Facia panel upper and lower mounting bolt location (Sec 30) (LHD shown, RHD similar)

22 With the help of an assistant remove the facia panel from the car.
23 Refitting is a reversal of removal.

31.7B   ... front screws (arrowed) ...

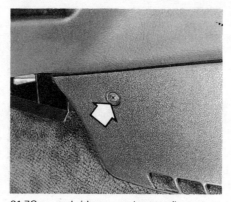

31.7C   ... and side screws (arrowed)

31.8   Electric window switch multi-plugs

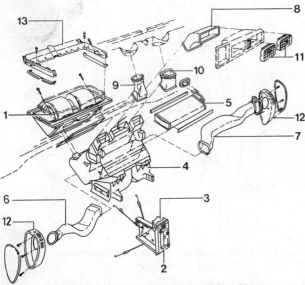

Fig. 11.14 Heater components (Sec 33)

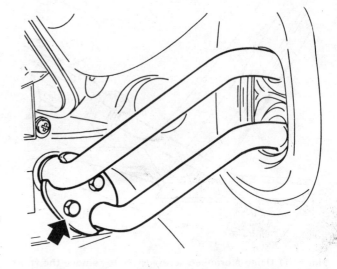

Fig. 11.15 Heater pipe retainer (Sec 33)

1 Fan motor assembly	8 Air duct (centre)
2 Control panel	9 Air duct (windscreen)
3 Fan motor switch	10 Air duct (windscreen)
4 Heater unit	11 Centre fresh air vents
5 Matrix	12 Side window defroster
6 Air duct (left-hand)	nozzle
7 Air duct (right-hand)	13 Fan shroud

32   Heater control panel – removal and refitting

1   Disconnect the battery negative lead.
2   Prise the cover from the cigarette lighter.
3   Disconnect the air distribution flap cable at the heater (photo).
4   Remove the two lower screws then release the top of the control panel and withdraw until the multi-plug and illumination wire can be disconnected (photos).
5   Disconnect the control cables and remove the panel (photos).
6   Refitting is a reversal of removal.

33   Heater matrix – removal and refitting

1   Remove the pedal bracket (Chapter 9).
2   Drain the cooling system (Chapter 2).
3   Unbolt the heater pipe retainer and disconnect the heater pipes. Be prepared for some spillage of coolant.
4   Remove the retaining screws and withdraw the matrix from the heater.

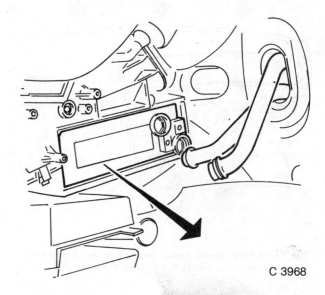

C 3968

Fig. 11.16 Removing the heater matrix (Sec 33)

5   Refitting is a reversal of removal but fit new O-ring seals to the two pipes. Refill the cooling system with reference to Chapter 2.

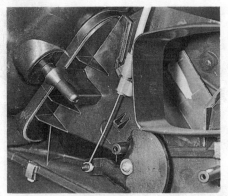

32.3 Heater air distribution flap cable

32.4A Removing the heater control panel lower screws

32.4B Disconnecting the heater control panel multi-plug

32.5A Right-hand side heater control cables

32.5B Releasing the left-hand side heater control outer cable

34 Heater unit – removal and refitting

1   Remove the facia panel (Section 30).
2   Remove the wiper arms and blades (Chapter 12).
3   Unscrew the nuts from the wiper spindle housings.
4   Pull off the weatherstrip and remove the water deflector.
5   Remove the heater matrix (Section 33).
6   Unscrew the fan motor retaining bolts.
7   Unbolt the heater unit from the bulkhead and remove from inside the car. Disconnect the remaining control cables (photo).
8   Refitting is a reversal of removal, but seal the mounting bolts to the bulkhead using a suitable sealant.

35 Heater fan motor – removal and refitting

1   Disconnect the battery negative lead.
2   Remove the wiper arms and blades (Chapter 12).
3   Unscrew the nuts from the wiper spindle housings.
4   Pull off the weatherstrip and remove the water deflector (photo).
5   Disconnect the wiring multi-plug, then unbolt and remove the wiper motor.
6   Disconnect the wiring plug from the fan motor.
7   Remove the screws and lift off the fan shroud.
8   Remove the fan wheel covers.
9   Remove the mounting screws, then manoeuvre the motor assembly out from the vehicle. Note that the motor must be rotated in order for it to pass by the windscreen wiper bracket.
10   Disconnect the wires and remove the series resistor from the bracket.
11   Refitting is a reversal of removal.

36 Centre fresh air vents – removal, refitting and adjustment

1   Using a hooked instrument, carefully pull the air vents from the facia panel (photo).
2   Turn the knurled adjustment wheel to minimum and operate the heater. Check that no air comes out of the vent holes. If adjustment is necessary disconnect the control rod, pull out the rod as far as possible, then reconnect it to the arm (photo).
3   Press the air vents fully into the facia panel.

37 Side fresh air vent – removal and refitting

1   Prise off the side cover.
2   Extract the three screws and withdraw the air vent assembly from the facia panel. Remove the vents.
3   Refitting is a reversal of removal.

38 Air conditioning system – description and precautions

1   An air conditioning system is fitted as standard equipment on later high-specification models, and was available as an optional extra on some lower-specification models. In conjunction with the heater, the system enables any reasonable air temperature to be achieved inside the car, it also reduces the humidity of the incoming air, aiding demisting even when cooling is not required.

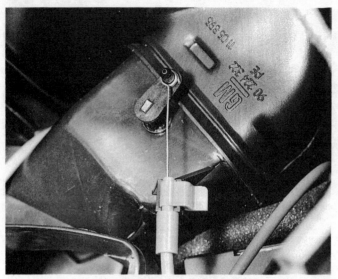

34.7   Heater flap control cable

35.4   Heater fan motor with water deflector removed

36.1   Removing a centre fresh air vent

36.2   Centre fresh air vent control rod and arm

2   The refrigeration side of the air conditioning system functions in a similar way to a domestic refrigerator. A compressor, belt-driven from the crankshaft pulley, draws refrigerant in its gaseous phase from an evaporator. The compressed refrigerant passes through a condenser where it loses heat and enters its liquid phase. After dehydration, the refrigerant returns to the evaporator where it absorbs heat from the air passing over the evaporator fins. The refrigerant becomes a gas again and the cycle is repeated.

3   Various subsidiary controls and sensors protect the system against excessive temperature and pressures. Additionally, engine idle speed is increased when the system is in use to compensate for the additional load imposed by the compressor.

4   Although the refrigerant is not itself toxic, in the presence of a naked flame (or a lighted cigarette) it forms a highly toxic gas. Liquid refrigerant spilled on the skin will cause frostbite.

5   Considering the above points, and the need for specialised equipment for discharging and recharging the system, any work which requires the disconnection of a refrigerant line must be left to a

specialist.

6   Do not allow refrigerant lines to be exposed to temperatures in excess of 110°C (230°F), for example during welding or paint drying operations.

7   Do not operate the air conditioning system if it is known to be short of refrigerant, or damage may result.

---

39   Air conditioning system components – removal and refitting

Auxiliary fan

1   Remove the radiator grille (Section 11).

2   Loosen the horn mounting bolt and swing the horn to one side.

3   Unbolt the bracket from the front member and fan.

4   Disconnect the multi-plug, then turn the fan and remove it, taking care not to damage the condenser fins.

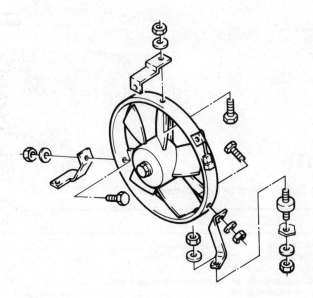

Fig. 11.17 Air conditioning auxiliary fan components
(Sec 39)

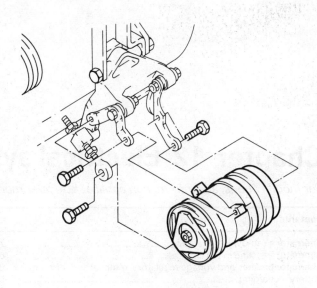

Fig. 11.18 Air conditioning compressor bolt location
(Sec 39)

5   Refitting is a reversal of removal.

Compressor (leaving refrigerant lines connected)
6   From the compressor, disconnect the wiring plugs for the magnetic clutch, the high pressure safety switch, and the auxiliary fan switch.
7   Loosen the pivot and adjustment bolts.

8   Unscrew the outer adjustment locknut to release the tension on the drivebelt then slip the drivebelt from the pulley.
9   Remove the pivot and adjustment bolts, and support the compressor to one side.
10   Refitting is a reversal of the removal procedure, tensioning the drivebelt as described in Section 13 of Chapter 2.

Chapter 12 Electrical system

For modifications, and information applicable to later models, see Supplement at end of manual

Contents

Specifications

System type .... 12 volt, negative earth

Battery
Type .... Lead-acid, maintenance-free
Capacity .... 44 Amp-hour

Alternator
Make .... Bosch
Type .... Rotating field, integral voltage regulator
Output current (maximum):
    18SV engine .... 55 or 70 Amps
    18SEH and 20SE engine .... 70 Amps
Output voltage .... 13.8 to 14.8 volts (2000 to 2500 rpm)
Minimum diameter of slip rings .... 31.5 mm (1.24 in)
Minimum brush length .... 5.0 mm (0.2 in)
Field winding resistance .... 3.4 ohms
Stator winding resistance .... 0.14 ohm

Starter motor
Make .... Bosch (0 001 108 047)
Type .... Pre-engaged
Minimum brush length .... 4.5 mm (0.177 in)
Current draw (no load) .... 75A at 2900 rpm
Current draw (locked):
    At 12 volts .... 475 to 600 A
    At 14 volts .... 625 to 800 A
Minimum diameter of commutator .... 31.2 mm (1.228 in)

Fuses (typical)

Number	Rating (Amps)	Circuit(s) protected
1	10	LH parking lamp, LH tail lamp
2	10	RH parking lamp, RH tail lamp
3	10	LH main beam
4	10	RH main beam
5	10	LH dipped beam
6	10	RH dipped beam
7	–	Not used
8	15	Stop-lamps, turn signal lamps, ABS
9	30	Reverse lamps, windscreen wipers, horn
10	10	Rear foglamp
11	–	Not used
12	30	Heater motor
13	20	Cigarette lighter, heated front seats, glovebox light
14	20	Constant current for caravan or trailer, level control system
15	15	Hazard warning flashers, clock, luggage compartment lamp, courtesy light, radio
16	20	Fuel injection system
17	20	Fog lamps
18	20	Heated rear window
19	30	Front electric windows
20	30	Rear electric windows
21	10	Instrument panel, number plate light, engine compartment light
22	30	Air conditioning system additional cooling fan
23	30	Central door locking system, heated rear seats
24	20	Long range headlamps
25	30	Electrically operated sunroof, front electric windows
26	10	Headlamp washer system
27	10	Automatic transmission

Wiper blades

Champion X-4803

Bulbs (typical)

Function	Wattage
Headlamp main/dip	60/55
Driving lights	55
Parking light	5
Direction indicator lamp (front and rear)	21
Stop-lamp	21
Rear foglamp	21
Tail lamp	10
Number plate light	5 or 10
Reversing lamp	21

Torque wrench settings

	Nm	lbf ft
Alternator bracket	25	19
Starter motor	45	33

1   General description

The electrical system is of 12 volt, negative earth type. Electrical power is produced by an alternator, belt-driven from the crankshaft pulley. A lead-acid battery provides a reserve of power for starting the engine and for periods when the electrical load exceeds the alternator's output.

As is normal practice in car electrical systems, most components only receive a live feed, the earth return being made via the bodywork or other metal structure instead of by means of a wire. This should be borne in mind when investigating faults: loose or corroded component mountings can have the same effect as a broken feed wire.

The reader whose competence or interest extends beyond the items covered in this Chapter may wish to study the Automobile Electrical Manual; available from the publishers of this book.

2   Routine maintenance

1   Carry out the following procedures at the intervals given in *Routine maintenance* at the front of this manual. Refer to the appropriate sections of this Chapter for adjustment or renewal procedures.
2   Check the function of all lights, both interior and exterior.
3   Check the function of the horn.
4   Check the level of washer fluid in the reservoir and top up if necessary.
5   Check that all washer jets are clean and adjusted correctly.
6   Examine all wiper blades for deterioration and splitting, clean them, and if necessary renew them.
7   Check the headlamp beam alignment, and if necessary, check the front foglamps.
8   Check the operation of all switches, instruments and any optional equipment.

3   Electrical system – precautions

It is necessary to take extra care when working on the electrical system to avoid damage to semiconductor devices (diodes and transistors) and to avoid the risk of personal injury. In addition to the precautions given in Safety First! *at the beginning of this manual, observe the following when working on the system.*

4.4   Battery clamp and bolt

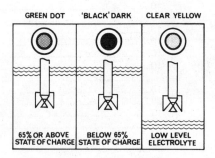

BUILT-IN HYDROMETER

Fig. 12.1 Battery 'magic eye' indicator hydrometer readings
(Sec 5)

1   Always remove rings, watches, etc before working on the electrical system. Even with the battery disconnected, capacitive discharge could occur if a component live terminal is earthed through a metal object. This could cause a shock, or a nasty burn.
2   Do not reverse the battery connections. Components such as the alternator or any other having semiconductor circuitry could be irreparably damaged.
3   Never disconnect the battery terminals, or alternator wiring connections, when the engine is running.
4   The battery leads and alternator connections must be disconnected before carrying out any electric welding on the car.
5   Never use an ohmmeter of the type incorporating a hand-cranked generator for circuit or continuity testing.

4   Battery – removal and refitting

1   The battery is located in the front left-hand side of the engine compartment.
2   Loosen the clamp nut and bolt on the negative (–) terminal clamp, remove the clamp and bend it to one side.
3   Lift the plastic cover and similarly disconnect the positive (+) terminal clamp.
4   Unscrew the clamp bolt at the base of the battery (photo), and
5   Refitting is a reversal of removal, connecting the negative (–) terminal clamp last. Apply a little petroleum jelly to the terminal posts and clamps before tightening them.

5   Battery – charging

1   In normal use the battery should be kept charged by the alternator. Except in extremely adverse conditions a regular need to charge the battery from an external source suggests that the battery or alternator is faulty, or that a short-circuit is draining the battery.
2   Charging from an external source may be useful to temporarily revive a flagging battery. A battery which is not in use should be given a refresher charge every six to eight weeks.
3   The state of charge of the battery fitted as original equipment is shown by a 'magic eye' indicator on the top face of the battery (Fig. 12.1). If the indicator is green the battery is charged. It if turns darker and eventually to black then the battery needs charging. If the indicator is

clear or yellow this indicates that the electrolyte level is too low to allow further use and the battery should be renewed.
4   Disconnect both leads or better still remove the battery before charging it.
5   As a general guide the charging rate (in amps) should not exceed one tenth of the battery capacity (in amp-hours). Make sure that dual voltage equipment is set to 12 volts.
6   Connect the charger to the battery, observing the correct polarity (+ to +, and – to –), then switch on the mains. Switch off the mains before disconnecting the charger. Ensure adequate ventilation during charging. If using the 'magic eye' indicator to determine the state of charge, shake the battery occasionally to encourage the indicator to move.
7   Rapid or boost charging should be avoided as there is a risk of explosion due to the rapid build-up of gas inside the battery.

6   Alternator – testing in the car

1   Should it appear that the alternator is not charging the battery, check first that the drivebelt is intact and in good condition and that its tension is correct (Chapter 2). Also check the condition and security of the alternator electrical connections and the battery leads.
2   Accurate assessment of alternator output requires special equipment and a degree of skill. A rough idea of whether output is adequate can be gained by using a voltmeter (range 0 to 15 or 0 to 20 volts) as follows.
3   Connect the voltmeter across the battery terminals. Switch on the headlights and note the voltage reading: it should be between 12 and 13 volts.
4   Start the engine and run it at a fast idle (approx 1500 rpm) Read the voltmeter: it should indicate 13 to 14 volts.
5   With the engine still running at a fast idle, switch on as many electrical consumers as possible (heated rear window, heater blower etc). The voltage at the battery should be maintained at 13 to 14 volts. Increase the engine speed slightly if necessary to keep the voltage up.
6   If alternator output is low or zero, check the brushes, as described in Section 8. If the brushes are OK, seek expert advice.
7   Occasionally the condition may arise where the alternator output is excessive. Clues to this condition are constantly blowing bulbs; brightness of lights varying considerably with engine speed; overheating of alternator and battery, possibly with steam or fumes coming from the battery. This condition is almost certainly due to a defective voltage regulator, but expert advice should be sought.

7   Alternator – removal and refitting

1   Disconnect the battery negative lead.
2   Note the electrical connections at the rear of the alternator then disconnect them.

7.3 Loosening the alternator adjustment bolt

7.4A Removing the alternator

7.4B Removing the alternator mounting bracket

8.2A Remove the screws ...

8.2B ... and withdraw the brush holder and voltage regulator

8.3 Measuring the length of the alternator brushes

8.8 Alternator slip rings (arrowed)

11.3 Electrical connections on the starter motor solenoid

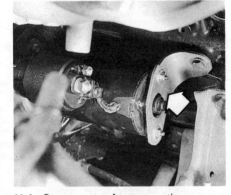

11.4 Starter motor front mounting bracket (arrowed)

3 Loosen the adjustment and pivot bolts, swivel the alternator towards the engine, and remove the drivebelt from the pulley (photo).
4 Remove the adjustment and pivot bolts and withdraw the alternator from the engine. If necessary unbolt the bracket from the block (photos).
5 Refitting is a reversal of removal but tension the drivebelt as described in Chapter 2.

8 Alternator brushes and voltage regulator – removal and refitting

Note: *On some models it may be preferable to remove the alternator as described in Section 7 due to limited access*

1 Disconnect the battery negative lead.
2 Remove the two screws and withdraw the brush holder and voltage regulator from the rear of the alternator (photos).
3 Measure the length of the brushes (photo). If they are worn below the minimum specified length, they must be renewed as follows.

4 Hold the brush wire with a pair of engineer's pliers and unsolder it from the brush box. Lift away the two brushes.
5 Insert the new brushes and check to make sure that they are free to move in their guides. If they bind, lightly polish with a very fine file.
6 Solder the brush wire ends to the brush box taking care that solder is not allowed to pass to the stranded wire.
7 Whenever new brushes are fitted, new springs should also be fitted.
8 Clean the alternator slip rings with a fuel-moistened cloth (photo).
9 Refitting is a reversal of removal.

9 Starter motor – general description

The starter motor is mounted on the rear face of the crankcase and is of Bosch manufacture. It is of the pre-engaged type, ie the drive pinion is brought into mesh with the starter ring gear on the flywheel before the main current is applied.

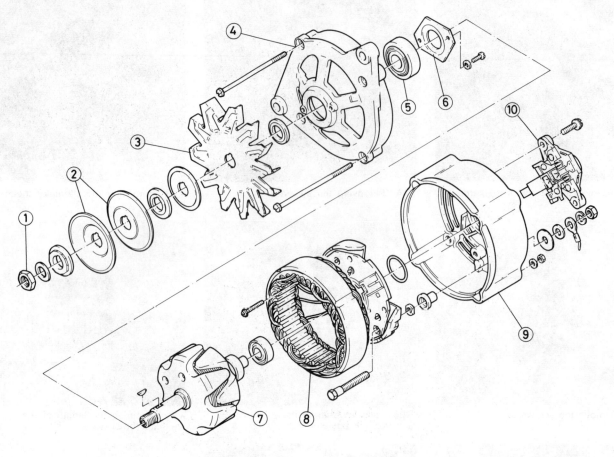

Fig. 12.2 Exploded view of the Bosch alternator (Sec 8)

1	Nut	4	Drive end housing	7	Rotor	10	Brush holder and voltage
2	Pulley	5	Bearing	8	Stator		regulator
3	Fan	6	Retaining plate	9	Brush end housing		

When the starter switch is operated, current flows from the battery to the solenoid which is mounted on the starter body. The plunger in the solenoid moves inwards, so causing a centrally pivoted lever to push the drive pinion into mesh with the starter ring gear. When the solenoid plunger reaches the end of its travel, it closes an internal contact and full starting current flows to the starter field coils. The armature is then able to rotate the crankshaft, so starting the engine.

A special freewheel clutch is fitted to the starter drive pinion so that as soon as the engine fires and starts to operate on its own it does not drive the starter motor.

When the starter switch is released, the solenoid is de-energised and a spring moves the plunger back to its rest position. This operates the pivoted lever to withdraw the drive pinion from engagement with the starter ring.

10   Starter motor – testing in the car

1   If the starter motor fails to operate when the switch is operated, provided that engine seizure is not the problem, there are five or six possible causes:

(a)   *The battery is faulty*
(b)   *The electrical connections between the switch, solenoid, battery and starter motor are somewhere failing to pass the necessary current from the battery through the starter to earth*
(c)   *The solenoid switch is faulty*

(d)   *The starter motor is mechanically or electrically defective*
(e)   *The starter motor pinion and/or flywheel ring gear is badly worn and in need of replacement*
(f)   *On automatic transmission models, the starter inhibitor switch may be defective or maladjusted. See Chapter 6.*

2   To check the battery, switch on the headlights. If they dim after a few seconds the battery is in a discharged state. If the lights glow brightly, operate the starter switch and see what happens to the lights. If they dim then you know that power is reaching the starter motor but failing to turn it. If the starter turns slowly when switched on, proceed to the next check.

3   If, when the starter switch is operated, the lights stay bright, then insufficient power is reaching the motor. Remove the battery connections, starter/solenoid power connections and the engine earth strap and thoroughly clean them and refit them. Smear petroleum jelly around the battery connections to prevent corrosion. Corroded connections are the most frequent cause of electric system malfunctions.

4   When the above checks and cleaning tasks have been carried out, but without success, you will possibly have heard a clicking noise each time the starter switch was operated. This was the solenoid switch operating, but it does not necessarily follow that the main contacts were closing properly (if no clicking has been heard from the solenoid, it is almost certainly defective). The solenoid contact can be checked by putting a voltmeter or bulb across the main cable connection on the starter side of the solenoid and earth. When the switch is operated, there should be a reading or lighted bulb. If there is no reading or lighted bulb, the solenoid unit is faulty and should be renewed.

5   If the starter motor operates but doesn't turn the engine, then it is most probable that the starter motor pinion and/or flywheel ring gear

13.1   Disconnecting the starter motor feed wire

13.2   Removing the solenoid screws

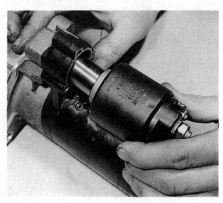

13.3A   Removing the solenoid switch housing ...

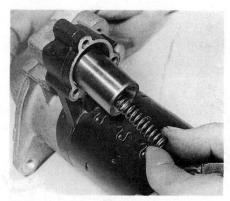

13.3B   ... spring ...

13.3C   ... and armature

are badly worn, in which case the starter motor will normally be noisy in operation.

6   Finally, if it is established that the solenoid is not faulty and 12 volts are getting to the starter, then the motor is faulty and should be removed for inspection.

11   Starter motor – removal and refitting

1   Disconnect the battery negative lead.
2   Jack up the front of the car and support it on axle stands.
3   Note the electrical connections on the solenoid then disconnect them (photo).
4   Unbolt the front starter motor bracket from the cylinder block (photo), then unscrew the mounting bolts and remove the starter motor from below. Remove the front bracket.
5   To refit the starter motor insert it through the block extension and tighten the mounting bolts to the specified torque. At this stage the front bracket nuts should be loose.
6   Insert the front bracket bolt finger-tight. Finger-tighten the bracket nuts.
7   Fully tighten the front bracket bolt and nuts.

12   Starter motor overhaul – general

1   Before embarking on a comprehensive overhaul of a well worn motor, compare the cost of the proposed repairs with the cost of a new or reconditioned motor. The difference may not be very great.
2   Premature failure of one component such as the solenoid, brushes

or pinion can be economically rectified by removing the motor, as just described, and dismantling, as described in the following Sections.

13   Starter solenoid – removal and refitting (starter motor removal)

1   At the front of the solenoid, undo the retaining nut and washer and slip the electrical feed wire off the terminal stud (photo).
2   Remove the two or three screws which secure the solenoid to the starter drive end housing (photo).
3   Withdraw the solenoid switch housing, spring and armature; unhook the armature from the pinion actuating arm (photo).
4   A defective solenoid must be renewed.
5   Refit in the reverse order to removal.

14   Starter motor brushes – inspection and removal

1   With the starter removed from the engine and on a clean bench, begin by removing the armature end cap which is secured by two small screws on the end of the motor (photo). Remove the armature retaining clip, washers and the rubber sealing ring which were exposed (photos). Undo and remove the two long bolts which hold the motor assembly together (photos). The end cover can now be removed to reveal the brushes and mounting plate (photo).
2   Take the brushes from the holder and slip the holder off the armature shaft. Retrieve the spacer washers between the brush plate and the armature block, where fitted.
3   Inspect the brushes; if they are worn down to less than the mini-

14.1A   Remove the screws ...

14.1B   ... retaining clip (arrowed) ...

14.1C   ... washer ...

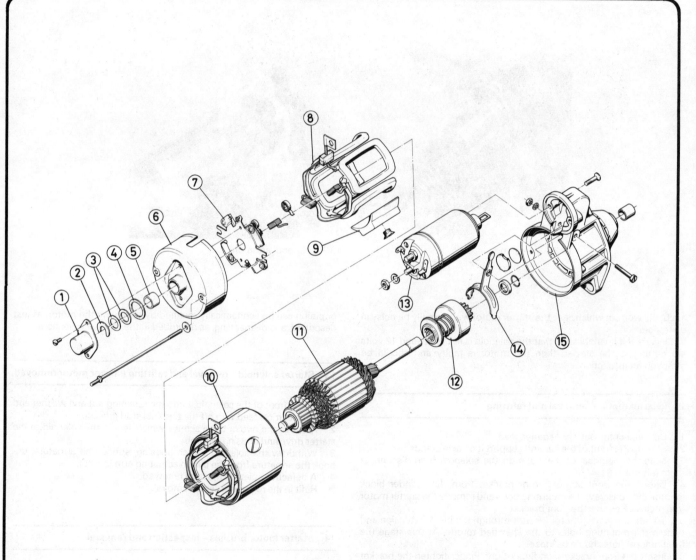

Fig. 12.3 Exploded view of the Bosch starter motor (Sec 9)

1 End cap	5 Bush	9 Permanent magnet	13 Solenoid
2 Circlip	6 End cover	10 Yoke	14 Actuating arm
3 Washers	7 Brush holder	11 Armature	15 Drive end housing
4 Sealing ring	8 Field windings	12 Pinion and one-way clutch	

14.1D ... and sealing ring

14.1E Unscrew the long bolts ...

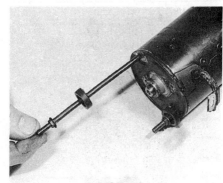

14.1F ... and remove them

14.1G Removing the end cover

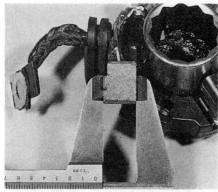

14.3 Measure the length of the starter motor brushes

15.5A Place a large socket over the end of the armature ...

15.5B ... and slide the brushes onto it

15.5C Brushplate and brushes retained with a socket

15.6A Remove the yoke ...

15.6B ... and withdraw the armature

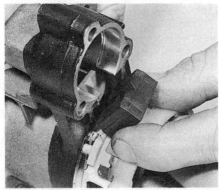

15.8A Removing the rubber pad

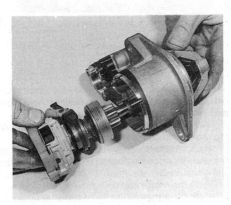

15.8B Removing the reduction gear unit

15.9A   Free the collar ...

15.9B   ... to remove the retaining ring ...

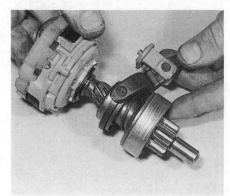

15.9C   ... then remove the pinion and one-way clutch

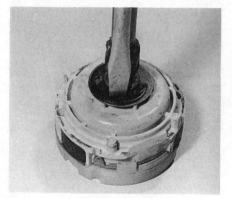

15.10A   Extract the circlip ...

15.10B   ... remove the washer ...

15.10C   ... unclip the cover ...

15.10D   ... remove the annulus ...

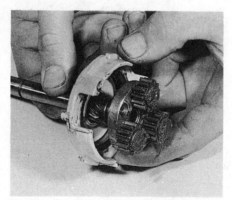

15.10E   ... and remove the gears

15.10F   Reduction gears and shaft

mum length given in Specifications, they should be renewed. Cut off the old brushes and solder on the new ones; hold the lead on the brush side with pliers to stop solder running up it (photo).

4   Wipe the starter motor armature and commutator with a non-fluffy rag moistened with petrol.

5   Reassemble the brushes into the holder and refit the holder over the armature shaft, remembering to fit the two washers between the holder and armature, where fitted.

6   Refit the motor end cover and secure with two long bolts.

7   Refit the armature shaft end cap after fitting the rubber sealing ring, washer and shaft clip.

15   Starter motor – dismantling and reassembly

1   The complete overhaul of a starter motor is beyond the resources of the average home mechanic as special tools and equipment for testing are necessary, but if the appropriate spares can be obtained repairs can be made by renewing parts. With the starter on the bench proceed as follows.

2   Remove the solenoid as described in Section 13. Undo the two screws and remove the end cap from the commutator cover.

3   Prise the clip off the end of the armature and, after carefully noting

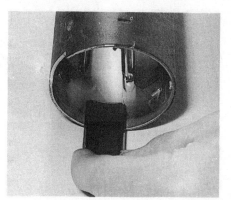

15.11 Removing the permanent magnets from the yoke

15.15 Checking the diameter of the commutator

16.1A Fuse/relay box

16.1B Relays located in the engine compartment

17.5 Disconnecting the combination switch wiring

the sequence of assembly, remove the washers and rubber sealing ring from the armature.

4 Mark the commutator cover relative to the starter yoke and then remove the two long bolts which hold the assembly together. Remove the commutator cover.

5 Lift the brush springs and then remove the brushplate from the assembly. Note and remove any shims that may be fitted. A large socket may be used to help retain the brushes in their holders (photos).

6 Remove the yoke together with the armature then pull out the armature (photos).

7 Where applicable unscrew the actuating arm pivot.

8 Prise out the rubber pad and remove the reduction gear unit from the drive end housing (photos).

9 To remove the pinion and one-way clutch, drive back the collar and extract the retaining ring (photos).

10 To dismantle the reduction gear unit, extract the circlip, remove the washer, unclip the cover, remove the annulus, and remove the gears (photo).

11 If necessary remove the permanent magnets from the yoke (photo).

12 With the starter motor dismantled, the various components can be cleaned and inspected for general wear and/or signs of damage. Use a petrol-damped cloth for cleaning, but avoid wetting electrical components. Dry thoroughly with a fluff-free cloth.

13 Renew worn or damaged carbon brushes as shown in Section 14.

14 If the starter motor has shown a tendency to jam or a reluctance to disengage then the starter pinion is almost certainly the culprit. Dirt accumulation on the shaft or on the pinion could cause this. After cleaning off any such dirt, check that the pinion can move freely in a spiral movement along the shaft. If it still tends to bind or stick, or if it is defective in any way, renew the pinion.

15 A badly worn or burnt commutator will need skimming on a lathe, but if it is only dirty or lightly marked, clean it up with a piece of fine grade glass paper wrapped round. If the commutator has to be skimmed have the job done by a specialist, but make sure that the minimum

diameter, as listed in the Specifications, is maintained (photo). After skimming, the separators should be undercut using a piece of old hacksaw blade ground down to the same thickness as the separators. Undercut to a depth of about 0.5 to 0.8 mm (0.02 to 0.03 in) and then clean up with fine grade glass cloth. Do not use emery on the commutator as abrasive particles could get embedded in the copper and cause rapid brush wear.

16 An armature with a bent shaft or other signs of damage must be renewed. Electrical checks should be undertaken by an auto-electrician with special equipment. Although simple continuity checks are possible with a lamp and low power source, more extensive checking is needed which is beyond the scope of the home mechanic.

17 Reassembly of the starter motor is a straightforward reversal of the dismantling sequence, but the following points should be noted:

(a) After assembling the clutch and pinion to the armature shaft, fit the retaining ring using a new snap-ring and then reposition the retainer

(b) Make sure that all shims and washers are fitted in the correct order

(c) Align the locating key and slot when assembling the yoke to the end housing

(d) Make sure that the carbon brushes slide freely in their boxes

(e) Lightly grease all sliding parts including the armature spiral spline, the actuating arm sliding surfaces, the clutch bearing surfaces and armature bearings. Of course, no grease must contaminate the commutator or brushes

16 Fuses and relays – general

1 All the car's electrical circuits are protected by fuses; most of the fuses are found in a fuse/relay box located under a cover to the right of and below the steering column (photo). Unclip the cover and pull out the

18.4A Press together the tabs ...

18.4B ... and pull out the switch

18.8 Fitting a centre facia switch

18.10 Fitting the headlamp range adjuster switch

18.12 Glovebox illumination switch

19.1 Courtesy light switch screw (arrowed)

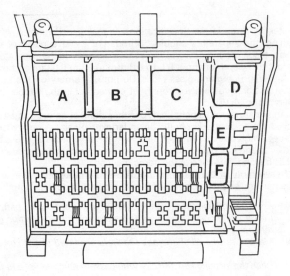

Fig. 12.4 Relays in the fusebox (Sec 16)

A *Warning buzzer*
B *Flasher unit*
C *Windscreen wash/wipe time relay*
D *Heated rear screen or horn relay*
E *Foglamp relay*
F *Long range headlamp relay*

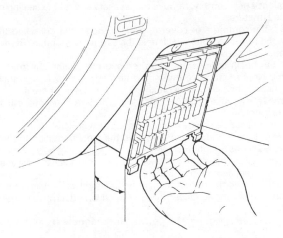

Fig. 12.5 Pulling out the fusebox (Sec 16)

fusebox. Relays are located in, and behind, the fusebox. On some models an additional relay box is located in the left-hand rear corner of the engine compartment (photo).

2   The fuse applications are given in the Specifications and this information is also to be found on the rear of the fuse cover.

3   A fuse remover and spare fuses are to be found in the bottom right corner of the fusebox.

4   When renewing a fuse, switch off the circuit(s) concerned first. If the new fuse blows immediately when switching on, find and rectify the cause. The most usual cause of a blown fuse is a short-circuit to earth somewhere along the wire feeding the component concerned. The wire may be disconnected, trapped or frayed. Pay special attention to wire that runs through grommets, under carpets etc.

5   Where a blown fuse serves more than one component, the defective circuit can be traced by switching on each component in turn until the replacement fuse blows.

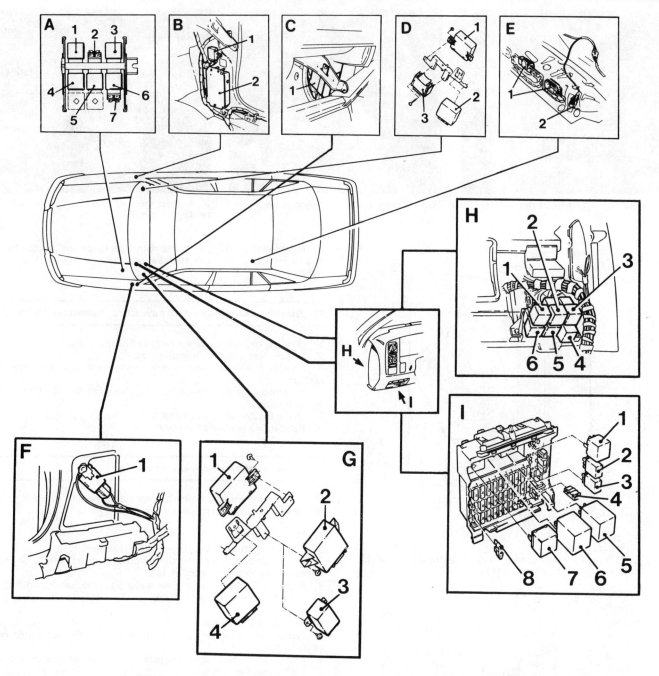

Fig. 12.6 Relay and control unit locations – pre-1989 models (later models similar) (Sec 16)

A Left-hand rear corner of engine compartment
1 Fuel injection system relay
2 Ignition fuse – 18 NV engine
3 Engine speed relay – 18 NV engine
4 ABS surge arrester relay
5 Headlamp wash/wipe relay
6 Auxiliary cooling fan relay
7 Fuse for auxiliary cooling fan

B Driver footwell panel
1 Central locking control unit
2 Motronic control unit

C Passenger footwell panel
1 Cruise control, control unit

D Right lower facia panel bracket
1 Diesel glow plug sensor
2 Automatic transmission downshift
3 Dipped beam relay

E Rear seat ramp
1 Rear seat heater relay
2 Vehicle level control sensor

F Passenger footwell panel
1 Heated outside mirror time relay

G Applicable to foreign markets only

H Relay holder behind fusebox
1 Air conditioning relay
2 Air conditioning fan relay
3 Cruise control relay
4 Rear screen wash/wipe time relay
5 Horn relay (1988 models on)
6 Air conditioning compressor relay

I Fusebox
1 Heated rear screen or horn
2 Fog lamp relay
3 Long range headlamp relay
4 Fuse remover
5 Windscreen wash/wipe time relay
6 Direction indicator unit
7 Warning buzzer
8 Fuse

19.2   Courtesy light switch removal

20.2   Disconnecting the clock wiring

21.3   Rear view of cigarette lighter (facia panel removed)

Fig. 12.7 Use a small screwdriver to depress the catch (Sec 18)

Fig. 12.8 Removing a centre facia switch (Sec 18)

6   **Never** attempt to bypass a fuse with silver foil or wire, nor fit a fuse of a higher rating than specified. Serious damage, or even fire, may result.

17   Steering column combination switches – removal and refitting

1   Unscrew the steering wheel height adjustment knob.
2   Disconnect the battery negative lead.
3   Remove the screws and withdraw the steering column shroud sections.
4   For better access remove the steering wheel as described in Chapter 10, Section 21.
5   Unclip the switch and disconnect the wiring plug (photo).
6   Refitting is a reversal of removal.

18   Facia switches – removal and refitting

1   Before removing any switch disconnect the battery negative lead. Reconnect the lead after refitting the switch.

Lighting switch
2   Turn the knob to the Low beam position and pull it out.
3   Using a small screwdriver in the bottom hole, depress the catch and remove the knob as shown in Fig. 12.7.
4   Press together the retaining tabs and pull out the switch (photos).
5   Refitting is a reversal of removal.

Centre facia switches
6   Protect the panel immediately above the switch with a strip of adhesive tape.
7   Using a screwdriver under the rocker switch and another on top of the switch, lever out the switch from the socket board as shown in Fig. 12.8.
8   Refit by pressing the switch into position (photo).

Headlamp range adjuster switch
9   Using a screwdriver under the switch, lever out the switch.
10   Refit by pressing the switch into position (photo).

Glovebox switch
11   Remove the glovebox with reference to Chapter 11.
12   Slide the switch from the side of the glovebox (photo).
13   Refit in reverse order.

19   Courtesy light switch – removal and refitting

1   Open the door and unscrew the cross-head screw (photo).
2   Remove the switch from the door pillar and pull the wire out sufficiently to prevent it from springing back into the pillar (photo).

22.2   Heater control switch removal

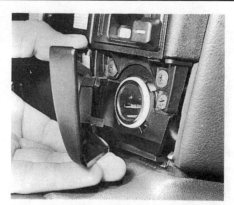

24.2   Removing the cigarette lighter cover

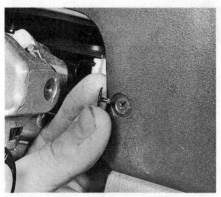

24.8A   Removing a plastic cap from the centre screws

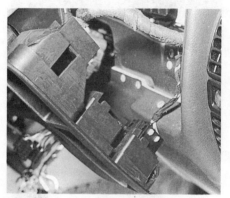

24.8B   Removing the surround panel

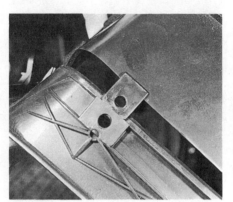

24.9   Unclipping the instrument panel bezel

24.10   Unscrewing the instrument panel retaining screws

3   Disconnect the wire and remove the switch.
4   Refitting is a reversal of removal.

20   Clock – removal and refitting

1   Disconnect the battery negative lead.
2   Carefully pull the clock from the facia. Disconnect the supply and illumination leads from the clock and remove it (photo).
3   Refitting is a reversal of removal.

21   Cigarette lighter – removal and refitting

1   Disconnect the battery earth lead.
2   Pull the heater element from the lighter socket.
3   Carefully prise the lighter socket out of the illuminating ring. Unplug the socket and remove it (photo).
4   Refitting is a reversal of removal. When inserting the socket into the illuminating ring, make sure that the ring lugs pass over the smooth part of the socket. Twist the socket clockwise to engage the lugs.

22   Heater control switch – removal and refitting

1   Remove the heater control panel as described in Chapter 11, Section 32.
2   Unclip the switch from the control panel (photo).
3   Refitting is a reversal of removal.

23   Ignition switch – removal and refitting

1   Disconnect the battery negative lead.
2   Unscrew the steering wheel height adjustment knob.
3   Remove the screws and withdraw the steering column shroud sections.
4   Pull off the multi-plug.
5   With the ignition key inserted and at position II, depress the small detent spring and pull out the lock cylinder.
6   Unscrew the two grub screws and remove the ignition switch.
7   Refitting is a reversal of removal.

24   Instrument panel – removal and refitting

1   Disconnect the battery negative lead.
2   Prise off the cigarette lighter cover, and remove the two screws revealed (photo).
3   Pull out the bottom of the heater control panel and unhook it at the top.
4   Remove the heater or air conditioning control panel.
5   Remove the lighting switch (Section 18)
6   Remove the headlamp range adjuster switch (Section 18)
7   Remove the steering column combination switches (Section 17).
8   Remove the eight screws and withdraw the surround panel from the facia (photos). Note that the centre screws are covered with plastic caps. Disconnect the wiring plug for the headlamp height adjuster.
9   Unclip the bezel from the surround (photo).

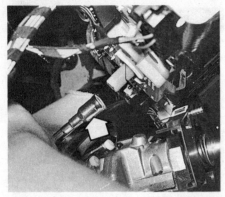

24.12 Disconnecting the speedometer cable (arrowed)

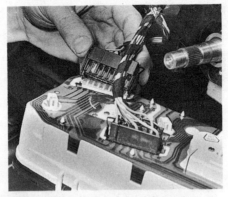

24.13A Disconnecting the left-hand wiring plugs ...

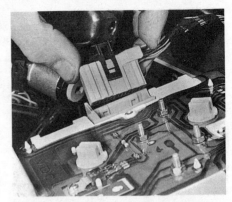

24.13B ... and right-hand wiring plug from the instrument panel

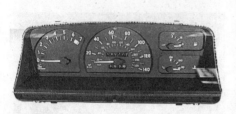

24.14A Instrument panel face

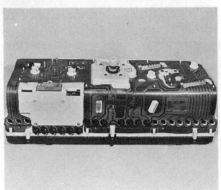

24.14B Rear view of instrument panel

25.4 Disconnecting the speedometer cable from the gearbox

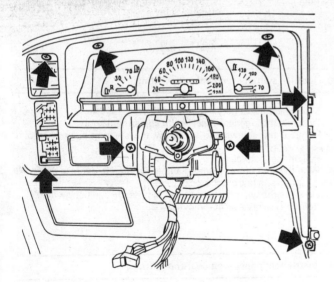

Fig. 12.9 Instrument panel surround screw locations (Sec 24) (LHD shown, RHD similar)

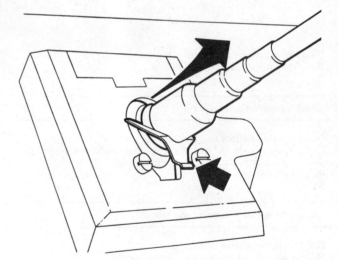

Fig. 12.10 Disconnecting the speedometer cable from the instrument panel (Sec 24)

10   Unscrew the instrument panel retaining screws (photo).
11   Release the speedometer cable from its retaining clips in the engine compartment.
12   Pull out the instrument panel, then depress the spring plate and disconnect the speedometer cable (photo).
13   Note the location of the wiring plugs and disconnect them (photos).
14   Remove the instrument panel (photos).
15   If required, access to the tachometer, temperature gauge, fuel gauge, voltage stabilizer, printed circuit board, and speedometer may

be gained by removing the casing held by five screws.
16   Refitting is a reversal of removal.

25   Speedometer cable – renewal

1   Remove the instrument panel as described in Section 24.
2   Working in the engine compartment draw the cable through the bulkhead and recover the grommet.

26.3 Horn mounting and wiring

27.2 Cover on rear of headlamp

27.3 Removing the parking lamp bulbholder

27.4 Removing the headlamp bulb wiring

27.5 Bulb retaining spring clip (arrowed)

27.6 Removing the headlamp bulb

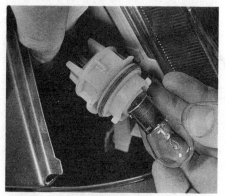

27.9 Front direction indicator lamp bulb removal

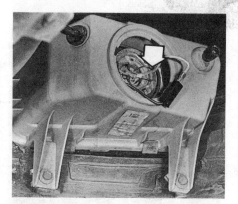

27.12 Front fog lamp wiring and bulb retaining spring clip (arrowed)

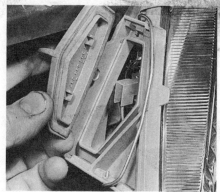

27.15 Front driving lamp cover removal

3   Jack up the front of the car and support on axle stands.
4   Unscrew the knurled nut and disconnect the cable from the gearbox (photo). Remove the cable.
5   Refitting is a reversal of removal, but make sure that the cable is not kinked or bent sharply.

26 Horn – removal and refitting

1   The horn is located behind the radiator grille. First remove the grille as described in Chapter 11.
2   Disconnect the battery negative lead.
3   Disconnect the two horn wires, then unbolt the horn from the bracket (photo).
4   If the horn does not work use a voltmeter to check that 12 volts is

available at one of the wires with the ignition on and the horn push depressed.
5   Refitting is a reversal of removal.

27 Bulbs – renewal

1   When renewing a bulb always switch off the respective circuit, and when charging halogen bulbs do not touch the glass part of the bulb. If the glass is inadvertently touched, clean it with white spirit.

Headlamp and parking lamp
2   Release the spring clip then swivel out the cover and remove it from the rear of the headlamp (photo).
3   Pull out the parking lamp bulbholder and extract the bulb witho turning it (photo).

27.17A Release the spring clip (arrowed) ...

27.17B ... and withdraw the bulb

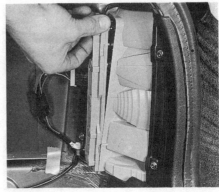

27.20A Rear lamp cluster cover removal (Saloon)

27.20B Rear lamp cluster bulbholder retaining lugs (arrowed)

27.21 Removing a bulb from the rear lamp cluster (Saloon)

27.22 Disconnecting the rear lamp cluster bulbholder wiring plug (Saloon)

27.25 Rear lamp cluster bulbholder removal (Estate)

27.28 Removing the number plate lamp surround (Saloon)

27.29A Remove the number plate lamp ...

4   Pull the wiring plug from the headlight bulb terminals (photo).
5   Squeeze together the ends of the spring clip and swivel it outwards (photo).
6   Remove the old bulb (photo).
7   Fit the new bulb using a reversal of the removal procedure, but make sure that the lug(s) on the bulb engage with the recess(es) provided.

Front direction indicator bulb
8   Twist and remove the bulbholder from the rear of the lamp.
9   Depress and twist the bulb to remove it (photo).
10   Fit the new bulb and reconnect the bulbholder.

Front foglamps
11   Reach under the bumper and remove the cover from the rear of the lamp by turning it anti-clockwise.
12   Release the spring clip, remove the bulb, and disconnect the wiring

(photo).
13   Fit the new bulb in reverse order, making sure that the lugs engage the recesses.

Front driving lamps
14   Remove the radiator grille (Chapter 11)
15   Release the spring clip and remove the cover (photo).
16   Pull the wire from the bulb terminal.
17   Release the spring clip and withdraw the bulb (photos).
18   Fit the new bulb in reverse order.

Rear lamp cluster (Saloon)
19   Unclip the lamp cover.
20   Press the two lugs apart and withdraw the bulbholder (photos).
21   Depress and twist the relevant bulb to remove it (photo).
22   The bulbholder may be removed if required by disconnecting the wiring plug (photo).

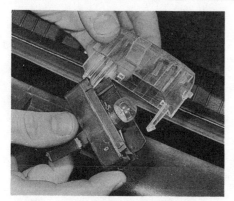

27.29B ... and withdraw the lens

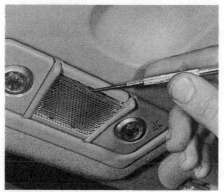

27.34A Removing the front interior lamp lens ...

27.34B ... for access to the bulb

27.34C Rear interior lamp removal

27.35A Glovebox illumination bulb removal

27.35B Engine compartment lamp bulb removal

27.35C Rear luggage compartment lamp bulb removal

27.38 Reading lamp bulb removal

27.40 Removing the side repeater lamp lens ...

23 Fit the new bulb in reverse order.

Rear lamp cluster (Estate)
24 Turn the catch and open the trim cover.
25 Release the lug and withdraw the bulbholder (photo).
26 Depress and twist the relevant bulb to remove it.
27 Fit the new bulb in reverse order.

Number plate lamp (Saloon)
28 Open the boot lid and prise off the lamp surround with a screwdriver (photo).
29 Remove the lamp then depress the lugs and withdraw the lens (photo).
30 Depress and twist the bulb to remove it.

Number plate lamp (Estate)
31 Open the tailgate. Remove the screws and withdraw the lens.
32 Release the festoon type bulb from the terminals.
33 Fit the new bulb in reverse order.

Interior lamps, luggage compartment lamp, engine compartment lamp, and glovebox lamp
34 Using a small screwdriver prise out the lamp and lens (photo).
35 Release the festoon type bulb from the terminals (photos).
36 Fit the new bulb in reverse order.

Reading lamp
37 Using a small screwdriver prise the complete lamp from the headlining.
38 Pull out the bulbholder and extract the wedge type bulb (photo).

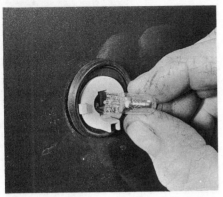

27.41　... and bulb

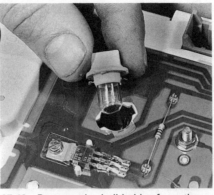

27.43　Remove the bulbholder from the instrument panel ...

27.44　... and extract the bulb

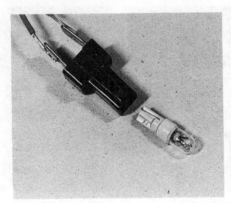

27.46　Heater control illumination light bulb removal

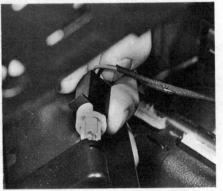

27.48　Ashtray illumination light bulb removal

39　Fit the new bulb in reverse order.

Side repeater lamp
40　Twist and remove the lens (photo).
41　Extract the wedge type bulb (photo).

Instrument panel warning and illumination lights
42　Remove the instrument panel (Section 24).
43　Twist and remove the bulbholder (photo).
44　Extract the wedge type bulb (photo).

Heater control illumination lamp
45　Remove the heater control panel as described in Chapter 11, Section 32.
46　Pull the bulb from the bulbholder (photo).

Ashtray illumination light
47　Remove the facia front panel with reference to Chapter 11.
48　Pull out the bulbholder and extract the bulb (photo)

28　Front direction indicator lamp – removal and refitting

1　Remove the bulb as described in Section 27.
2　Pull back and release the spring clip, then withdraw the lamp forwards.
3　Refitting is a reversal of removal but make sure that the lamp locates correctly on the lugs (Fig. 12.11)

29　Headlamp – removal and refitting

1　Remove the front direction indicator lamp (Section 28).
2　Remove the radiator grille (Chapter 11).
3　Disconnect the headlamp wiring plug (photo).
4　On models with a headlamp range control, disconnect the wiring plug (photo).
5　On models with a headlamp wash/wipe system the front bumper must be moved to one side. To do this, unscrew the bolt located beneath the wheel arch, unclip the wheel arch protector, and release the bumper sideways. The wiper arm may also be removed at this stage and the washer tube disconnected (photos).
6　Unscrew the three mounting bolts and withdraw the headlamp from the location slot (photos).
7　Where applicable remove the headlamp wiper motor (two screws) and the headlamp range control motor (photos).
8　The lens and gasket may be renewed by prising off the spring clips (photo).
9　Refitting is a reversal of removal but adjust the headlamp alignment as described in the next Section.

30　Headlamp – beam alignment

1　Correct alignment of the headlamp beams is most important, not only to ensure good vision for the driver but also to protect other drivers from being dazzled. Accurate alignment should be carried out by a GM

29.3 Disconnecting the headlamp wiring plug

29.4 Disconnecting the headlamp range control wiring

29.5A To remove the headlamp, unscrew the front bumper bolt ...

29.5B ... unclip the wheel arch protector ...

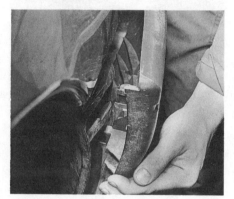

29.5C ... and release the bumper sideways

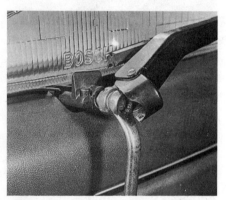

29.5D Removing the headlamp wiper arm

29.5E Disconnecting the washer tube

29.6A Headlamp mounting bolts (arrowed)

29.6B Headlamp bottom location slot

dealer using special optical setting equipment.

2   In an emergency, adjustments may be made by turning the adjustment knobs shown in Fig. 12.12 or Fig. 12.13, however accurate adjustment should be carried out at the earliest opportunity.

3   Holts Amber Lamp is useful for temporarily changing the headlight colour to conform with the normal usage on Continental Europe.

31 Wiper blades and arms – removal and refitting

1   To remove a wiper blade, lift the wiper arm away from the glass. Swivel the blade on the arm, depress the catch on the U-shaped retainer and slide the blade off the arm (photo).

2   The wiper motor should be in its parked position before removing a wiper arm. Mark the position of the blade on the screen with adhesive tape as a guide for refitting.

3   Lift up the cover (where applicable) and unscrew the nut from the spindle (photo). Pull the arm from the spindle.

4   Refitting is a reversal of removal.

32 Windscreen wiper motor and linkage – removal and refitting

1   Remove the windscreen wiper arms as described in Section 31.

2   Disconnect the battery negative lead.

29.7A Headlamp wiper motor

29.7B Headlamp range control motor

29.8 Prising off the headlamp lens retaining spring clips

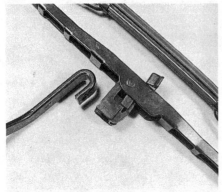

31.1 Removing a windscreen wiper blade

31.3A Removing a windscreen wiper arm

31.3B Tailgate wiper arm spindle nut

32.5 Windscreen wiper motor and wiring multi-plug

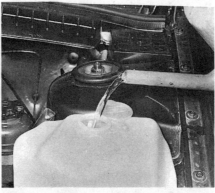

33.4 Topping up the washer fluid reservoir

34.5 Tailgate wiper motor

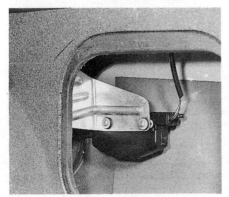

36.2 Fuel filler cap central locking servo

40.1A Removing the Allen screws covering the rod removal holes

40.1B Removing the radio

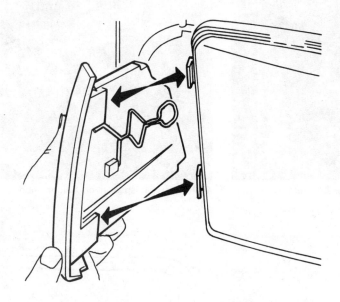

Fig. 12.11 Front direction indicator lamp location lugs (Sec 28)

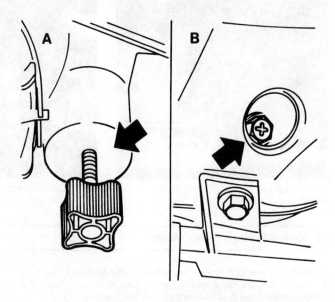

Fig. 12.12 Headlamp beam adjustment knobs on models without range control (Sec 30)

A   Vertical adjustment   *B   Horizontal adjustment*

3   Unscrew the plastic nuts securing the spindles to the windscreen valance.
4   Pull off the rubber moulding and remove the plastic water deflector.
5   Disconnect the wiring multi-plug from the motor (photo).
6   Unbolt the motor and withdraw it together with the linkage.
7   Refitting is a reversal of removal.

33   Windscreen washer pump – removal and refitting

1   Remove the battery (Section 4).
2   Unbolt the windscreen washer reservoir from the wheel arch and empty its contents into a suitable container.
3   Disconnect the wiring plug(s) then twist the pump slightly to remove it. Disconnect the washer hose.
4   Refitting is a reversal of removal. Top up the reservoir with a washer fluid solution (photo).

34   Tailgate wiper motor – removal and refitting

1   Remove the wiper arm as described in Section 31.
2   Remove the tailgate trim and, if fitted, the loudspeakers as described in Chapter 11.
3   Disconnect the battery negative lead.
4   Disconnect the wiring multi-plug from the motor. Also unscrew the earth lead screw.
5   Unbolt and remove the motor and bracket (photo).
6   Unbolt the motor from the bracket.
7   Refitting is a reversal of removal.

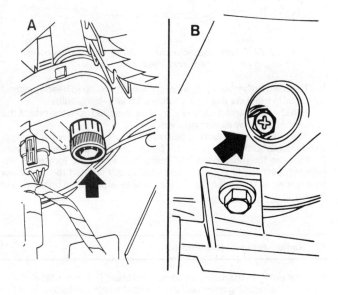

Fig. 12.13 Headlamp beam adjustment knobs on models with range control (Sec 30)

A   Vertical adjustment   *B   Horizontal adjustment*

35   Tailgate washer pump – removal and refitting

1   The tailgate washer pump is located in the same reservoir as the windscreen washer pump and its removal and refitting procedures are therefore as described in Section 33.

40.2 Multiple socket at rear of radio housing

40.3 Cassette storage box removal

40.4 Rear loudspeaker on Saloon models

36 Central locking system – general

Note: For component removal and refitting, refer to Chapter 13.
1   All models are fitted with a central door locking system to allow simultaneous locking of all doors and the fuel filler cap.
2   Each lock is provided with an electrically operated servo, and an electronic control unit generates the electrical impulses needed to operate the servos (photo).
3   The servos should operate when the locking knob or key is half way through its travel. Adjustment is made by loosening the appropriate servo screws, repositioning the servo and tightening the screws.
4   The electronic control unit is located behind the main facia panel.

37 Trip computer – general

1   A trip computer is optional equipment on some models. The computer collects fuel consumption and distance data and integrates them with respect to time. In this way it can provide estimates of fuel consumption (both instantaneous and average), average speed and range on fuel remaining. Normal time clock and stopwatch functions are available, and an external temperature sensor is also provided.
2   For detailed operating instructions, refer to the owner's handbook supplied with the vehicle.
3   Testing of the computer and its satellite components is beyond the scope of the average DIY mechanic.

38 Heated seats – general

1   Heated front and rear seats are optional equipment on some models. Heating elements are fitted inside the seats and controlled thermostatically.
2   In the event of malfunction, first check the wiring runs and connectors. If a heating element is proved faulty, a GM dealer should be consulted.

39 Check control system – general

1   Fitted to some higher specification models, the check control system monitors important fluid levels, brake pad wear and bulb failure. A bank of six or seven warning lights on the instrument panel conveys the information to the driver.
2   All the warning lights should come on for a few seconds when the ignition is first switched on; they should then all go out, except for the stop-lamp warning light which will go out once the brake pedal is operated. If any warning light stays on, or comes on during operation, the components or system indicated should be checked.

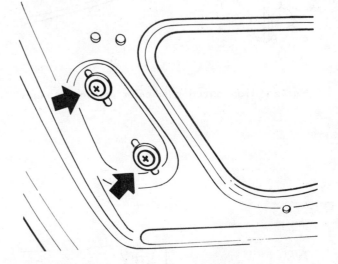

Fig. 12.14 Front door central locking servo mounting screws (Sec 36)

3   The main bulb failure indicator light monitors dipped headlights and tail lights. In brackets this light monitors the stop-lamp bulbs.
4   The check control display unit may be removed from the rear of the instrument panel by extracting three screws.
5   The bulb sensor is located behind the fusebox. If a tow bar is fitted, an additional bulb sensor is located behind the left-hand rear trim panel.
6   Sensors for the coolant and brake fluid levels are located in the relevant reservoir filler caps. A separate sensor is fitted to the washer fluid reservoir. The sensor for the engine oil level is located on the side of the sump.

40 Radio – removal and refitting

1   The radio is manufactured to the latest DIN standard and is removed by inserting two special rods into the holes on each side of the unit. The rods are pressed in until they snap into place, then used to pull the radio out of its aperture. The rods can be obtained from a car entertainment specialist. Note that the rod holes may be covered with side covers or Allen screws (photos).
2   On some models the radio is automatically disconnected from the battery, aerial and loudspeakers by means of a multiple socket, however on other models separate connections are provided (photo).
3   Where applicable the cassette storage box may be removed using the rods described in paragraph 1 (photo).
4   To remove the front loudspeakers remove the trim from the A-pillar then prise out the speakers and disconnect the wiring. Access to the

rear speakers is gained from the luggage compartment on Saloon models (photo). Removal of the door and tailgate mounted speakers is described in Chapter 11.

5   Refitting is a reversal of removal.

41 Radio equipment – suppression of interference

1   Adequate radio interference suppression equipment is fitted during manufacture. If vehicle-generated interference is a problem, make sure first that the radio is properly trimmed (see manufacturer's instructions) and that the aerial is well earthed.

2   Radio equipment which is fitted instead of the original items may be more sensitive to interference. If not already present, the use of an in-line choke in the radio power supply, as close as possible to the receiver, is often of benefit.

3   If interference from the windscreen wiper motor is a problem, an in-line choke can be fitted to it supply leads. Make sure that the choke is of adequate current carrying capacity.

4   The ignition system is already suppressed and no further attempt

should be made in that direction.

5   Consult a GM dealer or car entertainment specialist for further advice if necessary.

42 Wiring diagrams – general

1   The wiring diagrams are of the current flow type. Each circuit is shown in the simplest possible fashion. The bottom line of the diagram represents the 'earth' or negative connection; the numbers below this line are track numbers, which enable circuits and components to be located using the key.

2   The lines at the top of the diagram represent 'live' or positive connection points. The line labelled '30' is live at all times, whilst that labelled '15' is live only when the ignition is on.

3   Numbers in the square boxes on the diagram give the current tracks where the circuit is continued.

43 Fault diagnosis – electrical system

Symptom	Reason(s)
Starter motor does not turn – no voltage at motor	Battery terminals loose or corroded Battery discharged or defective Starter motor connections loose or broken Starter switch or solenoid faulty
Starter motor does not turn – voltage at motor	Starter motor internal defect
Starter motor turns very slowly	Battery nearly discharged or defective Battery terminals loose or corroded Starter motor internal defect
Starter motor noisy or rough	Mounting bolts loose Pinion or flywheel ring gear teeth damaged or worn
Alternator not charging battery	Drivebelt slipping or broken Alternator brushes worn Alternator connections loose or broken Alternator internal defect
Alternator overcharging battery	Alternator voltage regulator faulty
Battery will not hold charge	Short-circuit causing continual drain on battery Battery defective internally Battery case dirty and damp
Fuel or temperature gauge gives no reading	Sender unit defective Wire disconnected or broken Fuse blown Gauge faulty Instrument voltage stabiliser faulty (will affect all instruments)
Fuel or temperature gauge reads too high	Sender unit defective Wire earthed Gauge faulty Instrument voltage stabiliser faulty
Horn operates continuously	Horn push stuck down Cable to horn push earthed
Horn does not operate	Fuse blown Cable or connector broken or loose Horn contact ring dirty or corroded

Symptom	Reason(s)
Lights do not come on	Battery discharged Fuse(s) blown Light switch faulty Bulb blown
Lights give poor illumination	Lenses or reflectors dirty Bulbs blackened Incorrect wattage bulbs fitted
Wiper motor fails to work	Fuse blown Connections loosen or broken Relay defective Switch defective Motor defective
Wiper motor works slowly and draws little current	Brushes badly worn Commutator dirty or burnt
Wiper motor works slowly and draws heavy current	Linkage seized or otherwise damaged Motor internal fault
Wiper motor works, but blades do not move	Linkage broken or disconnected Motor gearbox badly worn
Defect in any other components	Fuse blown Relay faulty (when applicable) Supply wire broken or disconnected Switch faulty (when applicable) Earth return faulty (check for loose or corroded mountings) Component itself faulty

Chapter 13 Supplement:
Revisions and information on later models

Contents

1 Introduction

This Supplement contains information which is additional to, or a
revision of, the information contained in the first twelve Chapters.

The Sections in this Supplement follow the same order as the
Chapters to which they relate. The Specifications are all grouped
together at the beginning for convenience, but they too follow Chapter
order.

It is recommended that before any work commences, reference is
made to the appropriate Section(s) of this Supplement, in order to
establish any changes to procedures or specifications, before reading
the main Chapter(s). If no information on the relevant operation is
contained in this Chapter, then the operation can be carried out using
the information in the relevant original Chapter.

2 Specifications

Engine – 2.0 litre models with a catalytic converter
Note: *Unless otherwise stated, the specifications are as given for non-catalyst 2.0 litre models in Chapter 1*
Engine code C20NE
Compression ratio 9.2:1
Maximum output .... 115 bhp (85kW) @ 5200 rpm
Maximum torque .... 125.4 lbf ft @ 2600 rpm

Fuel and exhaust systems – 1990-on 2.0 litre models
Note: *Unless otherwise stated, the specifications are as given for earlier 2.0 litre models in Chapter 3*
System type .... Bosch Motronic M1.5 engine management system
Fuel pump operating pressure (engine idling at specified speed):
    Pressure regulator vacuum hose connected .... 1.8 to 2.2 bars
    Pressure regulator vacuum hose disconnected and plugged .... 2.5 to 3.0 bars
CO at idle (models with a catalytic converter) .... Less than 0.4%

Torque wrench setting

	Nm	lbf ft
Lambda sensor	30	22

Ignition system
Note: *Unless otherwise stated, the specifications are as given for earlier models in Chapter 4*
System type:
    1990-on 1.8 litre carburettor models .... MSTS (Microprocessor Spark Timing System) equipped with self-diagnosis facility
    1990-on 2.0 litre models .... Bosch Motronic M1.5 engine management system

Automatic transmission – 1990-on 2.0 litre models
Note: *Refer to Chapter 6 for information on AW 03-71L transmission fitted to all other models*
Type .... GM Powertrain computer-controlled with three operating modes, four forward speeds and one reverse
Designation AR25
Ratios:
    1st 2.40:1
    2nd 1.48:1
    3rd 1.00:1
    4th 0.72:1
    Reverse 1.92:1
Lubricant type/specification .... Dexron II type ATF (Duckhams Uni-Matic or D-Matic)
Capacity (approximate):
    From dry .... 6.4 litres (11.3 pints)
    After removing large sump .... 4.7 litres (8.3 pints)
    Drain and refill only .... 2.6 litres (4.7 pints)

Torque wrench settings

	Nm	lbf ft
Transmission sump bolts	12	9
Drain plug	25	18
Fluid filter bolts	20	15
Inhibitor switch bolts	12	9
Selector shaft lever nut	20	15
Transmission-to-engine bolts	45	33
Torque converter-to-driveplate bolts	30	22
Rear crossmember bolts	45	33

Final drive and driveshafts
Note: *Unless otherwise stated, the specifications are as given in Chapter 8*
Final drive ratio:
    1.8 models with automatic transmission 3.90:1
    2.0 litre models with a catalytic converter 3.90:1
Final drive lubricant capacity – models with modified rear cover .... See text

Braking system
Note: *Unless otherwise stated, the specifications are as given in Chapter 9*

Torque wrench settings

	Nm	lbf ft
Caliper guide pin bolt (ATE caliper)	30	22
Caliper mounting bracket-to-steering knuckle bolts:		
Stage 1	95	70
Stage 2	Angle-tighten a further 30 to 45°	Angle-tighten a further 30 to 45°
Caliper brake hose union bolt	40	30

Suspension and steering
Note: *Unless otherwise stated, the specifications are as given in Chapter 10*
Wheel sizes:
    Later low-specification models .... 6J x 15
    Later high-specification models .... 6J x 15 or 7J x 15*
* *These models have a space-saver 6J x 15 spare wheel, which must be used only in emergencies*
Tyre sizes .... 195/65 HR 15 or 195/65 VR 15 (depending on model)

3 Fuel and exhaust systems – 2.0 litre models

General information

1   From 1990 model year onwards, all 2.0 litre models are fitted with a Motronic M1.5 fuel injection system, instead of the ML4 system fitted to earlier models. The two systems are very similar in operation, the only notable change on the M1.5 system being that a throttle valve potentiometer is fitted, instead of the throttle valve switch used on the earlier ML4 system. The advantage of the potentiometer is that it informs the control unit of the exact position of the throttle valve, and not just whether the valve is open or closed. This allows the fuel/air mixture to be more accurately controlled.

2   From 1990 onwards, a 2.0 litre model with a catalytic converter was also offered. This model has the engine code C20NE, and has a closed-loop three-way catalytic converter to reduce harmful pollutants released into the atmosphere via the exhaust gases. The system is controlled by a lambda sensor which is screwed into the exhaust system downpipe. The lambda sensor tip is sensitive to oxygen, and provides the fuel injection system control unit with constant feedback about the condition of the exhaust gases. This enables the control unit to accurately adjust the amount of fuel being supplied to the engine, to calculate the required fuel/air mixture and so provide the best possible operating conditions for the converter. The lambda sensor tip also has a built-in heating element, which is controlled by the control unit. When the engine is cold, the control unit supplies current to the lambda sensor heating element, which in turn heats the exhaust gases as they pass over the sensor. The warmed exhaust gases then quickly bring the catalytic converter up to its normal operating temperature where it can operate efficiently.

3   On models with a catalytic converter, an evaporative emission control system is fitted. This prevents the release of fuel vapour into the atmosphere. With the ignition switched off, vapours from the fuel tank are fed to a carbon canister, where they are absorbed. When the engine is started, the electronic control unit opens a purge solenoid valve, and the fuel vapours are fed into the inlet manifold and mixed with fresh air. This cleans the carbon filter.

4   Unless otherwise stated below, procedures on these later models are as described for the 2.0 litre models in Chapter 3.

Mixture check and adjustment – models with a catalytic converter

5   On models with a catalytic converter, the fuel/air mixture is under the control of the lambda sensor, and therefore needs no adjustment. However, the performance of the closed-loop catalytic converter system should still be checked at regular intervals, using a good-quality, carefully-calibrated exhaust gas analyser. If the CO level at the tailpipe is too high, the complete fuel injection and ignition systems must be checked thoroughly, using Vauxhall diagnostic equipment. Once these have been checked and are known to be free from faults, the fault must be in the catalytic converter, which must then be renewed.

Throttle valve potentiometer – removal and refitting

6   The throttle valve potentiometer can be removed and refitted using the information given for the throttle valve switch, given in Chapter 3, Section 25, ignoring the remark about switch adjustment (photo). Adjustment of the throttle valve potentiometer is not necessary.

Lambda sensor (models with a catalytic converter) – removal and refitting

Note: *The lambda sensor must be unscrewed from the exhaust system downpipe when the engine is at normal operating temperature. The sensor is delicate, and will not work if it is dropped or knocked, if its power supply is disrupted, or if any cleaning materials or solvents are used on it.*

Removal

7   Warm the engine up to normal operating temperature, then switch it off. Firmly apply the handbrake, jack up the front of the vehicle and support it on axle stands.

8   Taking great care not to burn your hands on the hot exhaust pipe, disconnect the sensor wiring connector, and free the wiring from its retaining clips.

9   Carefully unscrew the lambda sensor, and remove it from the exhaust system along with its sealing washer.

3.6 Throttle potentiometer (arrowed) – Motronic M1.5 fuel injection system

Refitting

10   If the original lambda sensor is to be refitted, remove all traces of anti-seize compound from the threads, and apply a smear of the special grease (part number 19 48 602) to the threads of the sensor; this is available from your Vauxhall dealer. In the absence of the specified grease, a smear of good-quality, high-temperature anti-seize compound (such as Duckhams Copper 10) can be used. Note that new lambda sensors are supplied with the grease already applied to their threads. Examine the sealing washer for signs of damage, and renew if necessary.

11   Fit the sealing washer to the end of the lambda sensor, then screw the sensor into the downpipe and tighten it to the specified torque.

12   Ensuring that the wiring is correctly routed, reconnect the wiring connector and secure the wiring with all the necessary retaining clips.

13   Make a final check that the wiring is in no danger of contacting the exhaust system, then lower the vehicle to the ground.

Exhaust manifold (models with a catalytic converter) – removal and refitting

14   On these models, the exhaust manifold can be removed and refitted as described in Section 29 of Chapter 3, noting that it will be necessary to disconnect the lambda sensor wiring connector and release the wiring from its retaining clips before disconnecting the downpipe. On refitting, reconnect the wiring connector, and ensure that the wiring is correctly routed and retained by all the necessary retaining clips.

Exhaust system (models with a catalytic converter) – general information, removal and refitting

Note: *The catalytic converter is a fragile component which is easily damaged – do not strike any part of the system with tools, and take care not to drop it or strike it against anything else while handling it.*

15   On these models, the exhaust system is very similar to that fitted to non-catalyst-equipped 2.0 litre models, except that it consists of four sections – the fourth section being the catalytic converter itself, fitted between the downpipe and intermediate pipe.

16   The system can be removed and refitted using the information given in Section 30 of Chapter 3, noting that, prior to removing the complete system or the downpipe, it will be necessary to either disconnect the lambda sensor wiring connector and free the wiring from its retaining clips, or to remove the sensor itself, as described earlier in this Section. On refitting, install the sensor as described earlier in this Section, and/or ensure that the wiring is securely retained by all its necessary retaining clips, and is in no danger of contacting the exhaust system (as applicable).

Catalytic converter – general information and precautions

17   The catalytic converter is a reliable and simple device which needs no maintenance in itself, but there are some facts of which an owner

should be aware if the converter is to function properly for its full service life.

(a) *DO NOT use leaded petrol in a car with a catalytic converter – the lead will coat the precious metals, reducing their converting efficiency, and will eventually destroy the converter.*

(b) *Always keep the ignition and fuel systems well-maintained in accordance with the manufacturer's schedule – particularly, ensure that the air cleaner filter element, the fuel filter and the spark plugs are renewed at the correct intervals – if the intake air/fuel mixture is allowed to become too rich due to neglect, the unburned surplus will enter and burn in the catalytic converter, overheating the element and eventually destroying the converter.*

(c) *If the engine develops a misfire, do not drive the car at all (or at least as little as possible) until the fault is cured – the misfire will allow unburned fuel to enter the converter, which will result in its overheating, as noted in (b) above.*

(d) *DO NOT push- or tow-start the car – this will soak the catalytic converter in unburned fuel, causing it to overheat when the engine does start – see (b) above.*

(e) *DO NOT switch off the ignition at high engine speeds – ie do not 'blip' the throttle immediately before switching off the engine. If the ignition is switched off at anything above idle speed, unburned fuel will enter the (very hot) catalytic converter, with the possible risk of its igniting on the element and damaging the converter.*

(f) *DO NOT use fuel or engine oil additives – these may contain substances harmful to the catalytic converter.*

(g) *DO NOT continue to use the car if the engine burns oil to the extent of leaving a visible trail of blue smoke -- the unburned carbon deposits will clog the converter passages and reduce its efficiency; in severe cases, the element will overheat.*

(h) *Remember that the catalytic converter operates at very high temperatures – hence the heat shields on the car's underbody – and the casing will become hot enough to ignite combustible materials which brush against it. DO NOT, therefore, park the car in dry undergrowth, or over long grass or piles of dead leaves.*

(i) *Remember that the catalytic converter is FRAGILE – do not strike it with tools during servicing work, take great care when working on the exhaust system, and ensure that the converter is well clear of any jacks or other lifting gear used to raise the car. Do not drive the car over rough ground, road humps, etc., in such a way as to 'ground' the exhaust system.*

(j) *In some cases, particularly when the car is new and/or is used for stop/start driving, a sulphurous smell (like that of rotten eggs) may be noticed from the exhaust. This is common to many catalytic converter-equipped cars, and seems to be due to the small amount of sulphur found in some petrols reacting with hydrogen in the exhaust to produce hydrogen sulphide (H_2S) gas; while this gas is toxic, it is not produced in sufficient amounts to be a problem. Once the car has covered a few thousand miles, the problem should disappear – in the meanwhile, a change of driving style or of the brand of petrol used may effect a solution.*

(k) *The catalytic converter, used on a well-maintained and well-driven car, should last for between 50 000 and 100 000 miles – from this point on, careful checks of the CO level should be made at all specified service intervals, to ensure that the converter is still operating efficiently – if the converter is no longer effective, it must be renewed.*

Carbon canister (models with a catalytic converter) – removal and refitting
Removal
18   The carbon canister is mounted onto the engine compartment bulkhead. To remove the canister, slacken the hose clips and disconnect the hoses from the canister, noting their correct fitted positions. Slacken and remove the canister bracket mounting clamp bolt, then remove the clamp and lift the canister out of the engine compartment.

Refitting
19   Refitting is a reversal of the removal procedure, ensuring the hoses are reconnected to their original positions and the hose clamps are securely tightened.

Purge valve (models with a catalytic converter) – removal and refitting
Removal
20   Trace the outlet hose from the carbon canister (mounted on the engine compartment bulkhead) to the purge valve. Noting their correct fitted positions, slacken the retaining clips and disconnect the hoses from the valve.
21   Disconnect the valve wiring connector, then undo the retaining bolt and remove the valve from the engine compartment.

Refitting
22   Refitting is a reverse of the removal procedure, ensuring that the vacuum hoses are correctly refitted and securely retained by their retaining clips.

---

4   Ignition system – 1.8 litre carburettor models

General information
1   From the 1990 model year onwards, 1.8 litre carburettor models were fitted with a different version of the Microprocessor Spark Timing System (MSTS) ignition system. This later version, known as the EI Plus system, has a self-diagnosis facility, which can be accessed by a Vauxhall technician using the special 'TECH 1' electronic tester. This is a useful aid to fault diagnosis, should a problem arise.
2   The later EI Plus ignition system is very similar to the earlier system, apart from the following changes.

(a) *There is no octane rating plug in the ignition system. The ignition timing is set to run on unleaded petrol as standard, and requires no modification; if desired, leaded petrol can also be used without any adverse side effects.*

(b) *Checking of the ignition timing is no longer possible without the use of the special electronic Vauxhall test equipment.*

3   Bearing in mind the points made in paragraph 2, all other operations can be carried out using the information given for earlier 1.8 litre carburettor models in Chapter 4.

---

5   Automatic transmission

AR25 transmission – general information
1   From 1990 model year onwards, 2.0 litre models with automatic transmission were fitted with a new electronically-controlled four-speed automatic transmission. This new AR25 transmission unit has three driving modes; an Economy mode, a Sport mode and a Winter mode. The Economy mode, as the name suggests, is the mode for normal driving, in which the transmission shifts up at relatively low engine speeds to combine reasonable performance with economy. The transmission is automatically set to the Economy mode every time the ignition is switched on.
2   For increased performance, there is a Sport mode, selected using the button on the top of the selector lever. When the transmission is in Sport mode, an indicator lamp on the left-hand side of the instrument cluster is lit. In this mode, the transmission hangs on to each gear longer, shifting up at higher engine speeds to achieve maximum performance. To return to the Economy mode, simply press the selector button a second time.
3   The Winter mode is selected using the button on the centre console. When the Winter mode is selected, the LED indicator by the switch is lit. In this mode, the vehicle pulls away from rest with the transmission in third gear. This limits the torque supplied to the driving wheels, and allows the vehicle to start off safely on slippery surfaces such as snow and ice. The Winter mode can only be selected when the selector lever is in the 'D' position. To return the transmission to Economy mode, simply press the mode button for a second time, or move the selector lever to position '3' or 'R'. Note that the transmission will automatically exit the Winter mode and return to the Economy mode if the vehicle speed exceeds 50 mph (80 kph) or if the kickdown switch is depressed for more than 2 seconds.

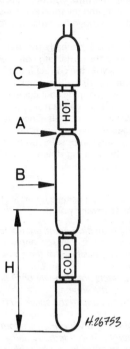

Fig. 13.1 AR25 automatic transmission filling levels (Sec 5)

A Filling level when ambient
   air temperature is above
   0°C (32°F)
B Filling level when ambient
   air temperature is below
   0°C (32°F)

C Filling level after transmission
   overhaul (transmission
   completely dry)
H Fluid level measurement from
   the base of dipstick

AR25 transmission – routine maintenance

Transmission fluid level check

4   To check the automatic transmission fluid level, first take the vehicle on a run of approximately 12 miles/20 km to warm the transmission up to its normal operating temperature. On your return, ensure that the vehicle is parked on level ground. With the engine running and the brakes applied, move the selector lever slowly from the 'P' position to the '1' position, and then return it to 'P'.

5   With the engine still idling and the selector lever in the 'P' position, withdraw the transmission dipstick, wipe it clean, then re-insert it fully into the tube. Withdraw the dipstick and note the level of the fluid. Repeat this procedure three times, and take the average reading as the true transmission fluid level.

6   With the engine and transmission at normal operating temperature, at ambient temperatures above 0°C (32°F), the fluid level should be within the 'HOT' portion of the dipstick (approximately 42 mm (1.65 in) up from the base of the dipstick). At ambient temperatures below 0°C (32°F), the fluid level should be halfway between the 'HOT' portion and the 'COLD' portion of the dipstick (approximately 32 mm (1.26 in) up from the base of the dipstick).

7   If necessary, top-up the transmission fluid level with the specified fluid via the dipstick tube, and recheck the fluid level as described above. Take great care not to allow any dust or dirt to enter the tube.

8   Once the level is correct, refit the dipstick and switch off the engine.

Transmission fluid renewal

9   On the AR25 transmission, the fluid should be renewed every 36 000 miles (60 000 km) or every 4 years, depending on which comes sooner. Although not strictly necessary, it is also recommended that the large transmission sump is removed at this interval and the transmission fluid filter cleaned. This will ensure that more of the transmission fluid is drained and renewed (only approximately half of the transmission fluid is drained when only the sump drain plug is removed), and that all debris is removed from the filter and sump.

10   If it is only wished to renew the transmission fluid, this can be carried out as described in Section 2 of Chapter 6, referring to the Specifications at the start of this Chapter for the approximate fluid quantity. On completion, fill the transmission with the specified type of fluid until the fluid level is at the correct point on the dipstick (see Fig. 13.1), then take the vehicle on a run, and check the fluid level as

5.17A Position a new gasket on the filter housing...

5.17B ...then refit the filter to the transmission...

5.17C ...and tighten its retaining bolts to the specified torque

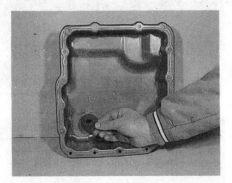

5.18A Install the cleaned magnet in the sump...

5.18B ...and refit the sump using a new gasket

described earlier in this Section. To clean the filter element as well, proceed as follows.

11   Firmly apply the handbrake, then jack up the front of the vehicle and support it on axle stands.

12   Position a container beneath the transmission sump, then unscrew the drain plug and allow the fluid to drain into the container. **Caution:** *If the vehicle has just been driven, the fluid will be extremely hot. Take great care to avoid being scalded.*

13   Examine the drain plug sealing washer, and renew if necessary. Once all the fluid has drained, wipe the threads clean, then refit the drain plug to the sump, tightening it to the specified torque.

14   Slacken and remove all the sump retaining bolts, then carefully lower the sump away from the transmission, being prepared for some fluid spillage. Note that the sump still contains a considerable amount of transmission fluid. Pour the fluid out of the sump and into the container, then remove the gasket and discard it.

15   Undo the three retaining bolts, then remove the filter from the underside of the transmission along with its sealing gasket. Discard the gasket; a new one should be used on refitting.

16   Clean the filter element in a bath of solvent, then examine the element for signs of clogging or damage. If the filter element is split or blocked, the filter must be renewed. Remove the magnet from inside the sump, and clean all traces of metal filings from it; the filings should be very fine – any sizeable chips of metal indicate a worn component in the transmission.

17   Ensure that the filter element is dry, then fit the new gasket onto the filter housing and offer up the filter to the transmission. Ensuring that the gasket remains correctly positioned, refit the retaining bolts and tighten them to the specified torque (photos).

18   Ensure that the sump and transmission sealing faces are clean and dry, then position the new gasket on the sump and refit the magnet. Refit the sump to the transmission, and tighten its retaining bolts to the specified torque (photos).

19   Lower the vehicle to the ground, then fill the transmission with the specified type of fluid until the fluid level is at the correct point on the dipstick (see Fig. 13.1); the approximate quantity is given in the Specifications at the start of this Chapter. On completion, take the vehicle on a run, and check the fluid level as described earlier in this Section.

AR25 transmission – removal and refitting

Removal

20   Firmly apply the handbrake, and place the selector lever in the 'N' position. Disconnect the battery negative terminal.

21   Withdraw the dipstick from the filler tube, then undo the dipstick tube retaining bolt and washer, and remove the tube from the transmission, noting its sealing O-ring.

22   Trace the transmission inhibitor switch wiring back to its wiring connector (which is clipped to the centre of the engine compartment bulkhead). Disconnect the connector, and free the switch wiring loom from all its relevant retaining clips and ties.

23   From within the engine compartment, release the transmission breather hose from all its retaining clips and ties.

24   Chock the rear wheels, then jack up the front of the vehicle and support it on axle stands.

25   From underneath the vehicle, release the inhibitor switch wiring and breather hose from any remaining clips.

26   On models not fitted with a catalytic converter, remove the exhaust system downpipe as described in Chapter 3, then unbolt the exhaust mounting bracket and heat shield. On models with a catalytic converter, remove the downpipe and converter, referring to the information given in Section 3 of this Chapter, then remove the mounting bracket and the catalytic converter heat shields.

27   Disconnect the two wiring connectors from the left-hand side of the transmission housing, and position the wiring clear of the transmission. **Note:** *When disconnecting the wiring connectors, hold the lower part of each connector firmly in position, to prevent it from being pulled out of the transmission.*

28   Release the speed sensor wiring from its retaining clip, and disconnect it at the wiring connector.

29   Slacken and remove the four retaining bolts, and remove the front crossmember from under the vehicle.

30   Carry out the operations described in paragraphs 9 to 17 of Section 14 in Chapter 6.

31   Place a jack with interposed block of wood beneath the transmission, and raise the jack until it is supporting the weight of the transmission.

32   Slacken and remove the nuts and bolts securing the rear crossmember to the transmission, and the four bolts securing the crossmember to the underbody, then remove the crossmember from underneath the vehicle.

33   With the jack positioned beneath the transmission taking the weight, slacken and remove the remaining bolts securing the transmission housing to the engine. Note the correct fitted positions of the bolts, to use as a reference on refitting, then make a final check that all necessary components have been disconnected.

34   With the bolts removed, move the trolley jack and transmission to the rear, to free it from its locating dowels. Once the transmission is free, lower the jack and manoeuvre the unit out from under the car, ensuring that the torque converter stays in position on the transmission shaft. If they are loose, remove the locating dowels from the transmission or engine, and keep them in a safe place.

Refitting

35   The transmission is refitted using a reversal of the removal procedure, bearing in mind the following points.

   (a)   *Apply a little high-melting-point grease to the splines of the transmission input shaft. Do not apply too much, however, otherwise there is a possibility of the grease contaminating the torque converter.*

   (b)   *Make sure the dowels are correctly positioned prior to refitting the transmission to the engine.*

   (c)   *Tighten all nuts and bolts to the specified torque setting (where given).*

   (d)   *Prior to installation, apply locking compound to the threads of the rear crossmember-to-underbody bolts.*

   (e)   *Ensure that the breather hose and wiring looms are correctly routed, and secured by all the necessary retaining clamps and new cable ties.*

   (f)   *On completion, refill the transmission with the specified type and quantity of fluid, and check the adjustment of the selector linkage as described later in this Section.*

Kickdown system (AR25 transmission) – general information and switch renewal

36   Unlike the earlier AW 03-71L transmission, the AR25 transmission kickdown system is fully electronically-controlled, and has no actuating cable. The system is triggered by the switch situated beneath the accelerator pedal.

37   To remove the switch, disconnect the wiring, then carefully prise the switch off its retainer. On refitting, ensure the switch is correctly seated on its retainer, then reconnect the wiring connector.

Selector lever linkage (AR25 transmission) – adjustment

38   The selector lever linkage can be adjusted using the information given in Chapter 6, Section 17 (photo). On completion, check the operation of the inhibitor switch and, if necessary, adjust as described later in this Section.

5.38 Selector lever linkage rod spring clip and pivot pin (arrowed)

Selector lever (AR25 transmission) – removal and refitting

Removal

39   Remove the centre console assembly as described in Chapter 11.

40   Firmly apply the handbrake, then jack up the front of the vehicle and support on axle stands.

41   From underneath the vehicle, release the spring clip, then withdraw the pivot pin and detach the linkage rod from the base of the selector lever.

42   Return to the inside of the vehicle, and carefully drill out the five rivets securing the selector lever housing to the body. Lift the selector lever and housing out of the vehicle.

Refitting

43   Remove all traces of sealing compound from the base of the selector lever housing and vehicle body.

44   Apply a bead of suitable sealing compound to the underside of the selector lever housing, then refit the housing to the vehicle.

45   Secure the selector lever housing in position using new pop-rivets.

46   From underneath the vehicle, reconnect the linkage rod to the base of the selector lever, securing the pivot pin in position with the spring clip.

47   Refit the centre console as described in Chapter 11.

48   Check the selector linkage adjustment and the inhibitor switch operation as described elsewhere in this Section.

Inhibitor switch (AR25 transmission) – removal, refitting and adjustment

Removal

49   Firmly apply the handbrake, and place the selector lever in position 'N'.

50   Trace the transmission inhibitor switch wiring back to its wiring connector (which is clipped to the centre of the engine compartment bulkhead). Disconnect the connector, and free the switch wiring loom from all its relevant retaining clips and ties.

51   Chock the rear wheels, then jack up the front of the vehicle and support it on axle stands.

52   From underneath the vehicle, release the inhibitor switch wiring from any further retaining clips (photo).

53   Unclip the inhibitor switch cover, then slacken and remove the nut securing the selector lever to the transmission, and pull the lever off the selector shaft.

5.52 Inhibitor switch location (arrowed) – AR25 transmission

54   Undo the two retaining bolts, and slide the inhibitor switch off the selector shaft.

Refitting and adjustment

55   Prior to refitting the switch, examine the selector shaft oil seal for signs of damage or oil leakage, and renew if necessary. To renew the oil seal, carefully lever the oil seal out of position using a small flat-bladed screwdriver. Apply a thin smear of grease to the lips of the new seal, then carefully pass the seal over the end of the shaft and press it into position in the transmission. If necessary, the seal can be tapped into position using a suitable tubular drift which bears only on the hard outer edge of the seal.

56   Locate the inhibitor switch on the selector shaft, then install its two retaining bolts, tightening them finger-tight only at this stage. Adjust the switch as follows. Before proceeding further, temporarily refit the selector lever to the shaft, and ensure that the transmission is still in neutral ('N' position).

57   There are two ways of adjusting the switch, either mechanically or electrically. The electrical method is the far more accurate method, but requires the use of a multimeter.

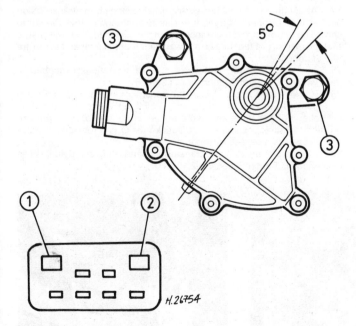

Fig. 13.2 AR25 transmission inhibitor switch electrical adjustment (Sec 5)

1 Wiring connector terminal 1
2 Wiring connector terminal 2
3 Inhibitor switch retaining bolts

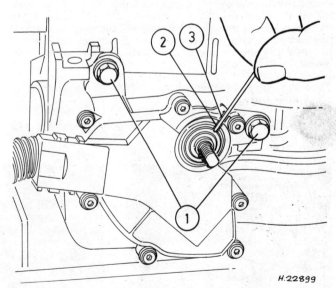

Fig. 13.3 Adjusting the AR25 transmission inhibitor switch using a suitable piece of welding rod (Sec 5)

1 Inhibitor switch retaining bolts
2 Inhibitor switch groove
3 Selector lever groove

5.66 AR25 electronic control unit location (water deflector lifted)

58   To electrically adjust the switch, connect a multimeter, set to the resistance function, across terminals 1 and 2 of the switch wiring connector (see Fig. 13.2). With the transmission in neutral, there should be continuity between the terminals. Pivot the switch slowly to determine the area of the switch where this occurs; this area forms an angle of approximately 5°. Position the switch in the centre of this area, then tighten its retaining bolts to the specified torque.

59   To adjust the switch mechanically, a welding rod of diameter 2.0 to 2.3 mm (0.08 to 0.09 in) is required. With the transmission in neutral, pivot the switch until the grooves on the switch and transmission selector lever align and the rod can be cleanly inserted (see Fig. 13.3). Hold the switch in this position, and tighten its retaining bolts to the specified torque. Check that the grooves are still correctly aligned, then remove the rod.

60   Once the inhibitor switch is correctly adjusted, refit the selector lever to the transmission selector shaft, and tighten its retaining nut to the specified torque.

61   Feed the switch wiring back up into the engine compartment, ensuring it is correctly routed.

62   From within the engine compartment, reconnect the inhibitor switch wiring connector, and secure the wiring in position with new cable ties.

63   Check the selector linkage adjustment as described in Chapter 6, Section 17, then check that the inhibitor switch operates correctly.

64   Refit the inhibitor switch cover, and lower the vehicle to the ground.

Transmission electronic control unit (AR25 transmission) – removal and refitting
Removal

65   The electronic control unit is situated under the bonnet (behind the left-hand end of the plastic water deflector).

66   To remove the unit, open up the bonnet, then peel back the sealing strip from the left-hand end of the water deflector. Carefully lift the water deflector to gain access to the control unit (photo).

67   Undo the retaining bolt and withdraw the control unit, disconnecting the wiring connector as it becomes accessible.

Refitting

68   Refitting is a reversal of the removal procedure, ensuring that the water deflector and sealing strip are correctly seated.

Sport mode switch (AR25 transmission) – removal and refitting
Removal

69   Using a small flat-bladed screwdriver, carefully prise out the gear indicator panel and slot cover from the surround panel, and remove them from the selector lever.

70   Undo the single retaining screw, then release the surround panel from the centre console. Pull the bulbholder out of the panel, and lift the panel off the selector lever.

71   Gently feed the Sport mode switch wiring in through the base of the selector lever, until the switch is forced out of position.

72   Using a soldering iron, carefully unsolder the two wires and remove the switch.

Refitting

73   Refitting is a reverse of the removal procedure, ensuring that the wires are securely soldered onto the switch. Check the operation of the switch prior to refitting the surround panel.

Winter mode switch (AR25 transmission) – removal and refitting
Removal

74   Unclip the middle console cover, and remove it from the centre console, disconnecting the switch wiring connector(s) as they become accessible.

75   Depress the switch retaining tangs, and remove the switch from the cover.

Refitting

76   Refitting is a reversal of the removal procedure.

Transmission fluid filter (AW 03-71L transmission) – cleaning

77   Although not strictly necessary, when changing the transmission fluid at the specified interval, it is also recommended that the sump should be removed and the transmission filter cleaned. This will ensure that the majority of the fluid is renewed, and that the filter and sump are free of debris.

78   To clean the filter, first carry out the operations described in paragraphs 13 to 15 of Section 2 of Chapter 6.

79   Remove the sump and clean the transmission filter as described in paragraphs 14 to 18 of this Section, noting that the filter is retained by six bolts and that there are two magnets in the sump. Also, prior to refitting the sump, examine the dipstick tube O-ring for signs of damage, and renew if necessary (photos).

80   On completion, refill the transmission and check the fluid level as described in Chapter 6, Section 2.

5.79A Fluid filter retaining bolts (arrowed) – AW 03-71L transmission

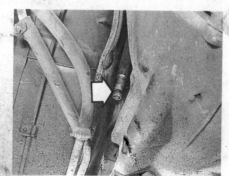

5.79B Ensure the dipstick tube O-ring (arrowed) is in good condition...

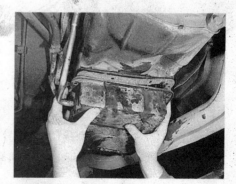

5.79C ...then refit the sump using a new gasket

6 Final drive and driveshafts

Final drive unit rear cover – modification

1   From approximately August 1990 onwards, most final drive units were fitted with a modified rear cover. The modified rear cover can be easily identified by the vertical cooling ribs cast into its outer surface; earlier covers have a smooth outer surface. The modified rear cover does not affect any of the procedures described in Chapter 8, but it does alter the lubricant capacity of the final drive; the final drive now requires an extra 0.1 litre (0.2 pints) of lubricant.

Final drive unit rear cover gasket – renewal

2   The final drive unit rear cover gasket can be renewed as described in Chapter 8, Section 5, noting the following points.

(a) A paper gasket is no longer fitted between the cover and housing. On refitting, ensure that the cover and housing mating surfaces are clean and dry, then apply a coat of suitable sealing compound to the cover flange mating surface.

(b) The rear cover retaining bolts **must** be renewed as a complete set whenever they are removed.

7 Braking system

Note: *Hydraulic fluid is poisonous; wash off immediately and thoroughly in the case of skin contact, and seek immediate medical advice if any fluid is swallowed or gets into the eyes. Certain types of hydraulic fluid are inflammable, and may ignite when allowed into contact with hot components; when servicing any hydraulic system, it is safest to assume that the fluid IS inflammable, and to take precautions against the risk of fire as though it is petrol that is being handled. Hydraulic fluid is also an effective paint stripper, and will attack plastics; if any is spilt, it should be washed off immediately, using copious quantities of fresh water. Finally, it is hygroscopic (it absorbs moisture from the air) – old fluid may be contaminated, and unfit for further use. When topping-up or renewing the fluid, always use the recommended type, and ensure that it comes from a freshly-opened sealed container.*

General information

1   On later models, a new type of front brake caliper, manufactured by ATE, was fitted. Operations concerning the new caliper, and all other modified procedures, are covered in this Section. All other procedures can be carried out using the information given in Chapter 9.

Front brake pads (ATE caliper) – inspection and renewal

Warning: *Renew both sets of front brake pads at the same time – never renew the pads on only one wheel, as uneven braking may result. Note that the dust created by wear of the pads may contain asbestos, which is a health hazard. Never blow it out with compressed air, and don't inhale any of it. An approved filtering mask should be worn when working on the brakes. DO NOT use petroleum-based solvents to clean brake parts – use brake cleaner or methylated spirit only.*

2   Firmly apply the handbrake, then jack up the front of the vehicle and support on axle stands. Remove both front roadwheels.

7.4 Carefully lever out the caliper housing spring using a flat-bladed screwdriver

3   The thickness of the brake pads (friction material and backing plate) can be measured via the aperture in the caliper. If any pad has worn beyond the specified minimum thickness (See Chapter 9 Specifications), all the pads must be renewed as an axle set. However, a far more thorough check can be made if the caliper is first removed, as follows.

4   Carefully lever out the large spring, and remove it from the outside of the caliper body (photo).

5   On vehicles equipped with check control, unclip the pad wear sensor from the caliper aperture, and position it clear of the caliper (photo).

6   Remove the dust caps from the caliper guide pin bolt holes, then slacken and remove the two guide pin bolts, and withdraw them from the caliper (photos).

7   Slide the caliper off the brake disc, and unclip the inner pad from the caliper piston. Tie the caliper to the suspension strut, using a suitable piece of wire, to avoid placing any strain on the flexible brake hose.

8   Remove the outer pad from the caliper mounting bracket.

9   First measure the thickness of each brake pad (friction material and backing plate). If either pad is worn at any point to the specified minimum thickness (see Chapter 9 Specifications), all four pads must be renewed. The pads should also be renewed if any are fouled with oil or grease; there is no satisfactory way of degreasing friction material once contaminated. If any of the brake pads are worn unevenly or fouled with oil or grease, trace and rectify the cause before reassembly. On vehicles equipped with check control, if the pad wear sensor has been in contact with the brake disc, that must also be renewed.

10   If the brake pads are still serviceable, carefully clean them using a clean, fine wire brush or similar, paying particular attention to the sides and back of the metal backing. Clean out the grooves in the friction material (where applicable), and pick out any large embedded particles of dirt or debris. Carefully clean the pad locations in the caliper body and mounting bracket. Check that the guide pins are free to slide easily in the

7.5 On vehicles equipped with check control, remove the pad wear sensor from the caliper aperture

7.6A Remove the dust covers...

7.6B ...then slacken and remove the caliper guide pin bolts

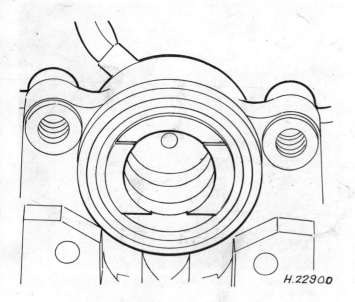

Fig. 13.4 Prior to refitting the inner pad, ensure caliper piston recess is positioned horizontally as shown (Sec 7)

caliper mounting bushes. Brush the dust and dirt from the caliper and piston, but **do not** inhale it, as it is injurious to health. Inspect the dust seal around the piston for damage, and the piston for evidence of fluid leaks, corrosion or damage. If attention to any of these components is necessary, refer to the information given in the following sub-section.

11   If new brake pads are being fitted, the caliper piston must be pushed back into the cylinder to make room for them. Either use a G-clamp or similar tool, or use suitable pieces of wood as levers. Provided that the master cylinder reservoir has not been overfilled with hydraulic fluid, there should be no spillage, but keep a careful watch on the fluid level while retracting the piston. If the fluid level rises above the maximum level mark, the surplus should be syphoned off using a syringe.

12   Prior to installing the inner pad, ensure that the recess on the caliper piston is positioned horizontally in relation to the caliper body (see Fig. 13.4). If necessary, rotate the piston until the recess is correctly positioned.

13   Once the piston is correctly positioned, clip the inner pad into position in the caliper piston, and install the outer pad in the caliper mounting bracket, ensuring that its friction material is facing the brake disc (photos).

14   Slide the caliper into position over the brake disc and outer pad.

15   Thoroughly clean the threads of the guide pin bolts, then apply a few drops of a suitable locking compound to them. Refit the bolts in the caliper holes, then tighten them to the specified torque and refit the dust covers.

16   On vehicles equipped with check control, clip the pad wear sensor into position on the inner brake pad. If a new sensor is being installed,

trace the wiring of the original sensor back to the connector, then disconnect it and remove the old sensor from the vehicle. Connect the wiring connector of the new sensor, ensuring that the wiring is correctly routed and retained by all the necessary clips.

17   Refit the caliper spring, ensuring that its ends are firmly located in the holes in the caliper body (photo).

18   Check that the caliper body slides smoothly on its guide pins, then depress the brake pedal repeatedly until the pads are pressed into firm contact with the brake disc, and normal (non-assisted) pedal pressure is restored.

19   Repeat the above procedure on the remaining front brake caliper.

20   Refit the roadwheels, then lower the car to the ground and tighten the roadwheel bolts to the specified torque setting.

21   Check the hydraulic fluid level as described in Chapter 9.

Front brake caliper (ATE caliper) – removal, overhaul and refitting

Note: *Before starting work, refer to the note at the beginning of this Section concerning the dangers of hydraulic fluid, and to the warning at the beginning of the previous sub-section concerning the dangers of asbestos dust.*

Removal

22   Chock the rear wheels, firmly apply the handbrake, then jack up the front of the car and support on axle stands. Remove the appropriate front roadwheel.

23   Minimise fluid loss either by removing the master cylinder reservoir cap and then tightening it down onto a piece of polythene to obtain an airtight seal (taking care not to damage the sender unit), or by using a brake hose clamp, a G-clamp or a similar tool to clamp the flexible hose.

24   Clean the area around the union, then undo the brake hose union bolt, and disconnect the hose from the caliper. Plug the end of the hose and the caliper orifice, to prevent dirt entering the hydraulic system. Discard the sealing washers; they must be renewed whenever disturbed.

25   On vehicles equipped with check control, unclip the pad wear sensor from the caliper aperture, and position it clear of the caliper.

26   Carefully lever out the large spring, and remove it from the outside of the caliper body.

27   Remove the dust caps from the caliper guide pin bolt holes, then slacken and remove the two bolts, and withdraw them from the caliper.

28   Carefully lift the caliper assembly off the brake disc, and remove the inner pad from the caliper piston. Note that the outer pad need not be disturbed, and can be left in position in the caliper mounting bracket.

Overhaul

29   With the caliper on the bench, wipe away all traces of dust and dirt, but *avoid inhaling the dust, as it is injurious to health.*

30   Withdraw the partially-ejected piston from the caliper body, and remove the dust seal. The piston can be withdrawn by hand, or can if necessary be pushed out by applying compressed air to the union bolt hole. Only low pressure should be required, such as is generated by a foot pump.

31   Using a small screwdriver, extract the piston hydraulic seal, taking great care not to damage the caliper bore.

32   Press the guide sleeves out of the caliper body using a suitable socket.

7.13A Clip the inner pad into the caliper piston...

7.13B ...then install the outer pad in the mounting bracket, and slide the caliper assembly into position

7.17 Refit the spring to the caliper housing, ensuring its ends are firmly located in the caliper holes

33   Thoroughly clean all components, using only methylated spirit, isopropyl alcohol or clean hydraulic fluid as a cleaning medium. Never use mineral-based solvents such as petrol or paraffin, as they will attack the hydraulic system's rubber components. Dry the components immediately, using compressed air or a clean, lint-free cloth. Use compressed air to blow clear the fluid passages. *Wear eye protection when using compressed air!*

34   Check all components, and renew any that are worn or damaged. Pay particular attention to the cylinder bore and piston; these should be renewed (note that this means the renewal of the complete body assembly) if they are scratched, worn or corroded in any way. Similarly check the condition of the guide pins and their sleeves; both guide pins should be undamaged and (when cleaned) a reasonably-tight sliding fit in the sleeves. If there is any doubt about the condition of any component, renew it.

35   If the assembly is fit for further use, obtain a new piston and dust seal, and a tube of brake cylinder paste (part number 90 295 751) from your Vauxhall dealer.

36   Smear a little brake cylinder paste onto the surfaces of the caliper bore, piston and piston seal.

37   Install the piston seal in the caliper bore, using only your fingers to manipulate it into its groove. Fit the new dust seal to the piston, then carefully refit the piston to the caliper bore, using a twisting motion, ensuring that it enters the bore squarely.

38   Press the piston fully into the bore, then rotate the piston so that its recess is positioned horizontally in relation to the caliper body (see Fig. 13.4). With the piston correctly positioned, press the dust seal into its groove in the caliper body.

39   Lubricate the caliper guide sleeves with a little soapy water, then press them into position in the caliper body.

Refitting

40   Clip the inner brake pad into position in the caliper piston, then slide the caliper over the brake disc and outer pad.

41   Thoroughly clean the threads of the guide pin bolts, and apply a few drops of suitable thread-locking compound to them. Refit the bolts in the caliper holes, then tighten them to the specified torque and refit the dust covers.

42   On vehicles with check control, clip the pad wear sensor into position on the inner brake pad.

43   Refit the caliper spring, ensuring that its ends are firmly located in the holes in the caliper body.

44   Position a new sealing washer on each side of the hose union, and refit the brake hose union bolt. Ensure that the brake hose union is correctly positioned against the lug on the caliper, and tighten the union bolt to the specified torque setting.

45   Remove the brake hose clamp, where fitted, and bleed the hydraulic system as described in Chapter 9. Note that, providing the precautions described were taken to minimise brake fluid loss, it should only be necessary to bleed the relevant front brake.

46   Refit the roadwheel, then lower the car to the ground and tighten the roadwheel bolts to the specified torque.

Front brake caliper mounting bracket bolts (all models) – revised tightening procedure

47   On all front brake calipers, the caliper mounting bracket-to-steering knuckle bolts are now tightened first to a specified torque, and then angle-tightened through a specified angle (see Specifications at the start of this Chapter). Also note that a few drops of suitable thread-locking compound should be applied to the threads of the bolts prior to installation.

48   Due to the revised tightening procedure, the mounting bracket bolts should be renewed whenever they are disturbed.

Handbrake lever and cable (models with a catalytic converter) – removal and refitting

49   On models with a catalytic converter, the handbrake cable and lever can be removed and refitted as described in the relevant Section of Chapter 9, noting that in both cases, it will first be necessary to remove both the catalytic converter heat shields to gain access to the cable adjustment nut.

ABS electronic control unit (1989-on models) – removal and refitting
Removal

50   From 1989 model year onwards, the ABS electronic control unit is

7.52 Removing the ABS electronic control unit – 1989-on models

situated underneath the front passenger seat. To remove the unit, first disconnect the battery negative terminal.

51   Push the passenger seat fully forwards, so that access to the unit can be gained from the rear of the seat.

52   Open up the plastic cover, then slide the control unit out of the rear of the plastic housing (photo). Disconnect the wiring connector, and remove the unit from the vehicle.

Refitting

53   Refitting is a reverse of the removal procedure.

---

8   Bodywork and fittings

Bonnet release cable – renewal and adjustment

1   Open up the bonnet, and remove the radiator grille as described in Chapter 11.

2   Slacken and remove the release cable clamping bolt and clamp from the bonnet locking platform (photo).

3   Detach the inner cable from the bonnet lock, then work back along the length of the cable, releasing it from any necessary retaining clips, and noting how it is routed.

4   From within the car, unclip the bonnet release lever from the right-hand footwell side trim panel, and remove the lever from the vehicle,

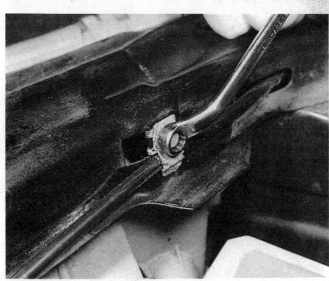

8.2 Removing the bonnet release cable clamping bolt

8.10 Disconnecting the front door master wiring connector

8.11A On electrically-operated mirrors, carefully lever the mirror glass out of position...

8.11B ...and disconnect its wiring connectors (arrowed)

withdrawing the cable as it is removed. Remove the rubber grommet and examine it for signs of damage, renewing as necessary.
5   Fit the grommet to the new cable and lever assembly, then have an assistant feed the cable through the bulkhead from the inside of the vehicle, while you ensure that the cable is correctly routed around the engine compartment.
6   Once the cable is correctly routed, clip the release lever into position on the side trim panel, and press the grommet into the bulkhead aperture.
7   Connect the cable to the bonnet lock, then refit the cable clamping bolt and plate, tightening the bolt finger-tight only. Secure the cable in position with all the necessary clamps and ties.
8   To adjust the bonnet release cable, position the outer cable in the clamp plate so that there is no free play present at the lock end of the inner cable. Once the outer cable is correctly positioned, tighten the clamping bolt securely. Have an assistant operate the release lever, and check that the lock catch moves sufficiently to release the bonnet. Close the bonnet, and check the operation of the release lever. Adjust as necessary.
9   Re-open the bonnet, and refit the radiator grille as described in Chapter 11.

Door – removal and refitting
10   Note that on some later models, when removing the door assembly (see Chapter 11, Section 18) it is no longer necessary to remove the inner trim panel to gain access to the various wiring connectors. All the wiring connectors are joined to a master wiring connector, fitted to the front edge of the door, which can be disconnected once the door has been opened (photo).

Door exterior mirror (electrically-operated) – glass removal and refitting
Removal
11   Position the mirror glass so that it is fully in at its lower, inner corner. Press the mirror glass in at its lower, inner corner, and carefully lever out the glass at its upper, outer corner, using a suitable flat-bladed tool, to release the glass from its retaining clips. Remove the glass from the mirror, disconnecting its wiring connectors as they become accessible (photos).

Refitting
12   Ensure that both the mirror adjustment rods are fully retracted into the motor assembly, then offer up the glass and reconnect its wiring connectors.
13   Align the glass with its central mounting point and adjustment rods, and press it firmly in until it clicks into position.
14   Switch on the ignition, and adjust the mirror to the required position.

Boot lid lock – removal and refitting
15   The boot lid lock can be removed and refitted using the information given in Chapter 11, Section 8, paragraphs 5 and 6.

Tailgate lock – removal and refitting
16   The tailgate lock can be removed and refitted using the information given in Chapter 11, Section 9, paragraphs 3, 6 and 8.

9   Electrical system

Exterior lamp units – removal and refitting
Rear lamp clusters
1   On Saloon models, open up the boot lid, then release the relevant luggage compartment trim panel to gain access to the lamp unit. Depress the two bulbholder retaining lugs, and remove the holder from the lamp unit. Undo the four retaining bolts, and remove the lamp unit from the vehicle.
2   On Estate models, from within the luggage compartment, turn the catch and open up the relevant lamp cover. Depress the retaining lugs and remove the bulbholder assembly. Undo the three retaining bolts, and remove the lamp unit from the vehicle (photo).
3   Refitting is a reverse of the removal procedure.

Front foglamps
4   Apply the handbrake, then jack up the front of the car and support on axle stands.
5   Disconnect the wiring connector from the relevant foglamp, then slacken and remove its retaining bolts, and withdraw the lamp from the rear of the bumper.
6   Refitting is a reverse of the removal procedure.

Indicator side repeater lamps
7   Where necessary, undo the mudflap retaining screws, then slacken and remove the retaining bolts from the front relevant wheel arch liner. Unclip the rear of the liner until access can be gained to the side repeater lamp wiring connector.

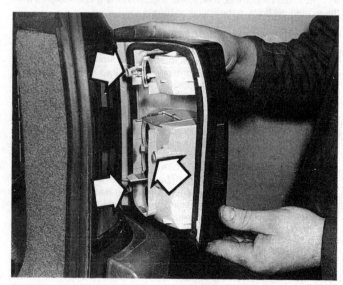

9.2 Removing rear lamp cluster – Estate model (retaining bolt locations arrowed)

9.8 Removing an indicator side repeater lamp

9.12 Removing headlamp wiper arm retaining nut

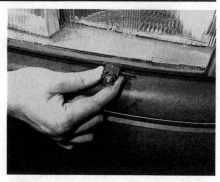

9.15 Removing a headlamp washer jet

8   Disconnect the wiring connector, then release its retaining tabs and withdraw the lamp from the wing (photo).
9   Refitting is a reversal of the removal procedure, ensuring that the wheel arch liner is correctly refitted and its retaining bolts are securely tightened.

Bulbs – renewal

Passenger sunvisor vanity mirror lamp
10   Lower the sunvisor then, using a small flat-bladed screwdriver, carefully prise off the lamp cover. Remove the bulb(s).
11   Refitting is a reverse of the removal procedure.

Headlamp wash/wipe components – removal and refitting

Wiper arm
12   Lift the spindle cover, then slacken and remove the wiper arm retaining nut (photo). Release the arm from the spindle splines, and remove it from the vehicle.
13   Refitting is a reverse of the removal procedure, ensuring that the wiper blade is correctly positioned on the spindle splines, and its retaining nut is securely tightened.

Washer jet
14   Remove the wiper arm as described above.
15   Pull the washer jet off the wiper motor spindle, and disconnect it from the washer tubing (photo). Tie a piece of string to the tubing, to prevent it disappearing behind the bumper.
16   Refitting is a reverse of the removal procedure.

Wiper motor
17   The wiper motor can be removed and refitted as described in Section 29 of Chapter 12.

Washer pump
18   The pump is identical to the windscreen washer pump, and can be removed and refitted using the information given in Chapter 12, Section 33.

Solenoid valve
19   Unbolt the windscreen washer reservoir from the wheel arch, and empty its contents into a suitable container.
20   Disconnect the solenoid wiring connector, then remove the solenoid from the reservoir.
21   Label the hoses, to ensure they are correctly reconnected on refitting, then disconnect them and remove the solenoid from the vehicle.
22   Refitting is a reversal of the removal procedure, ensuring that the washer hoses are reconnected correctly. On completion, refill the reservoir with fluid.

Headlamp wash/wipe relay
23   Refer to Chapter 12, Section 16.

Central locking system components – removal and refitting
24   Disconnect the battery negative terminal.

Door lock servo motor – pre-1988 models
25   Remove the door trim inner panel, as described in Chapter 11.
26   Peel back the plastic water shield from the door frame, to gain access to the servo unit.
27   Slacken and remove the servo motor retaining screws, then detach it from its control rod. Disconnect the wiring connector, and remove the servo motor from the door.
28   On refitting, reconnect the wiring connector to the servo, then connect the servo to the control rod. Refit the servo unit retaining screws, tightening them finger-tight only at this stage. Adjust the servo motor as follows.
29   Referring to Fig. 13.5, using a suitable marker pen, make a mark 'A' on the door locking knob control rod. Push the control rod down into the locked position, and mark the position of the mark on the control rod on the door frame 'B'. Pull the control rod up into the unlocked position, and again mark the position of the mark on the control rod on the door frame 'C'. Make a third alignment mark 'D' on the door frame, exactly halfway between marks 'B' and 'C'. Slowly move the control rod from the locked to unlocked position, while listening to servo motor switch. The switch in the servo should operate, indicated by an audible click, when the control rod is exactly halfway between the locked and unlocked position – ie when mark 'A' aligns with mark 'D'. Adjust the position of the servo motor until this is so, then securely tighten its retaining screws.

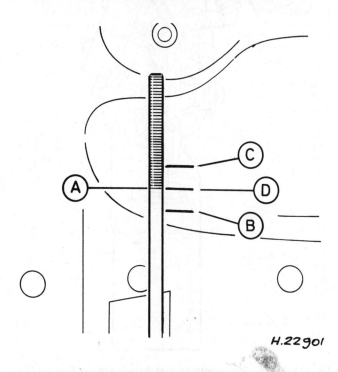

H.22901

Fig. 13.5 Door lock servo motor adjustment marks (see text for details) – pre-1988 models (Sec 9)

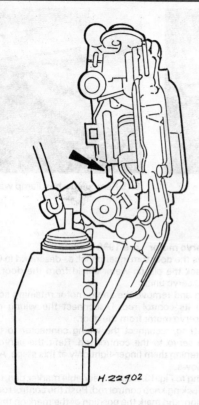

Fig. 13.6 Position servo motor so that lock lever abuts its stop (arrowed) – 1988-on driver's door lock assembly (Sec 9)

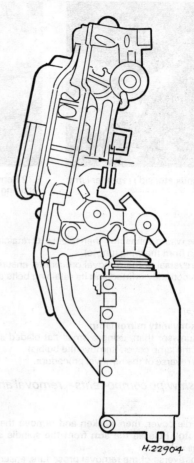

Fig. 13.7 On front passenger door lock assembly, position servo so that there is a gap of 2 mm (0.08 in) between lever and its stop – 1988-on models (Sec 9)

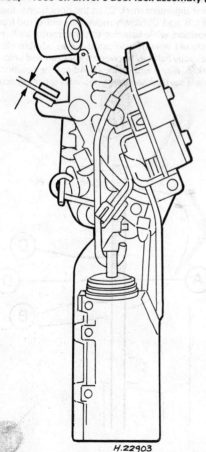

Fig. 13.8 Position servo motor so that there is a gap of 2 mm (0.08 in) between the lever and its stop – 1988-on rear passenger door lock assembly (Sec 9)

30   Once the servo motor is correctly adjusted, refit the plastic water shield to the door frame, and install the door trim panel as described in Chapter 11.

Door lock servo motor – 1988-on models

31   On 1988-on models, remove the lock assembly as described in Chapter 11. Undo the two servo motor retaining screws, then detach the motor and remove it from the bracket.

32   On refitting, reconnect the servo motor actuating lever to its control rod, then refit its retaining screws, tightening them finger-tight only. Prior to refitting the lock assembly, adjust the servo motor position as described in the relevant following paragraph.

33   *Driver's door*: press the actuating lever firmly into the servo motor and, while holding it securely in the locked position, adjust the position of the servo motor until the lock lever abuts its stop (see Fig. 13.6). Hold the servo in this position, and tighten its retaining screws securely.

34   *Front passenger door*: press the actuating lever firmly into the servo motor and, while holding it securely in the locked position, adjust the position of the servo motor until there is a clearance of 2 mm (0.08 in) between the lock lever and its stop (see Fig. 13.7). Hold the servo motor in this position, and tighten its retaining screws securely.

35   *Rear passenger doors*: press the actuating lever firmly into the servo motor and, while holding it securely in the locked position, adjust the position of the servo motor until there is a clearance of 2 mm (0.08 in) between the lock lever and its stop (see Fig. 13.8). Hold the servo motor in this position, and tighten its retaining screws securely.

36   Once the servo motor is correctly adjusted, refit the lock assembly to the door as described in Chapter 11.

Boot lid/tailgate servo motor

37   Open up the boot lid or tailgate, then slacken and remove the two servo motor retaining screws. Detach the servo from its operating rod, then disconnect its wiring connector and remove the servo motor.

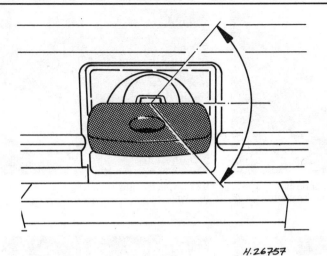

Fig. 13.9 Adjust the boot lid/tailgate servo position so that the servo switch operates when the key is at the same position on either side of the horizontal (Sec 9)

38   On refitting, connect the wiring connector, then engage the servo actuating lever with its operating rod. Refit the servo motor retaining screws, and tighten them by hand only at this stage. Adjust the position of the servo motor as follows.

39   Insert the key into the lock, and set the lock in the horizonal position. Slowly turn the key up and down while listening to the servo motor. The switch in the servo should operate, indicated by an audible click, when the key is at the same position on either side of the horizontal (see Fig. 13.9). Adjust the position of the servo motor until this is the case, then securely tighten its retaining screws.

Fuel filler cap servo motor

40   From within the luggage compartment, carefully peel back the right-hand trim panel until access to the servo motor can be gained.

41   Disconnect the wiring connector from the rear of the motor, then undo the two retaining screws and remove the motor from the vehicle.

42   Refitting is a reverse of the removal procedure.

Operating switch assembly

43   The operating switch assembly takes the form of two microswitches clipped onto the rear of the lock cylinder. There are two switches, one connected to the central locking system, and the other connected to the electric window system.

44   To remove a switch, first remove the door trim panel as described in Chapter 11.

45   Peel back the plastic water shield sufficiently to gain access to the exterior door handle.

46   Trace the wiring back from the microswitch assembly, and disconnect it at its wiring connectors. Unclip the switch assembly from the handle, and remove it from the door.

47   Refitting is a reversal of the removal procedure.

Electronic control unit

48   The central locking electronic control unit is located behind the

driver's footwell right-hand side trim panel (see Fig. 12.6, inset 'B', in Chapter 12).

49   To remove the unit, peel back the rubber moulding and remove the trim panel from the right-hand side of the driver's footwell.

50   Disconnect the wiring connector, then undo the two retaining bolts and remove the control unit from the vehicle.

51   Refitting is a reversal of the removal procedure.

Trip computer components – removal and refitting

52   Disconnect the battery negative terminal.

Trip computer

53   Remove the instrument panel as described in Chapter 12.

54   Push the trip computer out from the facia, and disconnect its wiring connector.

55   If a new trip computer is being installed, remove the program memory from the back of the original unit, and install it in the new computer. If the computer display bulb has failed, take the computer to a Vauxhall dealer to have the bulb renewed; a special tool is required to remove the bulb.

56   Refitting is a reverse of the removal procedure, noting that no pressure should be exerted on the front of the computer display panel, or damage may result.

Trip computer switch

57   Remove the middle cover from the console, and disconnect the trip computer switch wiring connector. If access to the switch connector cannot be gained via the cover aperture, remove the centre console retaining screws, and lift the console slightly until the connector can be reached. Refer to Chapter 11 for further information.

58   Once the switch wiring connector has been disconnected, depress the switch retaining tangs, and remove the switch from the cover.

59   Refitting is a reversal of the removal procedure.

Outside air temperature sensor

60   The outside air temperature sensor is fitted to the front bumper. To remove the sensor, unclip it from the bumper and disconnect its wiring connector.

61   Refit using a reverse of the removal procedure.

Cruise control components – removal and refitting

62   Disconnect the battery negative terminal.

Regulating unit

63   The regulating unit is mounted onto the engine compartment bulkhead. To remove the unit, first disconnect its wiring connector (photo).

64   Undo the three retaining screws, and release the regulating unit from the bulkhead (photos).

65   Release the small spring clip, and detach the accelerator cable ball end from the throttle linkage. Carefully prise off the spring clip, and detach the cruise control cable from the throttle linkage (photos). (Refer to photo 9.73 for a clearer view of the cable end fitting, if wished.)

66   Screw the adjusting screw fully into the guide piece, then unclip the guide piece from the regulating unit (photo).

67   Slide the guide piece away from the regulating unit, and detach the cruise control cable from the regulating unit belt (photo). Remove the regulating unit from the vehicle.

9.63 Disconnect the cruise control regulating unit wiring connector (arrowed)...

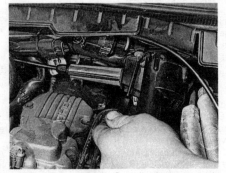

9.64A ...then undo the retaining screws...

9.64B ...and release the unit from the bulkhead

9.65A Detach the accelerator cable from the throttle linkage...

9.65B ...then prise off the spring clip (arrowed) and detach the cruise control cable

9.66 Unclip the guide piece from the regulating unit...

9.67 ...and detach the cable from the regulating unit belt (arrowed)

9.73 Removing the cruise control cable

9.77 Adjusting the cruise control cable

68   On refitting, attach the nipple of the cruise control cable to the regulating unit adjusting belt, then feed the adjusting belt into the guide piece, ensuring that the belt clip is correctly located in the guide piece elongated slot. Clip the guide piece into position in the regulating unit.

69   Refit the cruise control cable to the throttle linkage, and secure it in position with the spring clip. Reconnect the accelerator cable, and secure it in position with its spring clip.

70   Refit the regulating unit retaining screws, and tighten them securely. Reconnect the wiring connector.

71   Adjust the accelerator cable as described in Chapter 3, then adjust the cruise control cable as described in paragraph 77.

Cruise control cable
72   Carry out the operations described above in paragraphs 63 to 67.

73   Release the outer cable retaining clip from the throttle housing, and remove the cable from the engine compartment (photo).

74   If a new cable is being fitted, unscrew the guide piece from the adjusting nut of the original cable, and screw it fully onto the adjusting nut of the new cable.

75   On refitting, clip the outer cable into position on the throttle housing, then carry out the operations described in paragraphs 68 to 70.

76   Adjust the accelerator cable as described in Chapter 3, then adjust the cruise control cable as follows.

77   Screw the adjusting nut out of the guide piece, until all slack is removed from the cable and the throttle linkage just starts to move (photo). From this point, screw the adjusting nut two complete turns back into the guide piece, so that a small amount of free play exists in the cable.

Control unit
78   The control unit is located behind the glovebox, at the left-hand end of the facia (photo) – also see Fig. 12.6, inset 'C', in Chapter 12.

79   To gain access to the unit, open up the glovebox, then slacken and remove the five glovebox retaining bolts. Remove the glovebox from the facia, disconnecting the wiring connectors from the illumination lamp and switch as they become accessible. Note that, on models with air conditioning, it will also be necessary to detach the cool-air hose from the rear of the glovebox.

80   Disconnect the wiring connector from the control unit, then undo its retaining screw and remove the unit through the glovebox aperture.

81   Refitting is a reversal of the removal procedure.

Operating switches
82   The cruise control operating switches are situated on the end of the left-hand steering column combination switch assembly stalk. Refer to Chapter 12 for details of removal and refitting.

Cruise control relay
83   Refer to Chapter 12, Section 16 (Fig. 12.6).

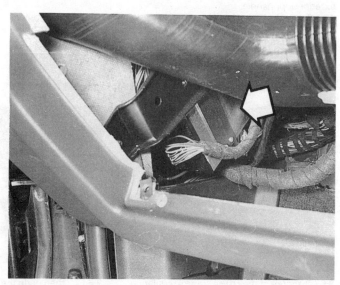

9.78 Cruise control electronic control unit location (arrowed)

9.97 Electric door mirror motor retaining screws (arrowed)

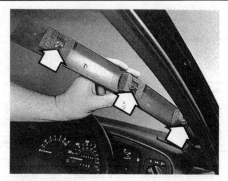

9.107 Remove the A-pillar trim (retaining clips arrowed)...

9.108 ...then unclip the speaker from the facia and disconnect its wiring connectors (arrowed)

Electric window components – removal and refitting
84   Disconnect the battery negative terminal.

Window motor and regulator assemblies
85   Refer to Chapter 11, Section 20 for the front doors, and to Chapter 11, Section 21 for the rear doors.

Centre console switches
86   Remove the centre console as described in Chapter 11.
87   Depress the retaining tabs, and remove the switch from the console.
88   Refitting is a reversal of the removal procedure.

Rear door switches
89   Carefully prise the switch out of the door trim panel, and disconnect its wiring connector.
90   Refitting is a reverse of the removal procedure.

Door lock operating switch
91   Refer to the information given for the central locking system in paragraphs 43 to 47 of this Section.

Electric windows (1988-on models) – reprogramming
92   On 1988-on models, whenever the battery is disconnected, or if any of the electric window components are removed, the electric window controls must be reprogrammed as follows to restore one-touch operation.
93   Close all doors, then switch on the ignition.
94   Close one of the windows by pressing the relevant operating switch until the window is fully closed. With the window closed, press and hold the switch down for a further two seconds.
95   Repeat the procedure on the remaining window(s).

Door exterior mirror (electrically-operated) – component removal and refitting
Mirror motor
96   Remove the mirror glass as described in Section 8 of this Chapter.
97   Undo the three retaining screws, then remove the motor from the mirror housing, disconnecting the wiring connector as it becomes accessible (photo).
98   Refitting is a reverse of the removal procedure.

Mirror operating switch
99   Remove the door trim panel as described in Chapter 11.
100   Depress the retaining tangs, and remove the switch from the door panel.
101   Refitting is a reverse of the removal procedure.

Mirror heating time relay
102   On pre-1989 models, the mirror heating time relay is situated behind the passenger footwell left-hand side panel (see Fig. 12.6, inset 'F', in Chapter 12). To remove the relay, peel back the rubber moulding, and remove the trim panel from the left-hand side of passenger footwell. Disconnect the wiring connector, and slide the relay off its retaining plate.
103   On 1989-on models, the mirror heating time relay may be combined with (or in place of) the rear screen wash/wipe time relay, which is situated in the relay holder behind the fusebox. Refer to Chapter 12,

Section 16 for further information (and to Fig. 12.6, inset 'H', relay number 4).

Anti-theft alarm system – general information
104   From 1990 onwards, an anti-theft alarm system was fitted to all high-specification Saloon models as standard equipment, and was offered as an optional extra on most other models. At the time of writing, very little information on the alarm system was available; any problems must therefore be referred to a Vauxhall dealer.

CD player and graphic equalizer – removal and refitting
105   Both the CD player and graphic equalizer (where fitted) can be removed using the information given in Chapter 12, Section 40. Prior to removal, make a note of the correct positions of all the wiring connectors, to help ensure they are correctly reconnected on refitting. At the time of writing, no information was available on the boot-mounted CD autochanger fitted to later high-specification models.

Loudspeakers – removal and refitting
Front door speakers
106   Refer to Chapter 11, Section 13.

Facia panel speakers
107   Carefully prise the trim panel away from the relevant A-pillar, noting that the trim panels are retained by three retaining clips (photo).
108   Prise the speaker out of the facia panel, disconnecting its wiring connectors as they become accessible (photo).
109   Refitting is a reversal of the removal procedure, ensuring the trim panel is clipped securely in position.

Rear speakers – Saloon models
110   Unclip the speaker cover from the rear parcel shelf.
111   Undo the four speaker retaining screws, then lift the speaker out and disconnect its wiring connectors.
112   Refitting is a reversal of the removal procedure.

Rear speakers – Estate models
113   Refer to Chapter 11, Section 10.

Windscreen aerial amplifier – removal and refitting
114   On models with an aerial which is built into the windscreen, an amplifier is incorporated in the aerial lead, to help boost the signal. The amplifier can be removed as follows.
115   Remove the right-hand front speaker from the facia panel as described above.
116   Remove the radio or the CD player as described in Chapter 12, noting also the information given in paragraph 105 where appropriate.
117   Trace the radio/CD player wiring back to the amplifier wiring connector, which is approximately 60 mm (2.5 in) from the main connector. Disconnect the amplifier supply wire.
118   Tie a piece of string to the radio end of the aerial lead, and disconnect the upper end of the lead from the windscreen.
119   Undo the retaining bolt, then withdraw the amplifier through the speaker aperture. Once the end of the aerial lead emerges, untie the string and leave it in position behind the facia; the string can then be used on refitting, to draw the aerial lead and amplifier wiring connector through into position in the radio aperture.
120   Refitting is a reverse of the removal.

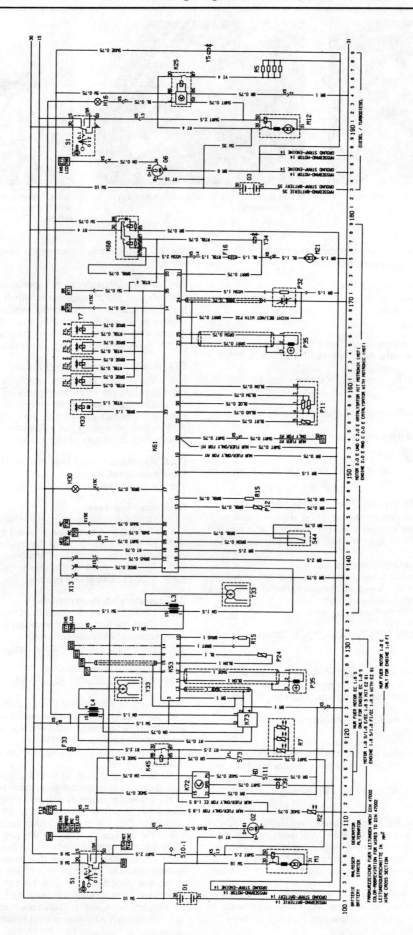

Fig. 13.10 Wiring diagram for 1987 to 1988 models

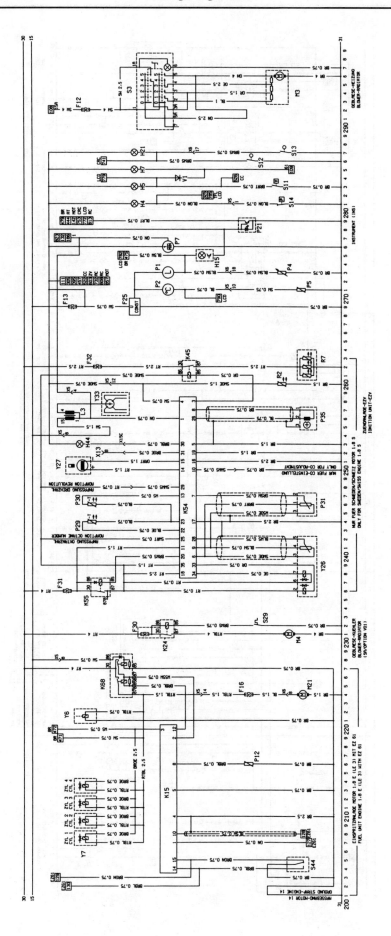

Fig. 13.10 Wiring diagram for 1987 to 1988 models (continued)

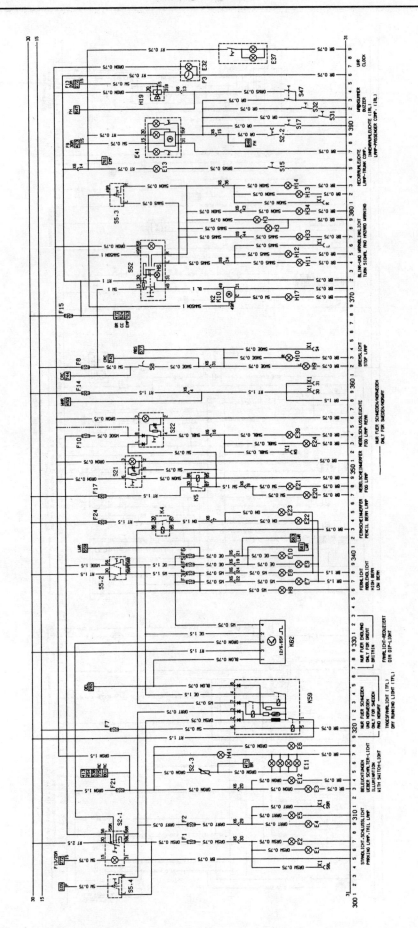

Fig. 13.10 Wiring diagram for 1987 to 1988 models (continued)

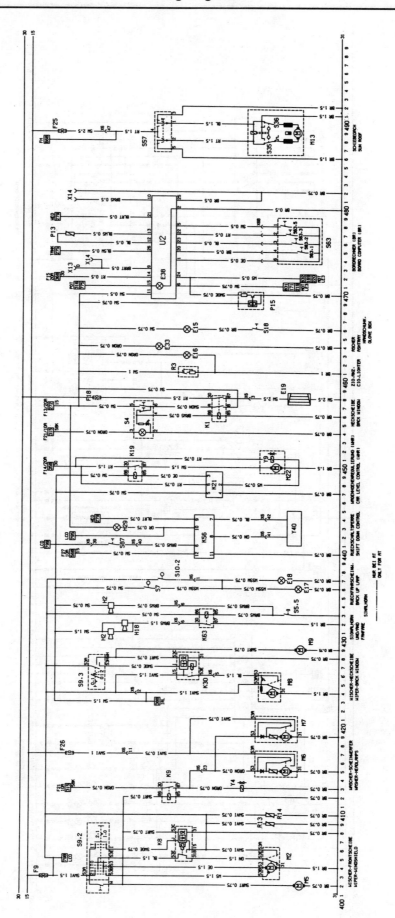

Fig. 13.10 Wiring diagram for 1987 to 1988 models (continued)

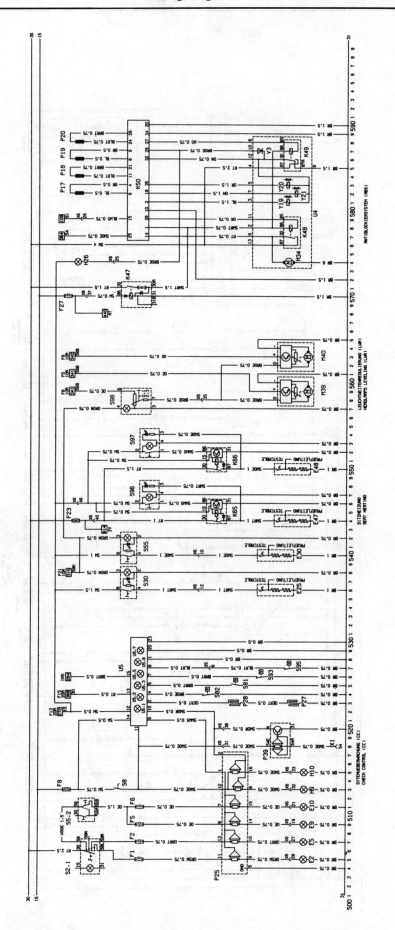

Fig. 13.10 Wiring diagram for 1987 to 1988 models (continued)

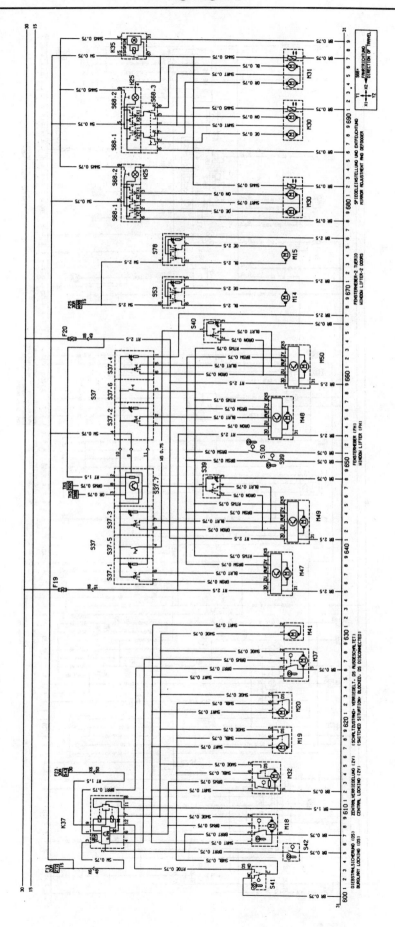

Fig. 13.10 Wiring diagram for 1987 to 1988 models (continued)

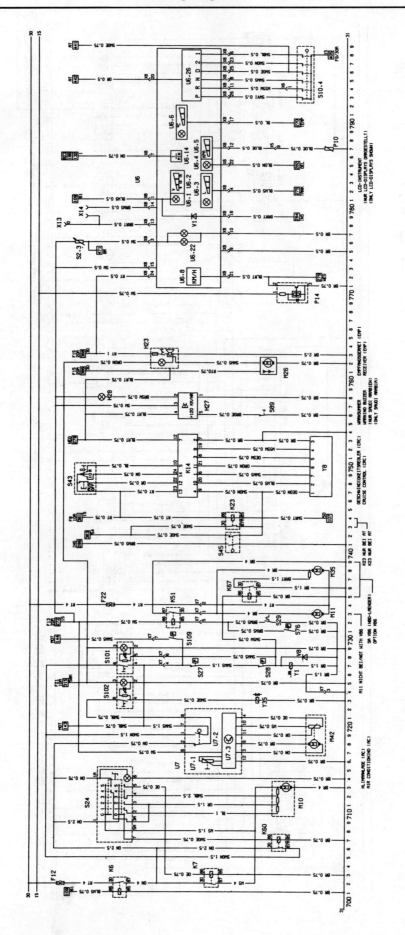

Fig. 13.10 Wiring diagram for 1987 to 1988 models (continued)

Key to Fig. 13.10

No	Description	Track	No	Description	Track
E1	LH parking light	306	H41	Warning light (only with LCD)	317
E2	LH tail light	307, 505	H44	EZV warning light	253
E3	Number plate light	313	K1	Heated rear window relay	456..458
E4	RH parking light	309	K2	Flasher unit	370, 371
E5	RH tail light	310, 507	K4	Spotlight relay	343, 344
E6	Engine compartment light	318	K5	Foglight relay	348, 349
E7	LH high beam	337	K6	Air conditioning relay	701, 702
E8	RH high beam	338	K7	Air conditioning fan relay	702, 703
E9	LH low beam	339, 509	K8	Windscreen wiper intermittent relay	405..406
E10	RH low beam	340, 511	K9	Headlamp washer relay	412, 413
E11	Instrument lights	316	K10	Trailer flasher unit	370, 371
E12	Selector lever light	314	K14	Cruise control	747..753
E13	Boot light	385	K15	Fuel injection timing control	204..220
E15	Glovebox light	466	K19	Level control relay	449, 450
E16	Cigarette lighter light	463	K21	Level control sensor	447..449
E17	LH reversing light	436	K23	Cruise control relay	743, 744
E18	RH reversing light	437	K24	Radiator fan relay	231, 232
E19	Heated rear window	458	K25	Preheater relay	193..196
E20	LH foglight	347	K30	Rear wiper intermittent relay	426..428
E21	RH foglight	348	K35	Heated exterior mirror delay relay	697..699
E22	LH spot light	344	K37	Central locking relay	606..611
E23	RH spot light	345	K45	Mixture preheater relay	117, 118, 261, 262
E24	LH rear foglight	353	K47	Over-voltage protection relay	570, 571
E25	LH heated front seat	536	K48	ABS pump relay	576..579
E30	RH heated front seat	540	K49	ABS solenoid valve relay	585..588
E32	Clock light	397	K50	ABS timing control	577..590
E33	Ashtray light	464	K51	Auxiliary radiator fan relay	732, 733
E37	Make-up mirror lamp	399	K53	Timing control (EV 61)	124..131
E38	Computer light	471	K54	Carburettor control unit (EZV)	238..258
E39	RH rear foglight	354	K55	Carburettor relay (EZV)	236, 237
E41	Courtesy light (with delay)	387..390	K56	Automatic kick-down control unit	440..444
E47	LH heated rear seat	544	K59	Day running light relay	319..325
E48	RH heated rear seat	550	K60	Compressor relay	706..707
F1 to			K61	Control unit (Motronic)	138..173
F26	Fuses in fusebox	various	K62	Control unit (dim-dip lights)	328..332
F25	Voltage stabiliser	269	K63	Dual horn relay	432, 433
F30	Fuse (radiator fan)	231	K65	LH seat heating relay	544..546
F31	Fuse (EZV carburettor)	236	K66	RH seat heating relay	550..552
F32	Fuse (mixture preheater)	262	K67	Radiator fan relay	735, 736
F33	Fuse (mixture preheater)	118	K68	Fuel injection relay	175..179, 224, 228
G1	Battery	101	K72	Engine revolution relay	113..115
G2	Alternator	108, 109	K73	Ignition module (EZ 61)	121, 122
G3	Battery (Diesel)	183	L3	Ignition coil (inductive sensor)	134, 135, 256, 257
G6	Alternator (Diesel)	184..186	L4	Ignition coil (inductive sensor, EZ 61)	122, 123
H2	Horn	431, 434	M1	Starter motor	105, 106
H3	Turn signal warning light	378, 379	M2	Windscreen wiper motor	403..406
H4	Oil pressure warning light	281	M3	Heater fan motor	293..296
H5	Handbrake/brake fluid warning light	283	M4	Radiator fan motor	231
H6	Hazard warning system warning light	373	M5	Washer pump	402
H7	No-charge warning light	285	M6	LH headlight wiper motor	415..417
H8	Main beam warning light	336	M7	RH headlight wiper motor	419..421
H9	LH stop-light	362, 513	M8	Rear window wiper motor	424..426
H10	RH stop-light	363, 515	M9	Rear window washer pump	429
H11	LH front turn signal light	374	M10	Air conditioning fan motor	710..713
H12	LH rear turn signal light	375	M11	Auxiliary radiator fan motor	733
H13	RH front turn signal light	382	M12	Starter motor (Diesel)	190, 191
H14	RH rear turn signal light	383	M13	Sunroof motor	488..491
H15	Low fuel warning light	275	M14	LH front door window motor	668..670
H16	Preheater warning light	193	M15	RH front door window motor	673..675
H17	Trailer turn signal warning light	370	M18	Front door locking motor	606..609
H18	Dual horns	432	M19	LH rear door locking motor	617..619
H19	Headlights on warning buzzer	394, 395	M20	RH rear door locking motor	621..623
H21	Clutch/parking brake warning light	287	M21	Fuel pump	175, 224
H23	Radio with electric aerial	762..763	M22	Level control compressor	450
H25	Mirror heater warning light	684, 694	M26	Electric aerial motor	761, 762
H26	ABS warning light	574	M30	LH exterior mirror adjustment and heating	679..682, 688..691
H27	Safety check warning buzzer	756..758			
H28	Seat belt warning light	758	M31	RH exterior mirror adjustment and heating	694..697
H29	4-speed automatic warning light	443	M32	Front door locking motor	612..615
H30	Engine warning light	148	M33	Idle control unit	157, 158
H33	LH repeater turn signal light	377	M34	ABS return pump	574
H34	RH repeater turn signal light	380	M35	Auxiliary radiator fan relay	738

Key to Fig. 13.10 (continued)

No	Description	Track
M37	Bootlid/tailgate locking motor	625..628
M39	LH headlight levelling motor	558..560
M40	RH headlight levelling motor	562..564
M41	Fuel filler cap locking motor	630, 631
M42	Air conditioning actuator	717..721
M47	LH front electric window motor	635..639
M48	RH front electric window motor	653..657
M49	LH rear electric window motor	641..645
M50	RH rear electric window motor	659..663
P1	Fuel gauge	273
P2	Temperature gauge	271
P3	Clock	396
P4	Fuel sensor	273
P5	Temperature sensor	271
P7	Tachometer	276
P10	Oil pressure sensor	787
P11	Airflow meter	156..160
P12	Temperature probe (coolant)	146, 216
P13	Outside air temperature sensor	476, 477
P15	Fuel flowmeter	469, 470
P17	LH front wheel sensor (ABS)	582, 583
P18	RH front wheel sensor (ABS)	584, 585
P19	LH rear wheel sensor (ABS)	586, 587
P20	RH rear wheel sensor (ABS)	588, 589
P21	Instrument optical frequency sensor	278, 279
P24	Oil temperature sensor	128, 129
P25	Bulb test sensor	505..517
P27	LH front brake lining sensor	523
P28	RH front brake lining sensor	523
P29	Inlet manifold temperature sensor	243, 244
P30	Coolant temperature sensor	246, 247
P31	Main throttle potentiometer	245, 247
P32	Heated Lambda sensor	170, 171
P35	Crankshaft inductive sensor 125..127, 165..167, 255..257	
P39	Trailer bulb test sensor	518, 520
R2	Carburettor preheater	111, 260
R3	Cigarette lighter	461
R5	Glow plugs	197
R7	Mixture preheater	118..120, 262
R13	LH heated washer jet	409
R14	RH heated washer jet	410
R15	Resistor	130, 131, 147
S1	Starter motor switch	105, 106, 190, 191
S2	Light switch assembly	
S2.1	Light switch	305..308, 506, 507
S2.2	Courtesy light switch	389
S2.3	Instrument lights dimmer	315, 776
S3	Heater fan switch	291..297
S4	Heated rear window switch	454..457
S5	Turn signal switch assembly	
S5.2	Headlight dip switch	338, 339, 511
S5.3	Turn signal switch	381..383
S5.4	Parking light switch	301..303
S5.5	Horn switch	433
S7	Reversing light switch	436
S8	Stop-light switch	362, 513
S9	Windscreen wiper switch assembly	
S9.2	Windscreen wiper switch (intermittent)	402..406
S9.3	Rear window wiper switch (intermittent)	427, 428
S10	Automatic transmission switch	
S10.1	Automatic transmission switch	106
S10.2	Reversing light switch	437
S10.4	Speed telltale switch	793..799
S11	Brake fluid level switch	283
S12	Clutch control switch	286
S13	Handbrake warning light switch	287
S14	Oil pressure switch	281
S15	Boot light switch	385
S17	LH courtesy light switch	390
S18	Glovebox light switch	466
S21	Foglight switch	349..351
S22	Rear foglight switch	354, 356

No	Description	Track
S24	Air conditioning fan switch	707..714
S27	Pressure switch	727
S28	Compressor cut-off switch	727
S29	Radiator fan switch	232, 732
S30	LH front heated door switch	536..538
S31	LH rear door courtesy light switch	391
S32	RH rear door courtesy light switch	392
S35	Sunroof micro switch	488
S36	Sunroof micro switch	490
S37	Electric window switch assembly	636..662
S37.1	LH front electric window switch	636..638
S37.2	RH front electric window switch	654..656
S37.3	LH rear electric window switch	662..644
S37.4	RH rear electric window switch	660..662
S37.5	Safety switch	640
S37.6	Anti-jamming switch	658
S37.7	Electronic control	645..648
S39	LH rear door window motor switch	602..604
S40	RH rear door window motor switch	664..666
S41	RH anti-theft lock switch	602..604
S42	LH central locking switch	605
S43	Cruise control switch	747..750
S44	Throttle valve switch	142, 143, 204, 205
S45	Cruise control clutch switch	741, 742
S47	Doors open/headlamps on warning switch	393, 394
S52	Hazard light switch	371..376
S53	LH front electric window switch	668..671
S55	RH front seat heating switch	540..542
S57	Sunroof switch	487..491
S63	Board computer switch assembly	474..478
S63.1	Function reset switch	475
S63.2	Clock hour adjustment switch	476
S63.3	Function selection switch	477
S63.5	Clock minute adjustment switch	478
S68	Exterior mirror switch	
S68.1	Exterior mirror adjustment switch	678..681, 686..690
S68.2	Exterior mirror heater switch	683, 684, 692, 693
S73	Temperature switch	117
S76	Compressor pressure switch	731
S78	RH front window motor switch	673..676
S81	Brake fluid low level switch	525
S82	Washer fluid low level switch	524
S87	4-speed automatic switch	441
S89	Seat belt switch	756
S93	Coolant low level switch	526
S95	Engine oil low level switch	527
S96	LH rear seat heating switch	546..548
S97	RH rear seat heating switch	552..554
S98	Headlight levelling switch	557..559
S99	RH front window switch (2V)	650
S100	LH front window switch (2V)	651
S101	Compressor switch	727..729
S102	Circulation switch	723..725
S109	Motronic compressor pressure switch	730
S111	Fuel cut-off vacuum switch	115
U2	Board computer	470..481
U4	ABS system	574..588
U5	Check control display assembly	521..530
U5.1	Tail light and low beam warning light	522
U5.2	Brake light warning light	523
U5.3	Low oil level warning light	525
U5.5	Low front brake lining warning light	526
U5.6	Low washer fluid warning light	528
U5.7	Low coolant level warning light	529
U6	LCD instrument assembly	771..798
U6.1	Charging indicator light	781
U6.2	Voltmeter	782..784
U6.3	Fuel indicator	782
U6.4	Oil pressure warning light	785
U6.5	Oil pressure gauge	787
U6.6	Coolant temperature indicator	790
U6.8	Speedometer	772

11

Key to Fig. 13.10 (continued)

No	Description	Track
U6.14	Tachometer	786
U6.22	Display lights	775, 776
U6.26	Automatic transmission lever display	793..798
U7	Air conditioning adjustment unit	716..721
U7.1	Temperature selector lever potentiometer	716
U7.2	Demister lever limit switch	718, 719
U7.3	Electronic control	716..721
V1	Brake fluid test bulb diode	284, 779
V3	ABS solenoid valve diode	587
V8	Compressor diode	728
X1	Trailer socket	various
X5 to X15E	Connectors	various
Y1	Air conditioning compressor	727
Y4	Headlight washer solenoid valve	413

No	Description	Track
Y5	Diesel solenoid valve	199
Y6	Auxiliary air slide valve	221, 222
Y7	Fuel injection solenoid valve	160..167, 207..214
Y8	Cruise control actuator	747..753
Y9	Level control solenoid	451
Y19	LH front ABS solenoid	581
Y20	RH front ABS solenoid	583
Y21	Rear axle ABS solenoid	582
Y26	Throttle valve positioner	236..242
Y27	Pre-throttle valve	250, 251
Y33	Distributor	125, 136, 258
Y34	Tank ventilation valve	177
Y35	Circulation valve	723
Y39	Fuel cut-off solenoid valve	114
Y40	4-speed automatic transmission	442, 444

Not all items are fitted to all models

Colour code
BL	Blue
BR	Brown
GE	Yellow
GN	Green
GR	Grey
HBL	Light blue
LI	Lilac
RT	Red
SW	Black
VI	Violet
WS	White

Abbreviations
ABS	Anti-lock brake system
AC	Air conditioning
AT	Automatic transmission
ATC	Automatic temperature control
AZV	Trailer hitch
BR	On-board computer
CC	Check control
D	Diesel
DS	Theft protection
DWA	Anti-theft warning system
DZM	Tachometer
EFC	Electric folding roof, convertible
EKS	Pinch guard (electric windows)
EMP	Radio
EUR	Euronorm engine
EZ +	El Plus with self-diagnosis
EZV	Ecotronic
FH	Window winders
GB	Great Britain
HS	Rear screen
HW	Rear screen wiper
HZG	Heating
HRL	Luggage compartment light
INS	Instrument
IRL	Interior light
KAT	Catalytic converter
KBS	Wiring harness
KV	Contact distributor
L3.1	Jetronic L3.1
LCD	LCD instrument
LHD	Left-hand drive
LWR	Headlight range control

M 1.5	Motronic M 1.5
M 2.5	Motronic M 2.5
MOT	Motronic in general
MT	Manual transmission
N	Norway
NS	Foglights
NSL	Rear foglights
OEL	Oil level control (oil pressure)
OPT	Optional equipment
P/N	Park/Neutral (automatic transmission)
PBSL	Park and brake shift block
POT	Potentiometer
RC	Electric ride control
RHD	Right-hand drive
S	Sweden
SD	Sliding roof
SH	Seat heating
SRA	Headlight cleaning system
TANK	Fuel gauge
TD	Turbodiesel
TEMP	Temperature gauge
TFL	Daytime driving light
TKS	Door contact switch
TSZI	Transistor ignition (inductive)
VGS	Carburettor
WEG	Odometer frequency sensor
WHR	Car level control
WS	Warning buzzer
ZV	Central door locking
ZYL	Cylinder
4WD	Four wheel drive

Wiring identification

eg GE WS 1.5
GE	Basic colour
WS	Identification colour
1.5	Section (mm²)

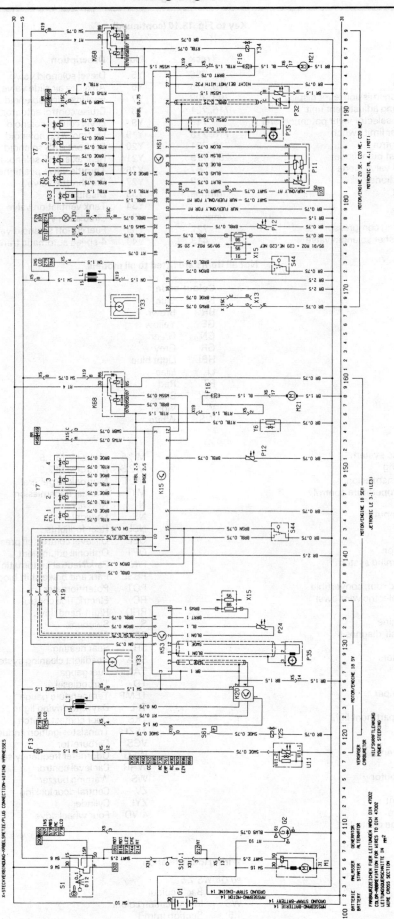

Fig. 13.11 Wiring diagram for 1989 to 1990 models

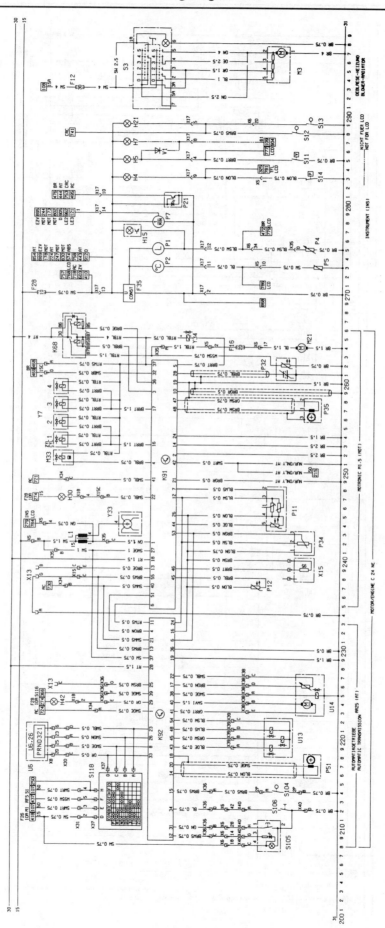

Fig. 13.11 Wiring diagram for 1989 to 1990 models (continued)

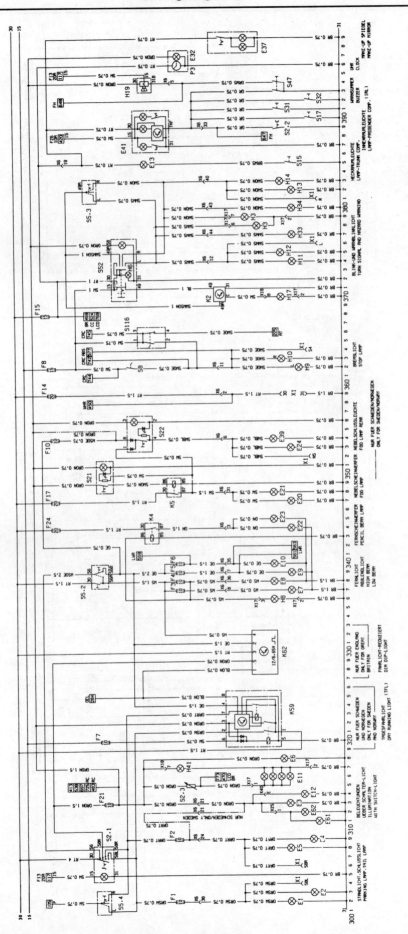

Fig. 13.11 Wiring diagram for 1989 to 1990 models (continued)

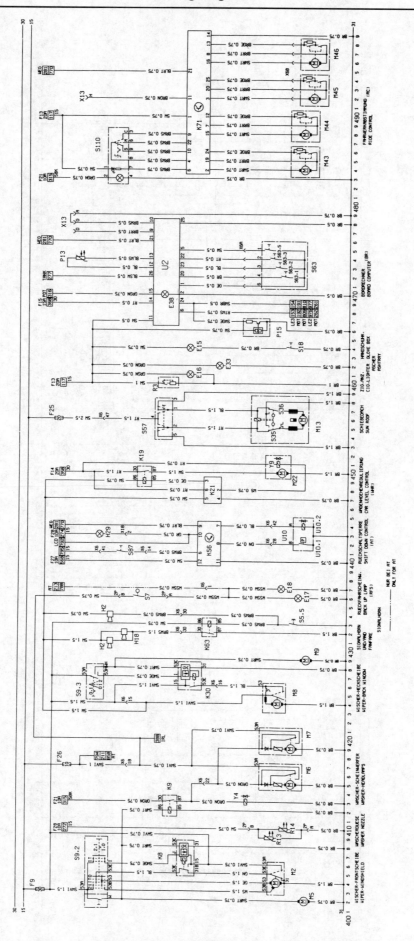

Fig. 13.11 Wiring diagram for 1989 to 1990 models (continued)

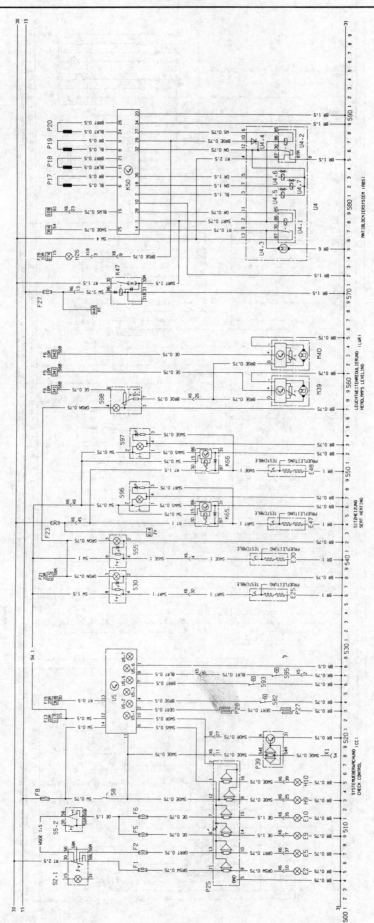

Fig. 13.11 Wiring diagram for 1989 to 1990 models (continued)

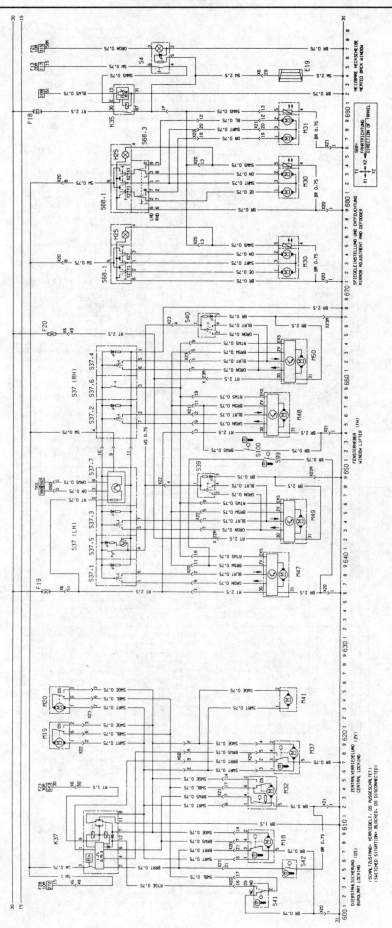

Fig. 13.11 Wiring diagram for 1989 to 1990 models (continued)

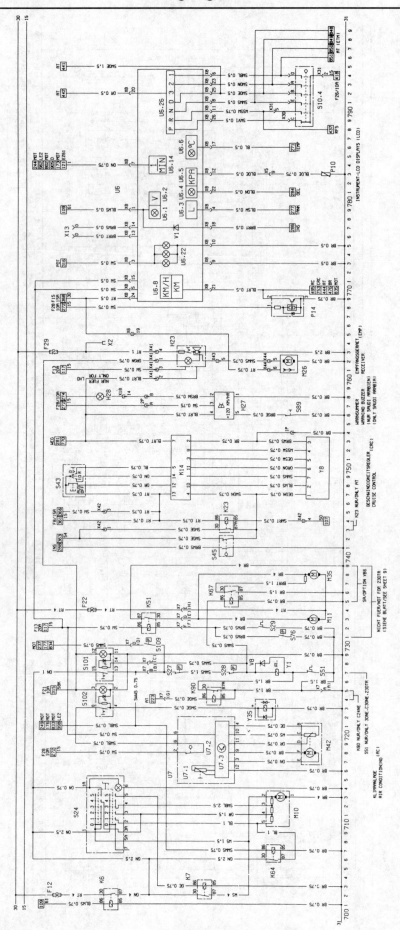

Fig. 13.11 Wiring diagram for 1989 to 1990 models (continued)

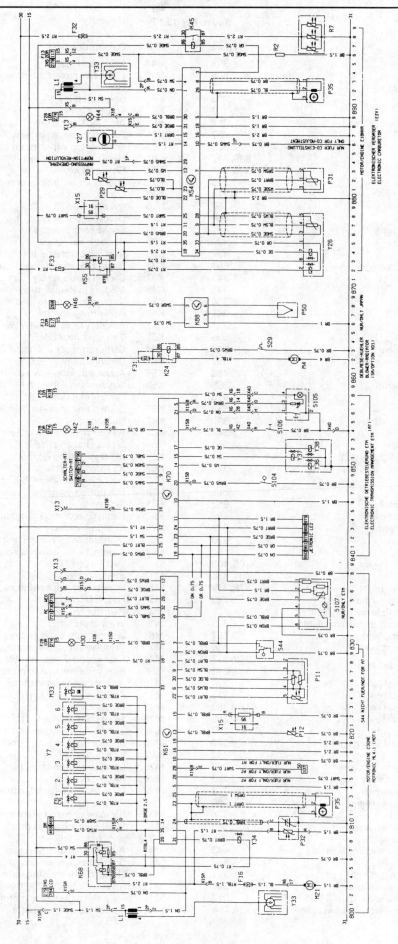

Fig. 13.11 Wiring diagram for 1989 to 1990 models (continued)

Key to Fig. 13.11

No	Description	Track	No	Description	Track
E1	LH parking light	302	H44	EZV warning light	889
E2	LH tail light	303, 505	H46	Catalytic converter temperature warning light	868
E3	Number plate light	313	K2	Flasher unit	370, 371
E4	RH parking light	309	K4	Spotlight relay	343, 344
E5	RH tail light	308, 507	K5	Foglight relay	348, 349
E6	Engine compartment light	318	K6	Air conditioning relay	701, 702
E7	LH high beam	337	K7	Air conditioning fan relay	702, 703
E8	RH high beam	338	K8	Windscreen wiper intermittent relay	405..408
E9	LH low beam	339, 509	K9	Headlamp washer relay	412, 413
E10	RH low beam	340, 511	K14	Cruise control	747..753
E11	Instrument lights	316	K15	Fuel injection timing control	141..154
E12	Selector lever light	314	K19	Level control relay	449, 450
E13	Boot light	385	K20	Ignition module	123, 124
E15	Glovebox light	464	K21	Level control sensor	447..449
E16	Cigarette lighter light	461	K23	Cruise control relay	743, 744
E17	LH reversing light	436	K24	Radiator fan relay	862, 863
E18	RH reversing light	437	K30	Rear wiper intermittent relay	426..428
E19	Heated rear window	694	K35	Heated exterior mirror delay relay	690..692
E20	LH foglight	347	K37	Central locking relay	606..611
E21	RH foglight	348	K45	Mixture preheater relay	897, 898
E22	LH spot light	344	K47	Over-voltage protection relay	570, 571
E23	RH spot light	345	K50	ABS timing control	577..590
E24	LH rear foglight	353	K51	Auxiliary radiator fan relay	732, 733
E25	LH heated front seat	536	K53	Timing control (EV 61)	127..134
E30	RH heated front seat	540	K54	Carburettor control unit (EZV)	874..894
E32	Clock light	397	K55	Carburettor relay (EZV)	872, 873
E33	Ashtray light	462	K56	Automatic kick-down control unit	440..444
E37	Make-up mirror lamp	399	K59	Day running light relay	319..325
E38	Computer light	470	K61	Control unit (Motronic)	168..194, 808..837
E39	RH rear foglight	354	K62	Control unit (dim-dip lights)	328..332
E41	Courtesy light (with delay)	387..390	K63	Dual horn relay	432, 433
E47	LH heated rear seat	544	K64	Air conditioning fan relay	706, 707
E48	RH heated rear seat	550	K65	LH seat heating relay	544..546
E61	LH number plate light (Japan)	311	K66	RH seat heating relay	550..552
E62	RH number plate light (Japan)	312	K67	Radiator fan relay	735, 736
F1 to			K68	Fuel injection relay	156..160, 195..199, 263..266, 803..808
F29	Fuses in fusebox	various	K70	Electronic transmission control unit	840..857
F31	Fuse (radiator fan)	862	K71	Ride control unit	484..499
F32	Fuse (mixture preheater)	898	K88	Catalytic converter temperature control unit	866..868
F33	Fuse (EZV carburettor)	872	K90	Compressor relay	724, 725
F35	Voltage stabiliser	270	K91	Motronic M1.5 control unit	235..262
G1	Battery	101	K92	Automatic transmission control unit	209..223
G2	Alternator	108, 109	L1	Ignition coil	123, 171, 242, 800, 892
H2	Horn	431, 434	M1	Starter motor	105, 106
H3	Turn signal warning light	378, 379	M2	Windscreen wiper motor	403..406
H4	Oil pressure warning light	283	M3	Heater fan motor	294..297
H5	Handbrake/brake fluid warning light	285	M4	Radiator fan motor	862
H6	Hazard warning system warning light	373	M5	Washer pump	402
H7	No-charge warning light	287	M6	LH headlight wiper motor	415..417
H8	Main beam warning light	336	M7	RH headlight wiper motor	419..421
H9	LH stop-light	362, 513	M8	Rear window wiper motor	424..426
H10	RH stop-light	363, 515	M9	Rear window washer pump	429
H11	LH front turn signal light	374	M10	Air conditioning fan motor	710..713
H12	LH rear turn signal light	375	M11	Auxiliary radiator fan motor	733
H13	RH front turn signal light	382	M13	Sunroof motor	455..457
H14	RH rear turn signal light	383	M18	Front door locking motor	606..609
H15	Low fuel warning light	277	M19	LH rear door locking motor	619..621
H17	Trailer turn signal warning light	370	M20	RH rear door locking motor	623..625
H18	Dual horns	432	M21	Fuel pump	158, 195, 264, 803
H19	Headlights on warning buzzer	394, 395	M22	Level control compressor	450
H21	Clutch/parking brake warning light	289	M26	Electric aerial motor	761, 762
H23	Radio with electric aerial	762, 763	M30	LH exterior mirror adjustment and heating	672..675, 681..684
H25	Mirror heater warning light	676, 685	M31	RH exterior mirror adjustment and heating	687..690
H26	ABS warning light	574	M32	Front door locking motor	612..615
H27	Safety check warning buzzer	756..758	M33	Idle control unit	180, 181, 251, 252, 824, 825
H28	Seat belt warning light	758	M35	Auxiliary radiator fan relay	738
H29	4-speed automatic warning light	443	M37	Bootlid/tailgate locking motor	616..619
H30	Engine warning light	178, 247, 830	M39	LH headlight levelling motor	558..560
H33	LH repeater turn signal light	377	M40	RH headlight levelling motor	562..564
H34	RH repeater turn signal light	380	M41	Fuel filler cap locking motor	623, 625
H41	Warning light (only with LCD)	317	M42	Air conditioning actuator	717..721
H42	Automatic transmission warning light	224, 854			

Key to Fig. 13.11 (continued)

No	Description	Track
M43	LH front ride control actuator	484..486
M44	RH front ride control actuator	488..490
M45	LH rear ride control actuator	492..494
M46	RH rear ride control actuator	496..498
M47	LH front electric window motor	636..640
M48	RH front electric window motor	654..658
M49	LH rear electric window motor	642..646
M50	RH rear electric window motor	660..664
P1	Fuel gauge	275
P2	Temperature gauge	273
P3	Clock	396
P4	Fuel sensor	275
P5	Temperature sensor	273
P7	Tachometer	278
P10	Oil pressure sensor	787
P11	Airflow meter	182..186, 244..248, 824..828
P12	Temperature probe (coolant)	151, 177, 237, 820
P13	Outside air temperature sensor	473, 474
P14	Distance sensor	770, 771
P15	Fuel flowmeter	466, 467
P17	LH front wheel sensor (ABS)	582, 583
P18	RH front wheel sensor (ABS)	584, 585
P19	LH rear wheel sensor (ABS)	586, 587
P20	RH rear wheel sensor (ABS)	588, 589
P21	Instrument optical frequency sensor	280, 281
P24	Oil temperature sensor	132
P25	Bulb test sensor	504..517
P27	LH front brake lining sensor	523
P28	RH front brake lining sensor	523
P29	Inlet manifold temperature sensor	881
P30	Coolant temperature sensor	882
P31	Main throttle potentiometer	881..883
P32	Heated Lambda sensor	191, 192, 261, 263, 809, 810
P34	Throttle valve position sensor	241..243
P35	Crankshaft inductive sensor	128..130, 187..189, 256..258, 811..813
P39	Trailer bulb test sensor	518, 520
P50	Catalytic converter temperature sensor	867, 868
P51	Speed sensor	216, 217
R2	Carburettor preheater	896
R3	Cigarette lighter	460
R7	Mixture preheater	898
R13	LH heated washer jet	409
R14	RH heated washer jet	410
S1	Starter motor switch	105, 106
S2	Light switch	
S2.1	Light switch	305..308, 506, 507
S2.2	Courtesy light switch	389
S2.3	Instrument lights dimmer	315
S3	Heater fan switch	292..298
S4	Heated rear window switch	695..697
S5	Turn signal switch assembly	
S5.2	Headlight dip switch	338, 339, 511
S5.3	Turn signal switch	381..383
S5.4	Parking light switch	301..303
S5.5	Horn switch	433
S7	Reversing light switch	436
S8	Stop-light switch	362, 513
S9	Windscreen wiper switch assembly	
S9.2	Windscreen wiper switch (intermittent)	402..406
S9.3	Rear window wiper switch (intermittent)	427, 428
S10	Automatic transmission switch	
S10.1	Automatic transmission switch	106
S10.4	Speed telltale switch	793..799
S11	Brake fluid level switch	285
S12	Clutch control switch	288
S13	Handbrake warning light switch	289
S14	Oil pressure switch	283
S15	Boot light switch	385
S17	LH courtesy light switch	390
S18	Glovebox light switch	464
S21	Foglight switch	349..351

No	Description	Track
S22	Rear foglight switch	354, 356
S24	Air conditioning fan switch	707..714
S27	Pressure switch	727
S28	Compressor cut-off switch	727
S29	Radiator fan switch	732, 863
S30	LH front heated seat switch	536..538
S31	LH rear door courtesy light switch	391
S32	RH rear door courtesy light switch	392
S35	Sunroof micro switch	455
S36	Sunroof micro switch	457
S37	Electric window switch assembly	637..663
S37.1	LH front electric window switch	637..639
S37.2	RH front electric window switch	655..657
S37.3	LH rear electric window switch	643..645
S37.4	RH rear electric window switch	661..663
S37.5	Safety switch	641
S37.6	Anti-jamming switch	659
S37.7	Electronic control	646..649
S39	LH rear door window motor switch	647..649
S40	RH rear door window motor switch	665..667
S41	RH anti-theft lock switch	602..604
S42	LH central locking switch	605
S43	Cruise control switch	747..750
S44	Throttle valve switch	142, 143, 172, 173, 829, 830
S45	Cruise control clutch switch	741, 742
S47	Doors open/headlamps on warning switch	393, 394
S51	Compressor coolant temperature switch	727
S52	Hazard light switch	371..376
S55	RH front seat heating switch	540..542
S57	Sunroof switch	453..459
S61	Power steering pressure switch	120
S63	Board computer switch assembly	471..475
S63.1	Function reset switch	472
S63.2	Clock hour adjustment switch	473
S63.3	Function selection switch	474
S63.5	Clock minute adjustment switch	475
S68	Exterior mirror switch	
S68.1	Exterior mirror adjustment switch	671..674, 679..683
S68.3	Exterior mirror left/right switch	680..684
S76	Compressor pressure switch	731
S82	Washer fluid low level switch	524
S87	4-speed automatic switch	441
S89	Seat belt switch	756
S93	Coolant low level switch	526
S95	Engine oil low level switch	527
S96	LH rear seat heating switch	546..548
S97	RH rear seat heating switch	552..554
S98	Headlight levelling switch	557..559
S99	RH front window switch (2V)	651
S100	LH front window switch (2V)	652
S101	Compressor switch	727..729
S102	Circulation switch	723..725
S104	Kickdown switch	214, 848
S105	Start-up assistance switch	208..210, 856..858
S106	Economy/power program switch	212, 854
S107	Throttle valve switch	831..837
S109	Motronic compressor pressure switch	730
S110	Ride control switch	483..488
S116	Stop light switch	365, 366
S118	Automatic transmission switch	211..216
U2	Board computer	467..478
U4	ABS system	575..588
U4.1	ABS pump relay	576..579
U4.2	ABS solenoid valve relay	585..588
U4.3	ABS pump	575
U4.4	ABS diode	587
U4.5	LH front ABS solenoid valve	581
U4.6	RH front ABS solenoid valve	583
U4.7	Rear ABS solenoid valve	582
U5	Check control display assembly	521..528
U5.1	Tail light and low beam warning light	522
U5.2	Brake light warning light	523

Key to Fig. 13.11 (continued)

No	Description	Track		No	Description	Track
U5.3	Low oil level warning light	525		U11.2	Carburettor preheater	117
U5.5	Low front brake lining warning light	526		U13	Clutch torque converter	219..222
U5.6	Low washer fluid warning light	528		U14	Adapter case	223..227
U5.7	Low coolant level warning light	529		V1	Brake fluid test bulb diode	286, 779
U6	LCD instrument assembly	771..798		V8	Compressor diode	728
U6.1	Charging indicator light	781		X1	Trailer socket	various
U6.2	Voltmeter	782..784		X5 to		
U6.3	Fuel indicator	782		X44	Connectors	various
U6.4	Oil pressure warning light	785		Y1	Air conditioning compressor	727
U6.5	Oil pressure gauge	787		Y4	Headlight washer solenoid valve	413
U6.6	Coolant temperature indicator	790		Y6	Auxiliary air slide valve	155
U6.8	Speedometer	772		Y7	Fuel injection solenoid valve	144..151, 182..189,
U6.14	Tachometer	786				253..260, 812..823
U6.22	Display lights	775..777		Y8	Cruise control actuator	747..753
U6.26	Automatic transmission lever display	218..221, 792..798		Y9	Level control solenoid	451
U7	Air conditioning adjustment unit	716..721		Y25	Acceleration solenoid valve	120
U7.1	Temperature selector lever potentiometer	716		Y26	Throttle valve positioner	872..878
U7.2	Demister lever limit switch	718, 719		Y27	Pre-throttle valve	886, 887
U7.3	Electronic control	716..721		Y33	Distributor	128, 168, 244, 801, 894
U10	4-speed automatic transmission			Y34	Tank ventilation valve	197, 265, 808
U10.1	4-speed automatic pressure switch	442		Y35	Circulation valve	723
U10.2	4-speed automatic solenoid valve	444		Y36	Automatic transmission solenoid valve (1)	850
U11	Carburettor assembly			Y37	Automatic transmission solenoid valve (2)	851
U11.1	Thermotime valve	118		Y38	Automatic transmission clutch solenoid valve	852

Not all items are fitted to all models

Colour code

BL	Blue		LI	Lilac
BR	Brown		RT	Red
GE	Yellow		SW	Black
GN	Green		VI	Violet
GR	Grey		WS	White
HBL	Light blue			

Abbreviations

ABS	Anti-lock brake system		M 1.5	Motronic M 1.5
AC	Air conditioning		M 2.5	Motronic M 2.5
AT	Automatic transmission		MOT	Motronic in general
ATC	Automatic temperature control		MT	Manual transmission
AZV	Trailer hitch		N	Norway
BR	On-board computer		NS	Foglights
CC	Check control		NSL	Rear foglights
D	Diesel		OEL	Oil level control (oil pressure)
DS	Theft protection		OPT	Optional equipment
DWA	Anti-theft warning system		P/N	Park/Neutral (automatic transmission)
DZM	Tachometer		PBSL	Park and brake shift block
EFC	Electric folding roof, convertible		POT	Potentiometer
EKS	Pinch guard (electric windows)		RC	Electronic ride control
EMP	Radio		RHD	Right-hand drive
EUR	Euronorm engine		S	Sweden
EZ +	El Plus with self-diagnosis		SD	Sliding roof
EZV	Ecotronic		SH	Seat heating
FH	Window winders		SRA	Headlight cleaning system
GB	Great Britain		TANK	Fuel gauge
HS	Rear screen		TD	Turbodiesel
HW	Rear screen wiper		TEMP	Temperature gauge
HZG	Heating		TFL	Daytime driving light
HRL	Luggage compartment light		TKS	Door contact switch
INS	Instrument		TSZI	Transistor ignition (inductive)
IRL	Interior light		VGS	Carburettor
KAT	Catalytic converter		WEG	Odometer frequency sensor
KBS	Wiring harness		WHR	Car level control
KV	Contact distribution		WS	Warning buzzer
L3.1	Jetronic L3.1		ZV	Central door locking
LCD	LCD instrument		ZYL	Cylinder
LHD	Left-hand drive		4WD	Four wheel drive
LWR	Headlight range control			

Wiring identification

eg GE WS 1.5

GE	Basic colour
WS	Identification colour
1.5	Section (mm^2)

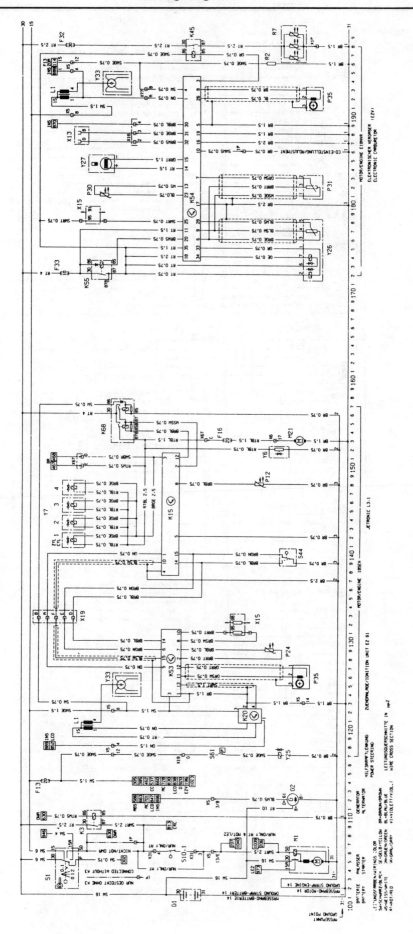

Fig. 13.12 Wiring diagram for 1991 to 1992 models

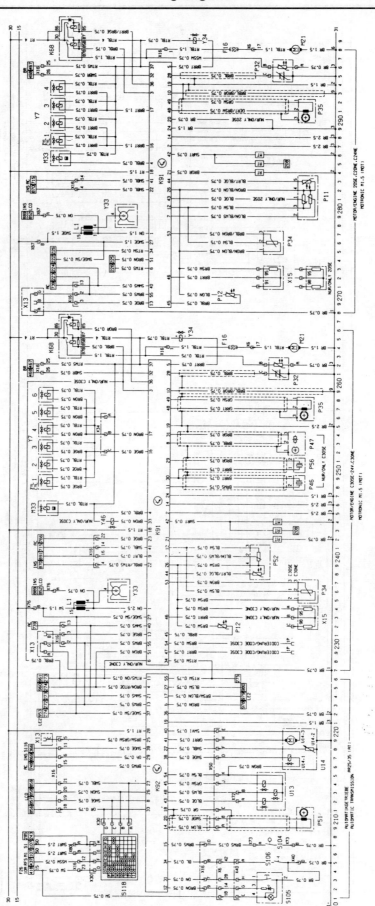

Fig. 13.12 Wiring diagram for 1991 to 1992 models (continued)

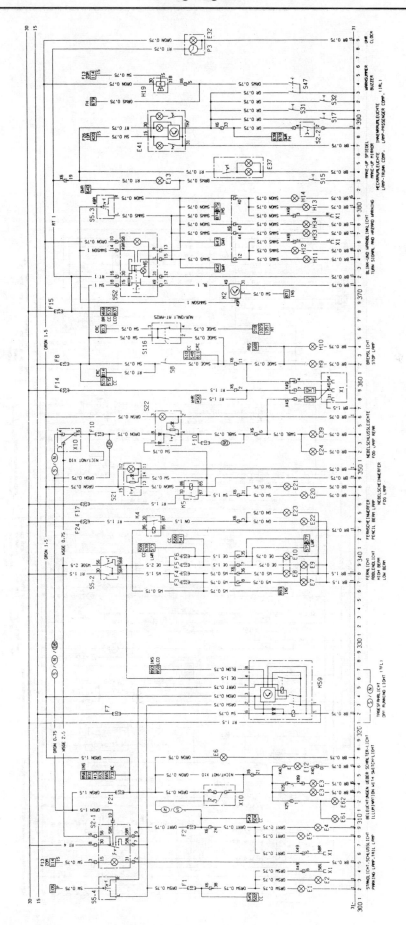

Fig. 13.12 Wiring diagram for 1991 to 1992 models (continued)

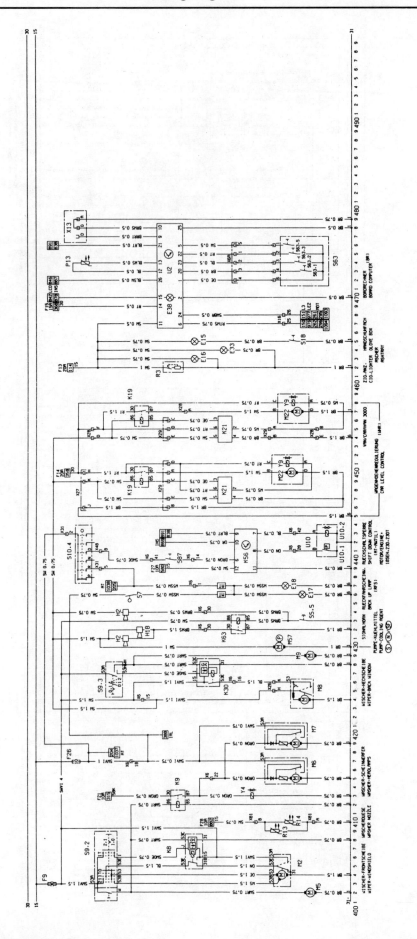

Fig. 13.12 Wiring diagram for 1991 to 1992 models (continued)

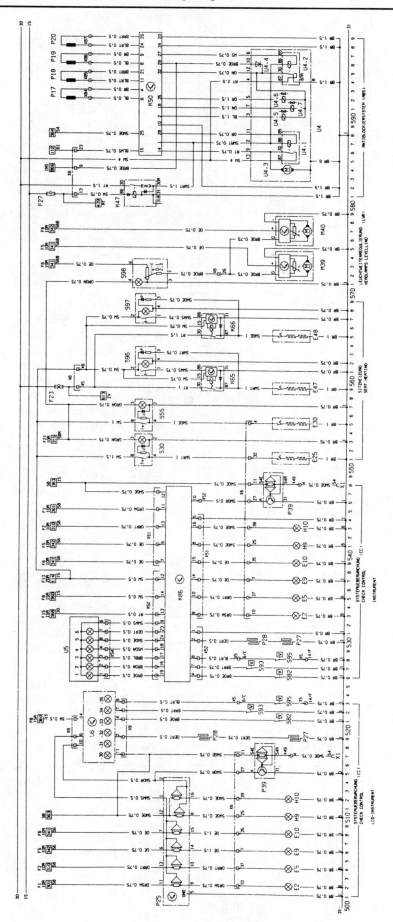

Fig. 13.12 Wiring diagram for 1991 to 1992 models (continued)

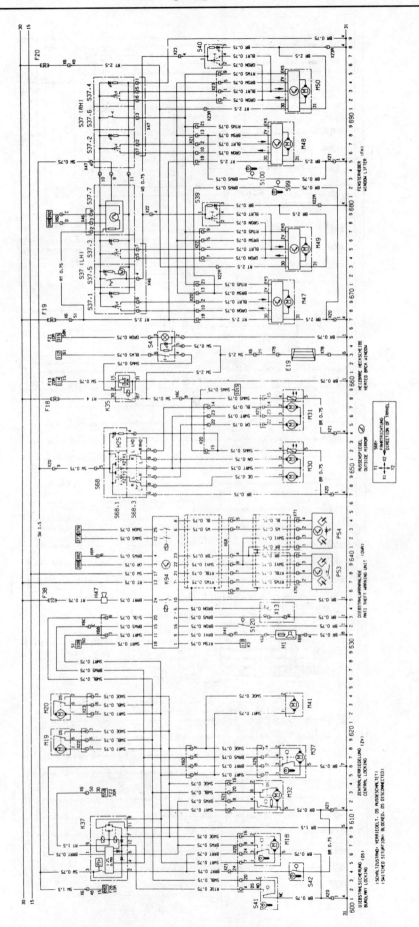

Fig. 13.12 Wiring diagram for 1991 to 1992 models (continued)

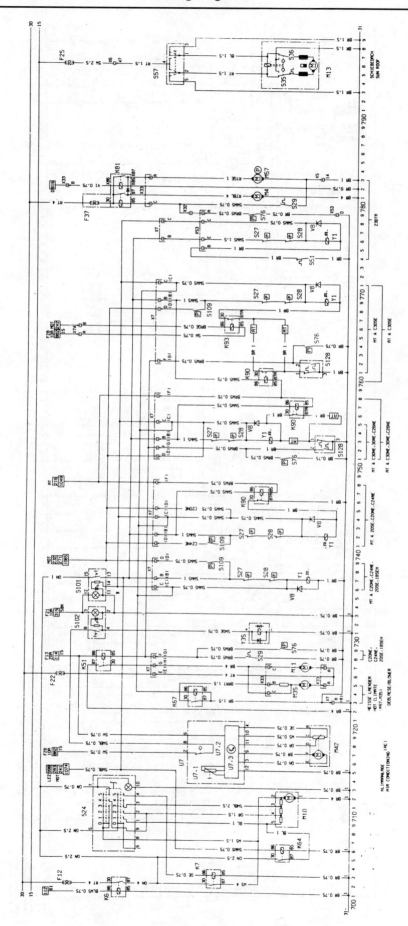

Fig. 13.12 Wiring diagram for 1991 to 1992 models (continued)

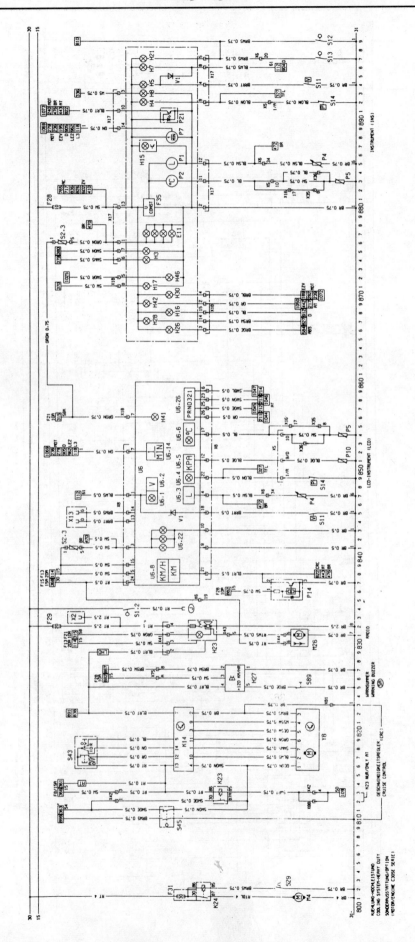

Fig. 13.12 Wiring diagram for 1991 to 1992 models (continued)

Key to Fig. 13.12

No	Description	Track	No	Description	Track
E1	Sidelight, left	302	H34	Direction indicator repeater light, right	378
E2	Tail light, left	303, 502, 503	H41	Warning light – lights	856
E3	Number plate light	313, 314	H42	Warning light – automatic transmission	869
E4	Sidelight, right	309	H46	Warning light – temperature, catalytic converter	872
E5	Tail light, right	308, 504, 535	H47	Siren – anti-theft warning unit	635
E6	Engine compartment light	317	K2	Flasher unit (in fusebox)	370, 371
E7	Main beam, left	337	K3	Relay – anti-theft warning unit	109, 110
E8	Main beam, right	338	K4	Relay – spotlights (in fusebox)	343, 344
E9	Dipped beam, left	339, 506, 537	K5	Relay – foglight (in fusebox)	347, 348
E10	Dipped beam, right	340, 508, 539	K6	Relay – air conditioning	701, 702
E11	Instrument lighting	877	K7	Relay – blower, air conditioning	702, 703
E12	Selector lever (auto) lighting, centre console	316	K8	Relay – windscreen wiper, intermittent (in fusebox)	405..408
E13	Boot light	383	K9	Relay – washer unit, headlights	412, 413
E15	Glovebox light	465	K14	Cruise control	816..822
E16	Cigarette lighter illumination	463	K15	Timing control – fuel injection	138..151
E17	Reversing light, left	436	K19	Relay – car level control	449, 450, 456, 457
E18	Reversing light, right	437	K20	Ignition module – ignition coil	121, 122
E19	Heated rear window	663	K21	Sensor – car level control	447..449, 454..456
E20	Foglight, left	347	K23	Relay – cruise control	812, 813
E21	Foglight, right	348	K24	Relay – radiator cooling fan	801, 802
E22	Spotlight, left	344	K30	Relay – tailgate wiper, intermittent	426..428
E23	Spotlight, right	345	K35	Relay – time delay, heated rear window & mirrors	658..660
E24	Foglight, rear, left	352	K37	Control unit – central locking	604..610
E25	Heating mat – front seat, left	551	K45	Relay – mixture preheating	197, 198
E30	Heating mat – front seat, right	555	K47	Relay – over-voltage protection	581, 582
E32	Light – clock	397	K50	Timing control – ABS	586..599
E33	Light – ashtray	464	K51	Relay – radiator cooling fan	727, 728
E37	Light – make-up mirror	384	K53	Timing control – EZ 61	124..131
E38	Light – on-board computer	470	K54	Control unit – carburettor	174..194
E39	Foglight, rear, right	354	K55	Relay – carburettor	172, 173
E41	Light – passenger compartment, delayed switch-off	387..389	K56	Control unit – kickdown control	439..443
E47	Heating mat – rear seat, left	559	K59	Relay – day running lights	321..327
E48	Heating mat – rear seat, right	565	K63	Relay – trumpet horn (in fusebox)	432, 433
E61	Number plate light, left (Japan)	310	K64	Relay – blower, air conditioning	705, 706
E62	Number plate light, right (Japan)	312	K65	Relay – heating mat, left	559..561
F1-F28	Fuses (in fusebox)	Various	K66	Relay – heating mat, right	565..567
F31	Fuse – radiator cooling fan	801	K67	Relay – radiator cooling fan, stage 1	723, 724
F32	Fuse – mixture preheating	198	K68	Relay – fuel injection	153..157, 263..266, 297..299
F33	Fuse – carburettor, electronic	172	K81	Relay – water pump	780..783
F35	Voltage stabilizer	880	K86	Control unit – check control	526..547
F37	Fuse – water pump	780	K90	Relay – compressor (AT)	746, 755, 760
F38	Fuse – anti-theft warning unit	635	K91	Control unit – Motronic M1.5	228..262, 269..296
G1	Battery	101	K92	Control unit – automatic transmission, AR25/35	202..226
G2	Alternator	111, 112	K93	Relay – compressor (Motronic)	766, 767
H1	Radio	630	K94	Control unit – anti-theft warning unit	630..644
H2	Horn	431, 434	L1	Ignition coil	120, 192, 234, 277
H3	Warning light – direction indicators	874, 875	M1	Starter	105, 106
H4	Warning light – oil pressure	892	M2	Motor – windscreen wiper	403..406
H5	Warning light – brake fluid	894	M4	Motor – radiator cooling fan	781, 801
H6	Warning light – hazard warning system	373	M5	Pump – windscreen washer	402
H7	Charging indicator light	896	M6	Motor – headlight wiper, left	415..417
H8	Warning light – main beam	893	M7	Motor – headlight wiper, right	419..421
H9	Stop-light, left	362, 510, 541	M8	Motor – tailgate wiper	424..426
H10	Stop-light, right	363, 512, 543	M9	Pump – tailgate washer	429
H11	Direction indicator light, front, left	374	M10	Motor – blower, air conditioning	709..712
H12	Direction indicator light, rear, left	375	M11	Motor – radiator auxiliary cooling fan	727
H13	Direction indicator light, front, right	380	M13	Motor – sunroof	795..797
H14	Direction indicator light, rear, right	381	M18	Motor – central locking, driver's door	605..608
H15	Warning light – fuel	887	M19	Motor – central locking, rear left door	618..620
H16	Warning light – glow time (diesel)	868	M20	Motor – central locking, rear right door	622..624
H17	Warning light – direction indicator light, trailer	871	M21	Pump – fuel	153, 264, 298
H18	Trumpet horn	432	M22	Compressor – car level control	450, 457
H19	Buzzer – headlights-on warning (in fusebox)	396, 397	M26	Motor – electric aerial	830, 831
H21	Warning light – clutch & handbrake	897	M30	Motor – exterior mirror, driver's side	649..652
H23	Radio aerial, electric	831, 832	M31	Motor – exterior mirror, passenger's side	655..658
H25	Warning light – mirror heating	654	M32	Motor – central locking, (front) passenger's door	611..614
H26	Warning light – ABS	866	M33	Power unit – idling	245, 246, 285, 286
H27	Warning buzzer – safety checking	825..827	M35	Motor – radiator auxiliary cooling fan	725
H28	Warning light – seat belt warning	867	M37	Motor – central locking, bootlid/tailgate	615..618
H30	Warning light – engine, electronic	870			
H33	Direction indicator repeater light, left	377			

Key to Fig. 13.12 (continued)

No	Description	Track
M39	Motor – headlight levelling, left	572..575
M40	Motor – headlight levelling, right	576..579
M41	Motor – central locking, door, fuel filler	622, 624
M42	Actuator – air conditioning	716..720
M47	Motor – electric window, front left	667..671
M48	Motor – electric window, front right	685..689
M49	Motor – electric window, rear left	673..677
M50	Motor – electric window, rear right	691..695
M57	Water pump	430, 783
P1	Fuel gauge	885
P2	Temperature gauge	883
P3	Clock	396
P4	Sensor – fuel	847, 885
P5	Sensor – water temperature	854, 883
P7	Tachometer	888
P10	Sensor – oil pressure	851
P11	Airflow meter	279..283
P12	Sensor – water temperature	148, 232, 270
P13	Sensor – outside air temperature	473, 474
P14	Sensor – distance	836, 837
P17	Sensor – ABS, front left	592
P18	Sensor – ABS, front right	594
P19	Sensor – ABS, rear left	596
P20	Sensor – ABS, rear right	598
P21	Instrument optical frequency sensor	890, 891
P24	Sensor – engine oil temperature	129
P25	Sensor – bulb test	501..514
P27	Sensor – brake lining, front left	519, 530
P28	Sensor – brake lining, front right	519, 530
P30	Water temperature sensor	181
P31	Main throttle potentiometer	181..183
P32	Sensor – exhaust gas oxygen content (heated)	261, 262, 295, 296
P34	Sensor – throttle valve position	235..237, 273..275
P35	Impulse sensor – crankshaft	126, 127, 192, 193, 256..258, 290..292, 515, 517, 546..548
P39	Sensor – bulb test, trailer	
P46	Sensor – knock control	248, 249
P47	Hall sensor – cylinder identification	252..254
P51	Sensor – speed	209, 210
P52	Airflow meter	238..241
P53	Sensor – anti-theft warning unit, driver's side	636..639
P54	Sensor – anti-theft warning unit, passenger's side	641..644
P56	Sensor – knock control	250, 251
R2	Carburettor – preheating	196
R3	Cigarette lighter	462
R7	Mixture – preheating	198
R13	Washer nozzle – heated, left	409
R14	Washer nozzle – heated, right	410
S1	Switch assembly – starter	105, 106
S1.2	Switch – starter	834
S2	Switch assembly – light	
S2.1	Switch – light	305..308
S2.2	Switch – passenger compartment light	389
S2.3	Dimmer – instrument lights	841, 876
S4	Switch – heated rear window & mirrors	663..665
S5	Direction indicator switch assembly	
S5.2	Switch – dipped beam	338, 339
S5.3	Switch – direction indicator	379..381
S5.4	Switch – sidelight	301..303
S5.5	Switch – horn	433
S7	Switch – reversing light	436
S8	Switch – stop-light	362
S9	Switch assembly – wipers	
S9.2	Switch – windscreen intermittent wipe	402..406
S9.3	Switch – tailgate intermittent wipe	427, 428
S10	Switch assembly – automatic transmission (AW71L)	
S10.1	Switch – park/neutral	106
S10.4	Switch – selector lever position	439..443
S11	Control switch – brake fluid, min capacity	845, 894
S12	Control switch – clutch	899
S13	Switch – handbrake	897

No	Description	Track
S14	Switch – oil pressure	849, 892
S15	Switch – luggage compartment light	383
S17	Contact switch – passenger's seat	390
S18	Switch – glovebox light	465
S21	Switch – foglight	348..350
S22	Switch – rear foglight	354, 356
S24	Switch – blower, air conditioning	707..713
S27	Switch – compressor, low pressure	737, 742, 753, 769, 776
S28	Switch – compressor, high pressure	737, 742, 753, 769, 776
S29	Switch – radiator cooling fan	728,780,802
S30	Switch – heating mat, front seat, left	551..553
S31	Contact switch – rear left door	391
S32	Contact switch – rear right door	392
S35	Micro-switch – sunroof	795
S36	Micro-switch – sunroof	797
S37	Switch assembly – electric windows	
S37.1	Switch – electric window, left	668..670
S37.2	Switch – electric window, right	686..688
S37.3	Switch – electric window, rear left	674..676
S37.4	Switch – electric window, rear right	692..694
S37.5	Safety switch	672
S37.6	Switch – anti-jam off (elec. window pinch-guard off)	690
S37.7	Control – electric window, automatic	677..680
S39	Switch – electric window, rear left door	678..680
S40	Switch – electric window, rear right door	696..698
S41	Switch – anti-theft locking, driver's door	601..603
S42	Switch – central locking, passenger's door	604
S43	Switch – cruise control	816..819
S44	Switch – throttle valve	139, 140
S45	Switch – clutch, cruise control	810, 811
S47	Contact switch – driver's door	392, 394
S51	Switch – compressor cooling agent	774
S52	Switch – hazard warning	371..376
S55	Switch – heating mat, front seat, right	555..557
S57	Switch – sunroof, open/close/tilt	793..799
S61	Pressure switch – power steering	117
S63	Switch assembly – on-board computer	
S63.1	Switch – function reset	473
S63.2	Switch – hour adjustment, clock	474
S63.3	Switch – function select	475
S63.5	Switch – minute adjustment, clock	476
S68	Switch assembly – exterior mirror	
S68.1	Switch – exterior mirror adjustment	647..652
S68.3	Switch – exterior mirror, left/right	647..652
S76	Switch – compressor, high pressure (blower)	729, 751, 764, 779
S82	Control switch – washer fluid	521, 526
S87	Switch – 4-speed automatic	440
S89	Switch – seat belt	825
S93	Control switch – coolant, min capacity	522, 527
S95	Control switch – engine oil, min capacity	523, 528
S96	Switch – heating mat, rear seat, left	561..563
S97	Switch – heating mat, rear seat, right	567..569
S98	Switch – headlight levelling	571..573
S99	Switch – electric window, driver's door, ZV	682
S100	Switch – electric window, passenger's door, ZV	683
S101	Switch – compressor	735, 737
S102	Switch – circulation	731..733
S104	Switch – kickdown	207
S105	Switch – Winter mode (automatic trans.)	201..203
S106	Switch – Economy/Sport mode (automatic trans.)	205
S109	Switch – compressor (Motronic)	739, 741, 768
S116	Switch – stop-light	365, 366
S118	Switch – automatic transmission	204..207
S120	Switch – bonnet	632
S128	Switch – temperature, radiator (blower-compressor)	752, 761
U2	On-board computer	467..478
U4	Hydraulic unit assembly – ABS	584..597
U4.1	Relay – pump, ABS	585..588

Key to Fig. 13.12 (continued)

No	Description	Track
U4.2	Relay – solenoid valves, ABS	594..597
U4.3	Pump – ABS	584
U4.4	Diode – ABS	596
U4.5	Solenoid valve – ABS, front left	590
U4.6	Solenoid valve – ABS, front right	592
U4.7	Solenoid valve – ABS, rear left	591
U5	Display assembly – check control	
U5.1	Warning light – washer fluid, min capacity	526
U5.2	Warning light – oil, min capacity	327
U5.3	Warning light – coolant, min capacity	528
U5.4	Warning light – tail light & dipped beam	529
U5.5	Warning light – stop-light failure	530
U5.6	Warning light – brake lining, front	531
U6	Instrument – LCD	
U6.1	Charging indicator light	847
U6.2	Voltmeter	848
U6.3	Fuel gauge	847
U6.4	Warning light – oil pressure	849
U6.5	Oil pressure gauge	851
U6.6	Water temperature gauge	854
U6.8	Speedometer	838
U6.14	Tachometer	852
U6.22	Warning lights	841..843
U6.26	Selector lever position indicator (auto. transmission)	856..859
U6.30	Warning light – washer fluid, min capacity	517
U6.31	Warning light – oil, min capacity	518
U6.32	Warning light – coolant, min capacity	519
U6.33	Warning light – tail light & dipped beam	520
U6.34	Warning light – stop-light failure	521
U6.35	Warning light – brake lining, front	522
U7	Air conditioning unit assembly	
U7.1	Potentiometer – temperature selector lever	715
U7.2	Limit switch – defroster lever	717
U7.3	Control unit – electronic	715..720
U10	Transmission assembly – 4-speed automatic	
U10.1	Pressure switch – 4-speed automatic	441
U10.2	Solenoid valve – 4-speed automatic	443
U13	Converter clutch – solenoid valves	212..215
U14	Adapter case	216..220
U14.1	Solenoid valve	217
U14.2	Sensor – fluid temperature	218
U14.3	Actuator	219
V1	Diode – brake fluid level test	845, 895
V8	Diode – compressor	736, 744, 755, 771, 778
X	Connectors and multi-plugs	
X1	Trailer socket	304, 306, 358..360, 376, 381, 517, 548
X2	Auxiliary user connector (in fusebox)	833
X5	Instrument panel & engine 14-pin/7-pin	106, 112, 117, 118, 122, 123, 190, 195, 196, 523, 528, 783, 849..854, 883, 892
X6	Instrument panel & body 51-pin	153, 201..205, 264, 298, 302, 309, 315, 337..340, 344, 348, 354, 359, 362, 374, 377, 378, 381, 383, 389, 394, 415, 417, 424, 426, 432, 434, 437, 440, 441, 443, 502..517, 533..561, 572, 581, 584, 590, 602, 613, 661, 667, 696, 796, 835, 847, 885, 897
X6A	Instrument panel & body 6-pin	471..475, 640
X6C	Instrument panel & door 3-pin	632, 658
X6D	Body & door 6-pin (ZV)	615..618, 678, 679
X7	Instrument panel & air conditioning 7-pin/ (8-pin- AT)	723, 726..728, 736..762, 768..778,
X8	LCD instrument 26-pin	837..859
X9	LCD instrument 26-pin (CC)	517..523
X10	Code countries 6-pin	312, 313, 354
X13	Diagnostic link 10-pin	187, 188, 219, 229..231, 268..270, 477..479, 494, 633, 634, 844, 845
X15	Octane plug 3-pin	131, 178, 232..334, 270..272
X16	Instrument panel & Motronic 26-pin	187..189, 202..233, 239..242, 261..264, 269..298, 468, 469, 856, 882
X17	Instrument 14-pin	874..897
X18	Instrument 16-pin	856, 866..872
X19	Engine & Jetronic 8-pin	117, 133
X20	Door frame & driver's door, 24-pin	318, 601..608, 650..657, 667..671
X21	Door frame & passenger's door, 24-pin	319, 604, 611..614, 655..658, 685..689
X22	Door frame & left rear door, 9-pin	618..620, 674..677, 679
X22A	Door frame & left rear door, 2-pin	673, 680
X23	Door frame & right rear door, 9-pin	622..624, 692..695, 697
X23A	Door frame & right rear door, 2-pin	691, 698
X25	Body & bootlid 5-pin	312, 615..618
X26	Body & tailgate 3-pin	313, 425, 426
X27	Body & car level control 3-pin	446..450
X28	Body & car level control 6-pin	454..457
X29	Car level control & high sensor 5-pin	446..456
X30	Motronic/Jetronic & auto. transmission switch 8-pin	204..207, 209
X31	Instrument panel & auto. transmission switch 5-pin	106, 439, 443
X32	Instrument panel & engine 1-pin	779
X33	Blower motor 3-pin	724..727, 780..783
X34	Motronic & fuel injection sol. valves 3-pin (C30SE)	252..256
X35	Motronic & fuel injection sol. valves 35-pin (C26NE)	855, 882
X36	Motronic & engine 1-pin (C24NE)	853, 884
X40	Body & centre console (automatic transmission) 8-pin	201..205, 314
X41	Instruments & radio 6-pin	631, 829..832
X42	Instruments & cruise control 4-pin (AR25 auto. trans.)	812, 813
X43	Body & radio 6-pin	831
X44	Body & loudspeaker 6-pin	830, 831
X46	Door & console 8-pin	668..679
X47	Door & console 7-pin	685..694
X48	Instrument panel & automatic transmission switch 5-pin	441
X49	Body & socket-trailer 7-pin	304, 306, 358..360, 376, 379, 517, 548
X50	Motronic/Jetronic & automatic transmission 10-pin	209..220
X51	Check control 16-pin	533..547
X52	Check control 26-pin	526..537, 546
X53	Instrument panel & compressor 5-pin	775..779
X54	Instrument 8-pin (CC)	526..532
X67	Instrument panel & Jetronic 5-pin	150, 151, 153, 276, 279
X68	Instrument panel & door 9-pin	631..644
X69	Radio 16-pin	631
X70	Door & anti-theft sensor – driver's side 4-pin	636..639
X71	Door & anti-theft sensor – passenger's side 4-pin	641..644
X72	Motronic & automatic transmission 2-pin	212, 213
X73	Instrument panel & kickdown switch 2-pin	207
X74	Instrument panel & air conditioning 2-pin	765..766
X75	Instrument panel & cruise control 2-pin	826, 827
X76	Instrument panel & Motronic 2-pin	234, 236
X77	Engine & EZV 2-pin	192, 193
X78	Body & tailgate (Van) 2-pin	663
X80	Engine & Motronic/Jetronic 2-pin	206, 207
X81	Instrument panel & heated washer nozzles 2-pin	410
X83	Instrument panel & cruise control 1-pin	812, 823
X84-87	Wheel sensor, ABS 2-pin	592..599
X88	Cruise control & auto. trans. switch (AW71L) 1-pin	812
X89	Tailgate & number plate light, 1-pin	313
Y1	Clutch – compressor, air conditioning	737, 742, 753, 769, 776
Y4	Solenoid valve – headlight washer	413

Key to Fig. 13.12 (continued)

No	Description	Track	No	Description	Track
Y6	Auxiliary air valve	152	Y26	Throttle valve positioner	172..178
Y7	Solenoid valves – fuel injection	141..148, 248..259, 287..294	Y27	Pre-throttle valve	184, 185
			Y33	Ignition distributor	125, 194, 236, 279
Y8	Actuator – cruise control	816..822	Y34	Solenoid valve – fuel tank ventilation	265, 299
Y9	Solenoid valve – car level control	451, 458	Y35	Valve – circulation	731
Y25	Solenoid valve – acceleration	117	Y46	Solenoid valve – inlet manifold	244

Not all items are fitted to all models

Colour code

BL	Blue
BR	Brown
GE	Yellow
GN	Green
GR	Grey
HBL	Light blue
LI	Lilac
RT	Red
SW	Black
VI	Violet
WS	White

Abbreviations

ABS	Anti-lock brake system		M 1.5	Motronic M 1.5
AC	Air conditioning		M 2.5	Motronic M 2.5
AT	Automatic transmission		MOT	Motronic in general
ATC	Automatic temperature control		MT	Manual transmission
AZV	Trailer hitch		N	Norway
BR	On-board computer		NS	Foglights
CC	Check control		NSL	Rear foglights
D	Diesel		OEL	Oil level control (oil pressure)
DS	Theft protection		OPT	Optional equipment
DWA	Anti-theft warning system		P/N	Park/Neutral (automatic transmission)
DZM	Tachometer		PBSL	Park and brake shift block
EFC	Electric folding roof, convertible		POT	Potentiometer
EKS	Pinch guard (electric windows)		RC	Electric ride control
EMP	Radio		RHD	Right-hand drive
EUR	Euronorm engine		S	Sweden
EZ +	El Plus with self-diagnosis		SD	Sliding roof
EZV	Ecotronic		SH	Seat heating
FH	Electric windows		SRA	Headlight cleaning system
GB	Great Britain		TANK	Fuel gauge
HS	Rear screen		TD	Turbodiesel
HW	Rear screen wiper		TEMP	Temperature gauge
HZG	Heating		TFL	Daytime driving light
HRL	Luggage compartment light		TKS	Door contact switch
INS	Instrument		TSZI	Transistor ignition (inductive)
IRL	Interior light		VGS	Carburettor
KAT	Catalytic converter		WEG	Odometer frequency sensor
KBS	Wiring harness		WHR	Car level control
KV	Contact distributor		WS	Warning buzzer
L3.1	Jetronic L3.1		ZV	Central door locking
LCD	LCD instrument		ZYL	Cylinder
LHD	Left-hand drive		4WD	Four wheel drive
LWR	Headlight range control			

Wiring identification

eg GE WS 1.5

GE	Basic colour
WS	Identification colour
1.5	Section (mm^2)

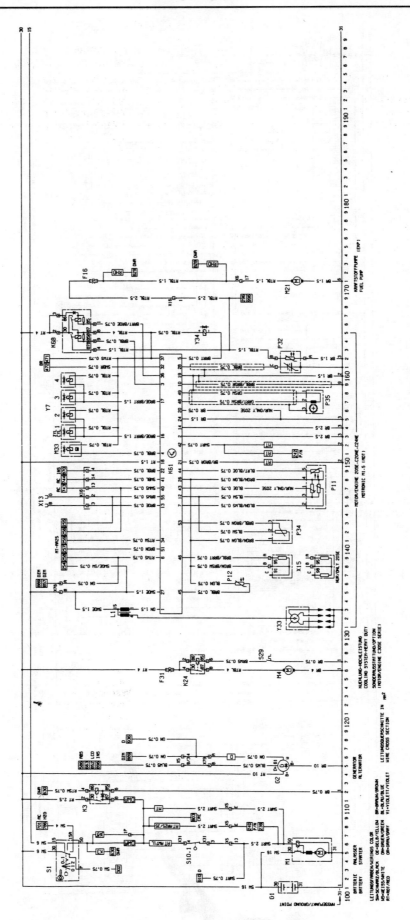

Fig. 13.13 Wiring diagram for 1993-on models

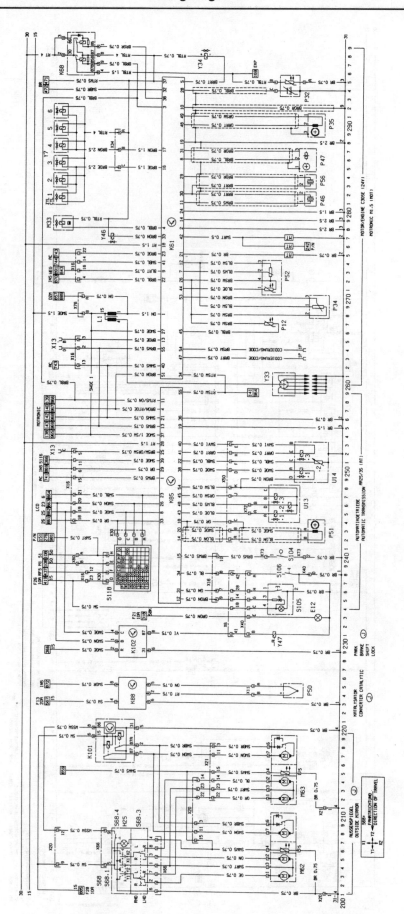

Fig. 13.13 Wiring diagram for 1993-on models (continued)

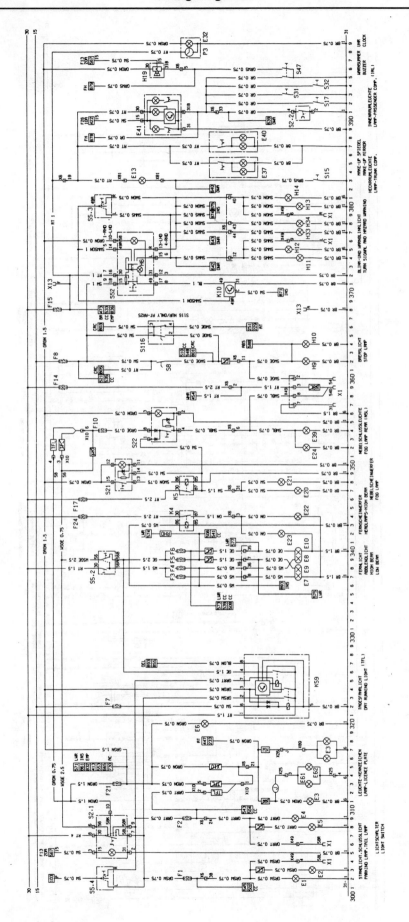

Fig. 13.13 Wiring diagram for 1993-on models (continued)

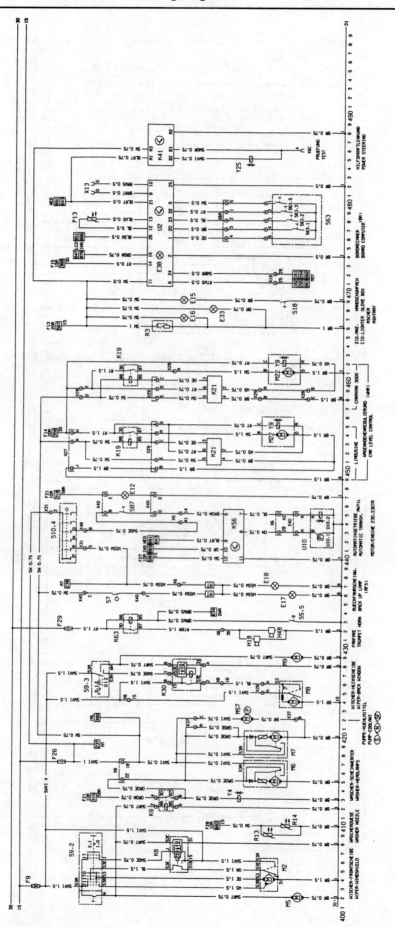

Fig. 13.13 Wiring diagram for 1993-on models (continued)

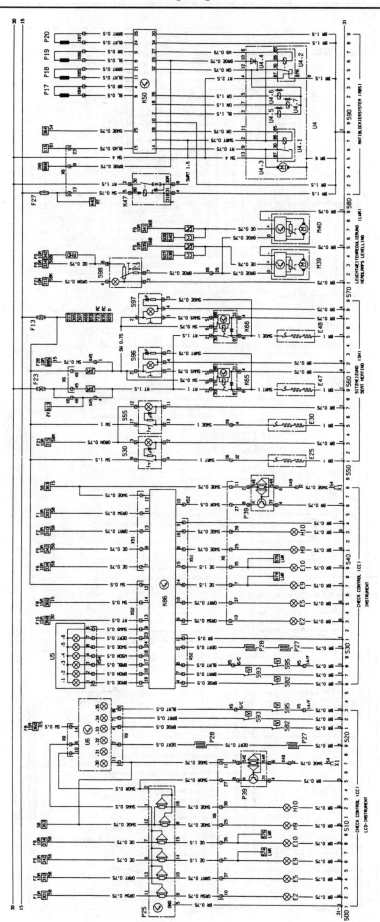

Fig. 13.13 Wiring diagram for 1993-on models (continued)

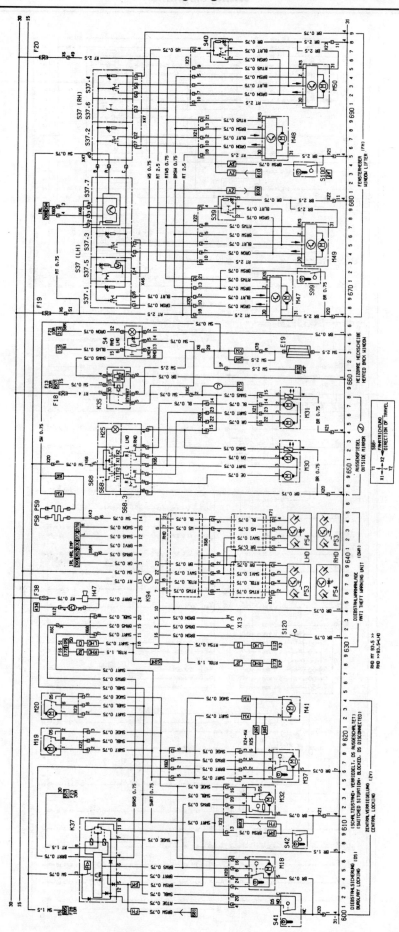

Fig. 13.13 Wiring diagram for 1993-on models (continued)

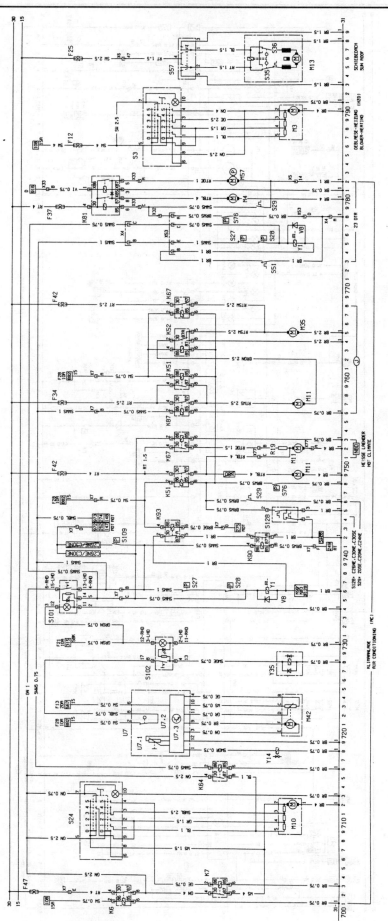

Fig. 13.13 Wiring diagram for 1993-on models (continued)

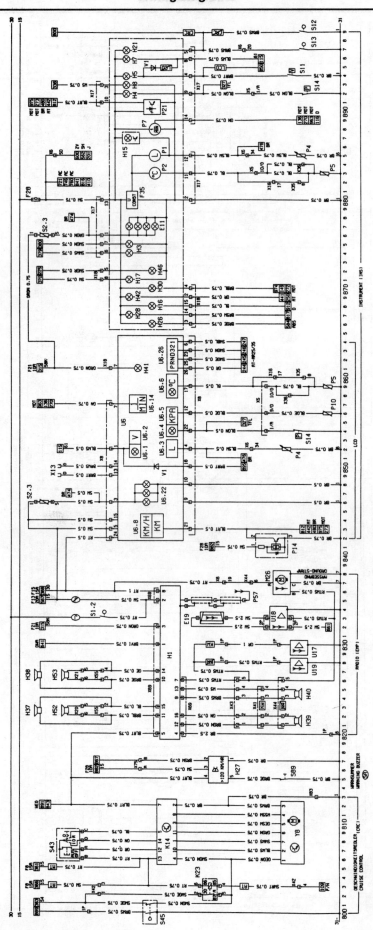

Fig. 13.13 Wiring diagram for 1993-on models (continued)

Key to Fig. 13.13

No	Description	Track	No	Description	Track
E1	Sidelight, left	302	H37	Loudspeaker – front left	821, 824
E2	Tail light, left	303, 502, 533	H38	Loudspeaker – front right	825, 828
E3	Number plate light	311, 316, 318	H39	Loudspeaker – rear left	821, 822
E4	Sidelight, right	309	H40	Loudspeaker – rear right	824, 825
E5	Tail light, right	308, 504, 535	H41	Warning light – lights	861
E6	Engine compartment light	320	H42	Warning light – automatic transmission	869
E7	Main beam, left	337	H46	Warning light – catalytic conv. temperature	872
E8	Main beam, right	339	H47	Siren – anti-theft warning unit	635
E9	Dipped beam, left	338, 506, 537	H48	Trumpet horn	432
E10	Dipped beam, right	340, 508, 539	H52	Loudspeaker – door, front left	822, 823
E11	Instrument lighting	877	H53	Loudspeaker – door, front right	826, 827
E12	Selector lever lighting (auto. trans.)	233, 447	K3	Relay – starter, anti-theft warning unit	111, 112
E13	Luggage compartment light	383	K4	Relay – headlights, main beam	343, 344
E15	Glovebox light	469	K5	Relay – foglights	347, 348
E16	Cigarette lighter illumination	467	K6	Relay – air conditioning	701, 702
E17	Reversing light, left	436	K7	Relay – blower, air conditioning	702, 703
E18	Reversing light, right	437	K8	Relay – windscreen intermittent wipe	405..408
E19	Heated rear window	663, 833	K9	Relay – headlight washer unit	412, 413
E20	Foglight, left	347	K10	Flasher unit	370, 371
E21	Foglight, right	348	K14	Cruise control	806..812
E22	Headlight main beam, left	344	K19	Relay – car level control	453, 454, 460, 461
E23	Headlight main beam, right	342	K21	Sensor – car level control	451..453, 458..460
E24	Foglight, rear, left	352	K23	Relay – cruise control	802, 803
E25	Heating mat – front seat, left	551	K24	Relay – blower, radiator	126, 127
E30	Heating mat – front seat, right	555	K30	Relay – tailgate intermittent wipe	426..428
E32	Light – clock	399	K35	Relay – time delay, heated rear window & mirrors	657..660
E33	Light – ashtray	468	K37	Control unit – central locking	602..610
E37	Light – make-up mirror, left	385,	K41	Control unit – power steering	485..488
E38	Light – on-board computer	474	K47	Relay – over-voltage protection (ABS)	581, 582
E39	Foglight, rear, right	354	K50	Timing control – ABS	586..599
E40	Light – make-up mirror, right	387	K51	Relay – radiator cooling fan	748, 749, 759, 760
E41	Interior light, delayed switch-off	389..391	K52	Relay – radiator cooling fan	763..765
E47	Heating mat – rear seat, left	559	K56	Control unit – kickdown control	440..445
E48	Heating mat – rear seat, right	565	K59	Relay – day running lights	321..327
E61	Number plate light, left (Japan)	313	K61	Control unit – Motronic	133..162, 261..295
E62	Number plate light, right (Japan)	314	K63	Relay – trumpet horn (in fusebox)	432, 433
F1-F28	Fuses (in fusebox)	various	K64	Relay – blower, air conditioning stage 1	715, 716
F31	Fuse – radiator cooling fan	126	K65	Relay – heating mat, rear left	559..561
F34	Fuse – radiator cooling fan	757	K66	Relay – heating mat, rear right	565..567
F35	Voltage stabilizer	880	K67	Relay – radiator cooling fan	752, 753, 767, 768
F37	Fuse – water pump	779	K68	Relay – fuel injection unit	163..167, 296..299
F38	Fuse – anti-theft warning unit	635	K81	Relay – water pump	779..782
F42	Fuse – radiator cooling fan (maxi)	749, 768	K85	Control unit – automatic transmission	235..259
F47	Fuse – air conditioning (maxi)	702	K86	Control unit – check control	526..547
G1	Battery	101	K87	Relay – radiator cooling fan	756, 757
G2	Alternator	114..116	K88	Control unit – catalytic conv. temperature	223..225
H1	Radio	820..836	K90	Relay – compressor (auto. trans.)	741, 742
H3	Warning light – direction indicator light	874, 875	K93	Relay – compressor (C30SE)	742, 743
H4	Warning light – oil pressure	892	K94	Control unit – anti-theft warning unit	630..644
H5	Warning light – brake fluid	894	K101	Relay – exterior mirror, parking position	217..220
H6	Warning light – hazard warning system	373	K102	Control unit – handbrake shift lock	229..231
H7	Charging indicator light	896	L1	Ignition coil	133, 268
H8	Warning light – main beam	893	M1	Starter	105, 106
H9	Stop-light, left	362, 510, 541	M2	Motor – windscreen wiper	403..406
H10	Stop-light, right	364, 512, 543	M3	Motor – heater blower	787..790
H11	Direction indicator light, front, left	374	M4	Motor – radiator cooling fan	126, 780
H12	Direction indicator light, rear, left	375	M5	Windscreen washer pump	402
H13	Direction indicator light, front, right	380	M6	Motor – headlight wiper, left	415..417
H14	Direction indicator light, rear, right	381	M7	Motor – headlight wiper, right	418..420
H15	Warning light – fuel	887	M8	Motor – tailgate wiper	424..426
H16	Warning light – glow time (diesel)	868	M9	Tailgate washer pump	429
H17	Warning light – trailer direction indicators	871	M10	Motor – blower, air conditioning	709..712
H18	Trumpet horn	431	M11	Motor – radiator cooling fan	749, 752, 757
H19	Buzzer – headlights-on warning (in fusebox)	396, 397	M13	Motor – sunroof	795..798
H21	Warning light – clutch & handbrake	897	M18	Motor – central locking, driver's door	603..606
H25	Warning light – mirror heating	207, 654	M19	Motor – central locking, rear left door	618..620
H26	Warning light – ABS	866	M20	Motor – central locking, rear right door	622..624
H27	Warning buzzer – safety checking	815..817	M21	Fuel pump	171
H28	Warning light – seat belt warning	867	M22	Compressor – car level control	454, 461
H30	Warning light – engine	870	M26	Motor – electric aerial	836..838
H33	Direction indicator repeater light, left	377	M30	Exterior mirror – driver's side	649..652
H34	Direction indicator repeater light, right	378			

No	Description	Track
M31	Exterior mirror – passenger's side	655..658
M32	Motor – central locking, passenger's door	611..614
M33	Actuator – idle speed	151, 152, 278, 279
M35	Motor – radiator cooling fan	765
M37	Motor – central locking, bootlid/tailgate	615..618
M39	Motor – headlight levelling, left	572..575
M40	Motor – headlight levelling, right	576..579
M41	Motor – fuel filler flap, central locking	622, 624
M42	Actuator – air conditioning	720..724
M47	Motor – electric window, driver's door	667..671
M48	Motor – electric window, passenger's door	685..689
M49	Motor – electric window, rear left	673..677
M50	Motor – electric window, rear right	691..695
M57	Water pump	422, 782
M62	Exterior mirror – driver's side	203..209
M63	Exterior mirror – passenger's side	212..218
P1	Fuel gauge	885
P2	Water temperature gauge	883
P3	Clock	398
P4	Sensor – fuel	852, 885
P5	Sensor – coolant temperature	859, 883
P7	Tachometer	888
P10	Sensor – oil pressure	852
P11	Airflow meter	145..149
P12	Coolant temperature sensor	136, 267
P13	Sensor – outside air temperature	478
P14	Sensor – distance (WEG)	841, 842
P17	Sensor – ABS, front left	592
P18	Sensor – ABS, front right	594
P19	Sensor – ABS, rear left	596
P20	Sensor – ABS, rear right	598
P21	Sensor – distance (WEG)	890, 891
P25	Sensor – bulb test	501..514
P27	Sensor – brake lining, front left	519, 530
P28	Sensor – brake lining, front right	519, 530
P32	Sensor – (heated), oxygen in exhaust gas	161, 162, 294, 295
P34	Potentiometer – throttle valve	141..143, 268..270
P35	Impulse sensor – crankshaft	156..158, 289..291
P39	Sensor – bulb test, trailer	515, 517, 546..548
P46	Sensor – knock control	281, 282
P47	Sensor – cylinder identification	285..287
P50	Temperature sensor – catalytic converter	224, 225
P51	Sensor – speed	242, 243
P52	Airflow meter	271..274
P53	Sensor – anti-theft unit, driver's side	636..644
P54	Sensor – anti-theft unit, passenger's side	636..644
P56	Sensor – knock control	283, 284
P57	Aerial	836
P58	Pane breakage sensor, rear left – anti-theft unit (KW)	644
P59	Pane breakage sensor, rear right – anti-theft unit (KW)	645
R3	Cigarette lighter	466
R13	Washer nozzle – heated, left	409
R14	Washer nozzle – heated, right	410
R19	Pre-resistor – radiator cooling fan	752
S1	Starter switch assembly	103..106
S1.2	Switch – key contact (Japan)	833
S2	Light switch assembly	
S2.1	Light switch	305..308
S2.2	Interior light switch	391
S2.3	Instrument light dimmer	846, 876
S3	Heater fan switch	785..791
S4	Switch – heated rear window & mirrors	663..665
S5	Direction indicator switch assembly	
S5.2	Switch – dipped beam	338, 339
S5.3	Switch – direction indicators	379..381
S5.4	Switch – sidelights	301..303
S5.5	Switch – horn	433
S7	Switch – reversing lights	486
S8	Switch – stop-lights	362
S9	Wiper switch assembly	
S9.2	Windscreen intermittent wipe switch	402..406

No	Description	Track
S9.3	Tailgate intermittent wipe switch	427, 428
S10	Switch assembly – auto. transmission (AW71L)	
S10.1	Switch – park/neutral	106
S10.4	Switch – selector lever position	441..445
S11	Control switch – brake fluid	894
S12	Control switch – clutch	899
S13	Switch – handbrake	897
S14	Switch – oil pressure	854, 892
S15	Switch – boot light	383
S17	Contact switch – passenger's door	392
S18	Switch – glovebox light	469
S21	Switch – foglight	348..350
S22	Switch – foglight, rear	353, 356
S24	Switch – blower, air conditioning	706..713
S27	Switch – compressor, low pressure	736, 775
S28	Switch – compressor, high pressure	736, 775
S29	Switch – coolant temperature	127, 746, 779
S30	Switch – heating mat, front seat, left	551..553
S31	Contact switch – rear left door	393
S32	Contact switch – rear right door	394
S35	Micro-switch – sunroof	795
S36	Micro-switch – sunroof	797
S37	Switch assembly – electric windows	
S37.1	Switch – electric window, driver's door	668..670
S37.2	Switch – electric window, passenger's door	686..688
S37.3	Switch – electric window, rear left	674..676
S37.4	Switch – electric window, rear right	692..694
S37.5	Safety switch	672
S37.6	Switch – anti-jam off (elec. window pinch guard off)	690
S37.7	Control – automatic, electric window	677..680
S39	Switch – electric window, rear left door	678..680
S40	Switch – electric window, rear right door	696..698
S41	Switch – anti-theft locking, driver's door	600..602
S42	Switch – central locking, passenger's door	609
S43	Switch – cruise control	806..809
S45	Switch – clutch, cruise control	800,801
S47	Contact switch – driver's door 2-pin	395, 396
S51	Switch – temperature, coolant (compressor)	773
S52	Switch – hazard warning	371..376
S55	Switch – heating mat, front seat, right	555..557
S57	Switch – sunroof	793..799
S63	Switch assembly – on-board computer	
S63.1	Switch – function reset	477
S63.2	Switch – hour adjustment, clock	478
S63.3	Switch – function select	479
S63.5	Switch – minute adjustment, clock	480
S68	Switch assembly – exterior mirror	
S68.1	Switch – exterior mirror adjustment	201..205, 647..652
S68.3	Switch – exterior mirror, left/right	201..206, 647..652
S68.4	Switch – exterior mirror, parking position	207, 208
S76	Switch – compressor, high pressure (blower)	748, 778
S82	Control switch – washer fluid, min. capacity	521, 526
S87	Switch – 4-speed automatic	445
S89	Switch – seat belt	815
S93	Control switch – coolant, min. capacity	522, 527
S95	Control switch – engine oil, min. capacity	523, 528
S96	Switch – heating mat, rear seat, left	561..563
S97	Switch – heating mat, rear seat, right	567..569
S98	Switch – headlight levelling	571..573
S99	Switch – electric window, driver's door	672
S100	Switch – electric window, passenger's door	684
S101	Switch – compressor	734, 736
S102	Switch – circulation	728..730
S104	Switch – kickdown	240
S105	Switch – Winter mode (auto. transmission)	234..236
S106	Switch – Economy/Sport mode (auto. trans.)	238
S109	Switch – compressor (Motronic)	741
S116	Switch – stop-light (AR25 auto. trans.)	365, 366
S118	Switch – automatic transmission	237..240
S120	Switch – bonnet	631
S128	Switch – coolant temperature	744, 745
U2	On-board computer	471..482

Key to Fig. 13.13 (continued)

No	Description	Track
U4	Hydraulic unit assembly – ABS	584..597
U4.1	Relay – ABS pump	585..588
U4.2	Relay – solenoid valves, ABS	594..597
U4.3	Pump – ABS hydraulic unit	584
U4.4	Diode – ABS hydraulic unit	596
U4.5	Solenoid valve – ABS, front left	590
U4.6	Solenoid valve – ABS, front right	592
U4.7	Solenoid valve – ABS, rear left	591
U5	Display assembly – check control system	
U5.1	Warning light – washer fluid, min. capacity	526
U5.2	Warning light – engine oil, min. capacity	527
U5.3	Warning light – coolant, min. capacity	528
U5.4	Warning light – tail light & dipped beam	529
U5.5	Warning light – stop-light failure	530
U5.6	Warning light – brake lining, front	531
U6	LCD instrument assembly	
U6.1	Charging indicator light	852
U6.2	Voltmeter	853
U6.3	Fuel gauge	852
U6.4	Warning light – oil pressure	854
U6.5	Oil pressure gauge	856
U6.6	Water temperature gauge	859
U6.8	Speedometer	843
U6.14	Tachometer	857
U6.22	Warning lights	846..848
U6.26	Selector lever indicator, auto. transmission	861..864
U6.30	Warning light – washer fluid, min. capacity	517
U6.31	Warning light – engine oil, min. capacity	518
U6.32	Warning light – coolant, min. capacity	519
U6.33	Warning light – tail light & dipped beam	521
U6.34	Warning light – stop-light failure	522
U6.35	Warning light – brake lining, front	523
U7	Air conditioning unit assembly	
U7.1	Potentiometer – temperature selector	719
U7.2	Limit switch – defroster lever	721
U7.3	Control unit – electronic	718..724
U10	Transmission assembly – 4-speed automatic	
U10.1	Pressure switch – 4-speed automatic	443
U10.2	Solenoid valve – 4-speed automatic	445
U13	Main automatic transmission housing	
U13.1	Solenoid valve – 2/3 shift	245
U13.3	Solenoid valve – 1/2/3/4 shift	246
U13.3	Solenoid valve – brake band	247
U14	Intermediate automatic transmission housing	
U14.1	Solenoid valve – converter clutch	250
U14.2	Temperature sensor – transmission fluid	251
U14.3	Solenoid valve – hydraulic pressure regulator	252
U17	Amplifier – aerial, roof (caravan)	830
U18	Amplifier – aerial, rear window	832..834
U19	Amplifier – windscreen aerial	828
V1	Diode – brake fluid level tester	850, 895
V8	Diode – compressor	735, 777
X	Connectors and multi-plugs	
X1	Trailer socket – 7-pin	304, 306, 357..360, 376, 379, 517, 548
X4	Instrument panel & air conditioning 3-pin (D)	775..778
X5	Instrument panel & engine 7-pin/ 14-pin (D)	106..116, 523, 528, 782, 854..859, 883, 892
X6	Instrument panel & body 51-pin	171, 231..238, 231..238, 302, 309, 315, 337..362, 374..396, 415, 417, 424, 426, 432, 437, 443..445, 502..517, 533..561, 572, 581..586, 663, 667, 696, 796, 837, 852, 885, 897
X6A	Instrument panel & body 6-pin	476..480, 640
X6C	Instrument panel & door 4-pin	486, 632, 658
X6D	Body & door 6-pin (ZV)	615..618, 678, 679
X7	Instrument panel & air conditioning 7-pin	702, 735..760
X8	Instrument panel & LCD instrument 26-pin	842..864
X9	Instrument panel & LCD instrument 26-pin (CC)	517..523

No	Description	Track
X10	Code countries 6-pin	312, 313, 351, 354
X11	Instrument panel & temperature sensor 2-pin	224, 225
X12	Code anti-theft warning unit 4-pin	634
X13	Diagnostic link 10-pin	145, 146, 252, 264, 265, 368, 371, 481, 482, 632, 633, 849, 850
X15	Octane plug 3-pin	138, 139
X16	Instrument panel & Motronic 26-pin	145..149, 169, 235..265, 272..275, 471, 472, 860, 882
X17	Instrument panel & instrument 14-pin	874..897
X18	Instrument panel & instrument 16-pin	861, 866..872
X20	Door & driver's door 24-pin	201..214, 600..606, 650..657, 667..671, 822, 823
X21	Door & passenger's door 24-pin	211..218, 609..614, 655..658, 685..689, 826, 827
X22	Door & rear door, left 11-pin	618..620, 673..680
X23	Door & rear door, right 11-pin	622..624, 691..698
X24	Body & tailgate 5-pin (KW)	615..618
X25	Body & bootlid 6-pin	314, 615..618
X26	Body & tailgate 3-pin (KW)	317, 425, 426
X27	Body & car level control 3-pin	450..454
X28	Body & car level control 6-pin	458..461
X29	Car level control & height sensor 5-pin	450..460
X30	Motronic & switch – auto. transmission 8-pin	237..242
X31	Instrument panel & switch – automatic transmission (AW71L) 5-pin	106, 441, 445
X32	Air conditioning & engine 1-pin	778
X33	Engine & blower 3-pin	779..782
X34	Motronic & fuel injection sol. valves 3-pin	285..289
X35	Motronic & fuel inj. valves (C26NE) 15-pin	860, 882
X36	Motronic & engine (C24NE) 1-pin	858, 884
X37	Body & water pump 3-pin	421, 422
X40	Body & console 8-pin	231..238, 436, 443..447
X41	Body & loudspeaker, rear 4-pin (KW)	821..825
X42	Instrument panel & cruise control (AR25 automatic transmission) 4-pin	802, 803
X43	Instrument panel & body 6-pin	644, 821..826
X44	Body & loudspeaker, rear 6-pin (limousine)	821..826, 837
X45	Door & console 5-pin	558, 562
X46	Door & console 8-pin	668..679
X47	Door & console 7-pin	685..694
X48	Instrument panel & switch – auto trans. 5-pin	443
X49	Body & trailer socket 9-pin	304, 306, 357..360, 376, 379, 517, 548
X50	Motronic & automatic transmission 10-pin	242..253
X51	Instrument panel 16-pin	533..547
X52	Instrument panel 26-pin	526..537, 546
X53	Instrument panel & compressor 5-pin	774..778
X54	Instrument panel & instrument 8-pin (CC)	526..532
X55	Instrument panel & door 4-pin	822..827
X66	Driver's door & switch – ext. mirror 9-pin	201..208, 647..654
X67	Instrument panel & Jetronic 5-pin	
X68	Instrument panel & door 9-pin	631, 633, 636..644
X69	Instrument panel & radio 16-pin	820..836
X70	Door & sensor – anti-theft unit 4-pin	636..639
X71	Door & sensor – anti-theft unit 4-pin	641..644
X72	Motronic & automatic transmission 2-pin	245, 246
X73	Instrument panel & kickdown sw. 4-pin (LHD)	240
X75	Instrument panel & warning buzzer 2-pin	816, 817
X76	Instrument panel & Motronic 2-pin	135, 136, 268, 270
X77	Air conditioning & blower, radiator 3-pin	751, 752
X78	Body & tailgate 2-pin (KW)	663
X79	Engine & alternator 2-pin (D)	115, 116
X80	Engine & Motronic 2-pin	239, 240
X81	Body & tailgate 2-pin (KW)	383
X83	Instrument panel & cruise control 1-pin	813
X84-87	Body & sensor – ABS 2-pin	592..599
X89	Tailgate & number plate light 1-pin	317
Y1	Clutch – compressor, air conditioning	736, 775
Y4	Solenoid valve – headlight washer	413
Y7	Fuel injection valves	153..160, 281..292
Y8	Actuator – cruise control	806..812

Key to Fig. 13.13 (continued)

No	Description	Track	No	Description	Track
Y9	Solenoid valve – car level control	455, 462	Y34	Solenoid valve – fuel tank ventilation	165, 298
Y14	Valve – coolant (Japan)	718	Y35	Valve – circulation	728
Y25	Solenoid valve – power steering	485	Y46	Solenoid valve – inlet manifold	277
Y33	Ignition distributor	132, 260	Y47	Lifting magnet – handbrake shift lock	231

Not all items are fitted to all models

Colour code

BL	Blue
BR	Brown
GE	Yellow
GN	Green
GR	Grey
HBL	Light blue
LI	Lilac
RT	Red
SW	Black
VI	Violet
WS	White

Abbreviations

ABS	Anti-lock brake system		M 2.7	Motronic M 2.7
AC	Air conditioning		M 2.8	Motronic M 2.8
AT	Automatic transmission		MID	Multi-info-display
ATC	Automatic temperature control		MOT	Motronic in general
AZV	Trailer hitch		MT	Manual transmission
BR	On-board computer		MUL	Multec in general
CC	Check control		NS	Front foglights
CRC	Cruise control		NSL	Rear foglights
D	Diesel		OEL	Oil/fluid level control (oil/fluid level)
DID	Dual-info-display		OPT	Optional equipment
DIS	Direct ignition system		PBSL	Park/brake lockout
DS	Theft protection		P/N	Park/Neutral (AT)
DWA	Anti-theft warning system		POT	Potentiometer
DZM	Tachometer		RC	Electronic ride control
EFC	Electric folding roof, convertible		RFS	Reversing lights
EKS	Pinch guard (electric windows)		RHD	Right-hand drive
EMP	Radio (receiver)		SD	Sliding roof
EZ +	El Plus with self-diagnosis		SH	Seat heating
FH	Window winders		SRA	Headlight washer system
HRL	Luggage/load compartment light		TANK	Fuel tank sensor
HS	Rear screen		TC	Traction control
HW	Rear screen wiper		TD	Turbodiesel
HZG	Heating		TEMP	Temperature gauge
INS	Instrument		TFL	Daytime driving light
IRL	Interior light		TKS	Door contact switch
KAT	Catalytic converter		TSZI	Transistor ignition (inductive)
KBS	Wiring harness		VGS	Carburettor
KV	Contact distribution		WEG	Odometer frequency sensor
L3.1	Jetronic L3.1		WHR	Car level control
LCD	LCD instrument		WS	Warning buzzer
LHD	Left-hand drive		ZV	Central door locking
LWR	Headlight range control		ZYL	Cylinder
M 1.5	Motronic M 1.5		4WD	Four wheel drive
M 1.5.2	Motronic M 1.5.2			

Wiring identification

eg GE WS 1.5

GE	Basic colour
WS	Identification colour
1.5	Section (mm²)

Index